GU01012148

Success in Geography: Physical and Mapwork

Success in
GEOGRAPHY: PHYSICAL AND MAPWORK

Peter Gilson, M.A.

John Murray

© Peter Gilson, 1976

All rights reserved. No part of this
publication may be reproduced, stored in
a retrieval system, or transmitted, in any
form or by any means, electronic, mechanical,
photocopying, recording or otherwise,
without the prior permission of
John Murray (Publishers) Ltd.,
50 Albemarle Street, London, W1X 4BD

Filmset in 'Monophoto' Times 9 on 11 pt. by
Richard Clay (The Chaucer Press), Ltd., Bungay, Suffolk
and printed in Great Britain by
Fletcher & Son Ltd., Norwich

Paperback 0 7195 3270 1

Foreword

This book, with its companion volume, *Geography: Human and Regional*, forms a basic course for O-level and similar examinations. It is also for readers who want to study the subject, in whole or in part, for their own interest.

Those who have an examination in view, however, need to make the best of available time, especially if they are working independently. Here are some guidelines which may help.

First of all, make yourself thoroughly familiar with the syllabus. Most teachers will explain it to students, but you can get your own copy by writing direct to the secretary of your appropriate examining board. In this book we deal with topics which are common to most syllabuses, but you may find you have certain options which have not been covered. There are, however, lists of Further Reading throughout the books and these will give you guidance on appropriate supplementary material.

When studying your syllabus, take a careful note of its organization and length. Choose your topics if a choice is offered. Go through your syllabus, comparing it with the Lists of Contents in this book and its companion volume. Make notes of the Units and Sections relevant to your study. If a topic is not listed, refer to the Further Reading sections and locate the appropriate book.

It will also be of great help to your study if you obtain some of the former papers set by your examining board. The board itself will be able to supply them.

The O-level course usually takes one or two years, depending on the number of subjects studied. You should plan your work carefully so that you have covered all the syllabus material a month or two before the examination. This will give you time for a complete revision of everything, thus building your confidence and reinforcing your understanding of what you have learned.

The next stage is tackling the work itself. Try to do this in complete privacy and quietness so that you achieve maximum concentration. Read a Unit of study through from beginning to end, slowly and carefully. Then try to recall its 'shape' or argument. Ask yourself, what were its chief points? What were the Sections into which it was divided? If you can't remember, read the Unit again.

Now you are ready to study the Unit in depth, taking one numbered Section at a time. Look up all unfamiliar words or place names—in the Glossary provided, a dictionary or an atlas. (It is absolutely essential for you to have a good atlas; it will be your constant companion throughout the course.)

As you study each Section, take notes, making a brief summary of the main points. The purpose of note-taking is to help you to understand and remember the essence of what you have learned. You will develop your own system of note-taking, but avoid merely copying the textbook verbatim. It is your own ideas and *understanding* of what you have read that counts. The purpose of these notes is that you keep going back to them from time to time, refreshing your mental image of the topic and reinforcing your memory and understanding.

When you think you have a good grasp of the Unit, test yourself by answering the questions given at the end. These are typical of the kind of examination questions you will eventually meet. When you are ready, you should also try to answer questions from the past papers of your board.

Normally you progress from one Unit of study to another when the first has been thoroughly assimilated, but if you have worked at a topic until it has become stale, it is an excellent idea to move on to something else for a change. You will eventually come back to the first topic new and refreshed.

As you progress in your course you should try to answer questions under conditions as close as practicable to those of the examination. Here, the *time* element becomes important. If, from your board's past papers, you see that five questions have to be answered in two hours, you should allow yourself about twenty minutes for each question. Spend a few minutes thinking about it and jotting down, on a spare piece of paper, a plan for the answer. List the main points or facts, get them into logical order, then begin to write. This preliminary organization will help you to make a clear, tidy presentation of your answer—avoiding crossings-out or afterthoughts—and this will go very much in your favour. Leave two or three minutes at the end for reading through again and correcting any obvious errors.

Give the same amount of time to each question. Don't be tempted (especially in the actual examination) to write at length on one subject if it means over-running your time and sacrificing something else. All questions count equally and valuable points will be lost if you leave any unanswered.

Where a question calls for a sketch map or diagram, remember that more information can be conveyed clearly in this way than in any number of words. Your illustrations should be as concise and accurate as possible, but should give only the information asked for; don't waste time putting in irrelevant details. In a sketch map there is no need to try and reproduce the intricacies of, say, a coastline. Your coastline can be simplified and rounded, but the map should be drawn quickly and be recognizable. As you work through the course, practise drawing maps of the countries you are studying so that you can easily reproduce them for the examination. In fact the best help you can give yourself, all along the way, is to shape your written and illustrated work towards examination requirements.

The study of geography does not end in the examination room. This is only a prelude to the appreciation and enjoyment of geography for its own sake. But at this stage you will be equipped with a knowledge and technique that will enable you to widen your studies, recognizing the relevance of geography, with its many facets, to everyday life and the world about you.

N.P. and P.G.

New Directions in Geography

The study of geography is in the throes of changes as, indeed, are all fields of learning if they are to continue to have relevance to changing economic and social conditions. Geography was shaped at first by the need to know the whereabouts of places and the physical conditions in a world which was being opened up by explorers and conquered by imperialists. The geography of the nineteenth century was, therefore, simple and descriptive; pupils were expected to learn by rote lists of places and products. This may have provided a body of useful knowledge, but it had no great *educational* value.

Early in the twentieth century a newer type of geography began to dominate the field. This took the form of cataloguing and classifying geographical phenomena and *explaining* their distribution. Its methods were twofold.

In the first place it was interested in *patterns* of distribution. It studied the geographical pattern of the cultivation of corn or cotton; of climatic types, vegetation and soils; of population, manufacturing and transport. These were represented on maps, and the maps were compared or correlated. Indeed, geography was at this time described as the 'science of correlations'. One pattern of distribution was explained in terms of another: crops in terms of climate and soil; manufacturing in terms of natural resources and transport facilities. It is easy to see, now, that explanation along these lines alone was always inadequate; there were many factors other than physical considerations which determined the distribution of human activities.

In the second place this geography was concerned with regions. A region was conceived as an area which was homogeneous or uniform in some important respect. Geographers contrasted highland regions with lowland; scarplands with clay vales; alluvial plains with plateaux. The land surface of Great Britain—as of every other country—was chopped up into regions, each delimited in terms of relief or landforms. But this was not the only criterion used. There were climatic, vegetation and soil regions. There were industrial and agricultural regions. The earth was dissected and every part ticketed and classified. There were, of course, problems in defining regions because there are no sharp divides in nature, and it was rare that geographers agreed on regional boundaries or, indeed, on the classification of regions. Nevertheless, the region proved to be a convenient framework both for the description of geographical phenomena and for their correlation and explanation.

This was the geography which held the field for the first half of the present century. It still prevails in the curricula of schools and the syllabuses of the Schools Examination Boards. It is the geography which underlies this book, which has been written to guide students through part of the O-level and similar examinations.

Since the 1950s, however, this 'traditional' geography has been under attack from those who feel it is too descriptive, giving no scope for analysis and providing no training to the student in solving the problems of the modern age. There has arisen what may for convenience be called the 'new geography'.

The new geography is, like the traditional, concerned with *spatial relations*, but it sees distributional patterns as continually changing. It seeks to isolate and evaluate the factors making for change, and in doing this it is prepared to use a battery of statistical tools. The region, focus of the older geography, is dispensed with in favour of the service area of a town, or the area from which commuters are drawn to a particular city, or the area served by a particular shopping centre or store. There are thousands of such areal units, and no geographer could possibly study, or even become acquainted with them all. The most he can be expected to do is to determine in general terms how people behave, trying to establish the principles which govern human behaviour in its geographical context. In other words, he can formulate a model of commuting, or shopping, or of any other normal type of human behaviour.

Models are merely generalizations. Sometimes they can be expressed in mathematical terms. But always they require to be tested against the real world. If a specific example fails to conform with the model, the geographer looks for the reason. Is the model in some respect inadequate? Is there some strongly distorting factor in this particular example? In this way the geographer, like any other social scientist, must refine his hypotheses in the light of new case studies. Geographical models can be constructed in any field of human activity from the distribution of market functions to the location of manufacturing or any other form of economic activity. In the final analysis *location* results from a human decision to locate some activity in a given place. How well-informed were the decision-makers, and how rational their judgment? Or was there an element of randomness in their choice? It is not difficult to show that the distribution of much economic activity, once explained so conclusively and so naïvely, is in fact a great deal less than rational.

Already we see modern geography taking shape as a problem-oriented study, capable of providing meaningful answers to countless questions which arise in everyday life. For instance, it is of greater importance to a large number of people to understand the factors influencing commuting distance from London than for them to know the boundaries of the London basin.

This, however, is the geography of the future. It has been accepted in the universities; it is entering into the A-level syllabuses. But at O-level it is still only a cloud, no bigger than a man's hand. In this way, too, the new geography appears in this book, a hint of it here and there, but always tempered by the needs of the current curricula and examination syllabuses.

N.P. and P.G.

Acknowledgments

Many people have contributed in various ways to this book, but I am particularly indebted to Norman Pounds, at whose suggestion it was written. Not only did he give advice and guidance, based on his own experience as author and scholar, he generously collaborated throughout and made valuable practical contributions to the text.

I am also grateful to Carolyn Nichols, who so skilfully and knowledgeably edited the book, and helped obtain many of the illustrations; to Irene Slade, editor of the *Success* series, who, in her own words, 'nagged me for several years'; to my wife and family who showed patience and tolerance during the entire course of the writing and production; to colleagues, students and friends whose interest and encouragement were always much appreciated.

I would like to thank the following who have kindly given permission for illustrations to be reproduced:

Aerofilms Ltd. (Figs. 2.14, 3.10, 5.7, 5.9, 5.11, 6.2);
Australian Information Service, London (Fig. 11.6);
The Finnish Embassy, London (Fig. 6.12);
The Director, Institute of Geological Sciences (NERC copyright) (Figs. 3.2, 3.7, 3.8, 4.7, 4.15, 5.2, 5.5);
National Film Board of Canada (Figs. 6.10, 8.2);
High Commissioner for New Zealand (Figs. 4.5, 6.8);
Oregon State Highway Division (Fig. 8.4);
Philip and Son Ltd. (Fig. 9.5);
Royal Naval Air Station, Culdrose (Fig. 5.3);
Santa Fe Railway (Figs. 3.9, 8.5);
Tennessee Valley Authority (Fig. 12.7);
USDA Forest Service (Figs. 6.4, 7.4, 11.8, 11.15);
USDA Soil Conservation Service (Figs. 12.3, 12.4, 12.5, 12.6);
US Department of Commerce, National Oceanic and Atmospheric Administration (Fig. 9.11 (*a*), (*b*) and (*c*));
US Department of Defense, Lower Mississippi Valley Division (Figs. 4.10, 4.12);
US Department of the Interior, National Park Service (Fig. 7.2)

The eight maps and keys to conventional signs that appear between pages 257 and 280 are reproduced from Ordnance Survey Maps with the sanction of the Controller of Her Majesty's Stationery Office (Crown copyright reserved). Acknowledgments are also due to HMSO for Figs. 9.15 and 13.5, also for Weather maps *A*, *B*, *C* and *D*.

P.G.

Contents

Unit One
Planetary Geography

Geography is the study of the earth's physical features and their effect on man's life and work. In this book we shall be studying the earth's physical geography—its relief, its rocks and soils, and its climate and vegetation. In the companion volume, *Success in Geography: Human and Regional* (*H & R*), we are more concerned with man's activities, such as his patterns of agriculture, industry, settlement and communications.

We cannot understand the earth properly, however, until we have some knowledge of its place in the solar system, so in this Unit we discuss some simple features of planetary geography.

1.1   Movement and Shape of the Earth

The solar system consists of nine planets which all orbit (revolve) around the sun. It takes about $365\frac{1}{4}$ days for our planet, earth, to complete its orbit. Planets nearer to the sun make the circuit more quickly and those further away take longer, as Table 1.1 shows.

Table 1.1   Planets of the solar system

Planet	Diameter (thousand km)	Average distance from the sun (million km)	Orbit time	
Mercury	4·8	57·9	88	
Venus	12·0	108	225	earth
Earth	12·7	150	365	days
Mars	6·7	228	687	
Jupiter	142·4	779	12	
Saturn	119·0	1 326	29·5	
Uranus	46·6	2 864	84	earth
Neptune	48·0	4 505	165	years
Pluto	5·9	5 792	248	

The earth's orbit is actually elliptical; at its nearest point the earth is 146 million km from the sun, at its most distant 151 million km.

The earth also rotates on its own *axis* at the same time as it is orbiting around the sun. The earth takes a 'day' of 24 hours to complete one rotation on its axis, spinning from west to east. The axis about which the earth turns, however, does not stand vertically, but slopes at an angle of $23\frac{1}{2}°$ from the vertical. This fact is of immense importance for life on earth, because there would be no variations in the seasons without it, as we shall see in Section 1.3. The rotation of the earth on its axis is what makes the sun appear to rise and set each day. We can visualize the sun as a stationary body, with the earth rotating from the west to the east as it orbits; the sun thus seems to rise in the east and set in the west, as Fig. 1.1 shows.

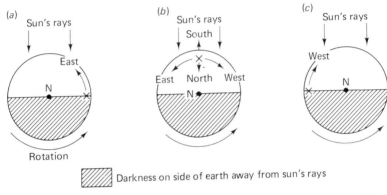

Fig. 1.1 *Apparent movement of the sun from east to west. N = North Pole*
(a) Sunrise: at X sun appears to 'rise' in the east
(b) Midday: at X sun is due south
(c) Sunset: at X sun appears to 'set' in the west

At one time people believed that the earth was flat, but we know now that it is spherical. We can demonstrate the shape of the earth easily, for example by looking through binoculars at a ship coming over the horizon. The first thing we see is its rigging, then its funnel appears and finally the hull. An eclipse of the moon also reveals the spherical shape of our planet, for the disc-shaped shadow of the earth can be seen passing across the lunar face. Finally, photographs taken from spacecraft also show the earth's form. The earth is not actually a perfect sphere: it is slightly flattened at the poles, which makes it a *spheroid*.

1.2   Longitude and Latitude

Any globe and most atlas maps showing the earth's surface have a network of two sets of lines printed on them, *longitude lines* and *latitude lines*. Together they enable the position of any place on the earth's surface to be defined exactly.

Lines of longitude and latitude are labelled in degrees (°), because each line that is drawn represents an angle at the centre of the earth, as Fig. 1.2 shows. Each degree of both latitude and longitude is further divided into minutes and seconds, so it is possible to specify the position of any place on the earth's surface with the utmost precision. Even moving ships and aircraft can be 'fixed' in this way at any moment.

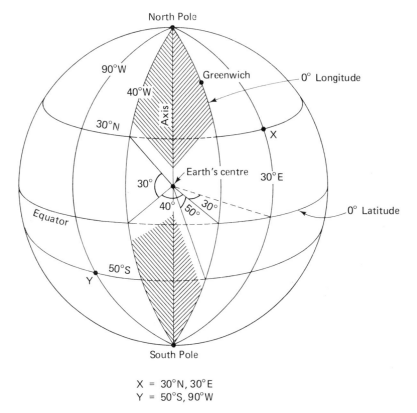

X = 30°N, 30°E
Y = 50°S, 90°W

Fig. 1.2 Latitude and longitude

(a) Longitude

Longitude lines or meridians radiate from the North Pole, draw further apart because of the earth's spheroidal shape, then converge and reunite at the South Pole (Fig. 1.2). In theory an infinite number of such lines could be drawn but for convenience they are usually printed on maps and globes at regular intervals of degrees, such as 10°, 15°, 20°.

One line of longitude is marked 0° and is sometimes called the Prime Meridian. It runs from the North Pole, through the site of the former Royal Observatory at Greenwich near London, to the South Pole, and it is the line from which all other lines of longitude are measured east (° E) or west (° W). Thus the line of longitude a quarter of the distance round the earth in a westerly direction is 90° W. At a similar distance to the east one finds 90° E, and the line of longitude at the opposite side of the earth to the Greenwich meridian is 180°. (180° W and 180° E are the *same* meridian; see Section 1.4(*b*).)

(*b*) Latitude
A place on the earth's surface can only be partially defined in terms of longitude, so we need the second set of lines, called lines or parallels of latitude, to locate its exact position between the North and South Poles. The *equator* circles the earth midway between the poles; it is the longest line of latitude and is marked 0°. All the other lines of latitude are drawn parallel to the equator, and they get smaller as they near the poles, because of the earth's spheroidal form. Those north of the equator (that is, in the northern hemisphere) are labelled in degrees north (° N) up to the North Pole (90° N), and those in the southern hemisphere in degrees south (° S) up to the South Pole (90° S). As with longitude, an infinite number of parallels could be drawn on a map but it is more convenient to show them at regular intervals.

(*c*) Special Parallels
Four parallels, in addition to the equator, have particular names and serve a special purpose. These are the lines drawn $23\frac{1}{2}°$ N and S, and $66\frac{1}{2}°$ N and S. The former pair are the Tropics of Cancer and Capricorn, the latter are the Arctic and Antarctic Cicles. These parallels divide the earth into six zones.

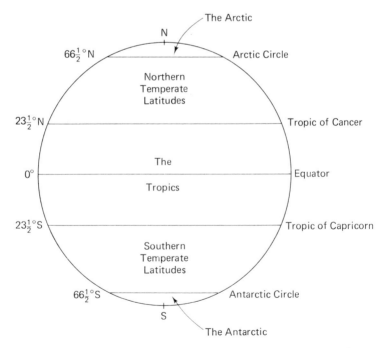

Fig. 1.3 Special parallels and zones

Their importance is related to the $23\frac{1}{2}°$ tilt of the earth's axis we mentioned in Section 1.1, and to the length of day and the sequence of the seasons which we shall look at in more detail in Section 1.3.

(*d*) **Great Circles**
You can, of course, draw lines around the earth in any direction. Great circles are lines of the same length as the equator, whose centre is the centre of the earth. They are never printed on maps in general use, but they are important because the shortest distance between any two points on the earth's surface is always part of the great circle on which they lie. If you fit a hoop of thin wire the same length as the equator on a small globe, say between Sydney, Australia and London, it will form a great circle and will indicate the shortest · route between the two cities. Lines of longitude are parts of great circles. The equator is also a great circle, but all other parallels are not.

Great circles are of immense importance in navigation. An ocean voyage, which commonly links ports and other fixed points, is likely to consist of a series of routes along great circles. Long air flights are also likely to follow great circles. The air route between, say, San Francisco and Copenhagen, probably lies by way of northern Canada and Greenland.

1.3   The Seasons

The summer and winter seasons are markedly different from each other over much of the earth's surface, particularly with regard to variations in the length of daylight and differences in temperature. (Summer days are generally longer and warmer than winter days.) The rotation of the earth on its axis gives us alternating daylight and darkness, as we saw in Section 1.1. The tilt of the axis, which is constant at $23\frac{1}{2}°$ from the vertical, and the earth's revolution around the sun are together responsible for seasonal variations in the length of the daylight period and in the sun's angle of elevation above the horizon (sometimes referred to as the *height of the sun in the sky*).

(*a*) **Daylight and Darkness**
At any moment the sun is illuminating half the earth's surface, but the half which is illuminated is constantly changing, as we saw in Fig. 1.1. The relative lengths of day and night are also different for most of the year, and the only time when daylight and darkness are of equal length everywhere on the earth is at the March and September equinoxes. Fig. 1.4 shows how this comes about: it illustrates four positions of the earth in its annual revolution around the sun. (To understand each position you should cover up the other three.)

In position *A* on Fig. 1.4 (21st June), at the June *solstice*, the North Pole is tilted towards the sun, which is overhead at the Tropic of Cancer ($23\frac{1}{2}°$ N). It is summer in the northern hemisphere and days are long. In fact, the whole of the North Polar region north of the Arctic Circle is illuminated continuously for a period of time which varies from 24 hours on the Arctic Circle to 6 months at the North Pole (Section 1.3(*b*) and Figs. 1.6 and 1.7). No part of

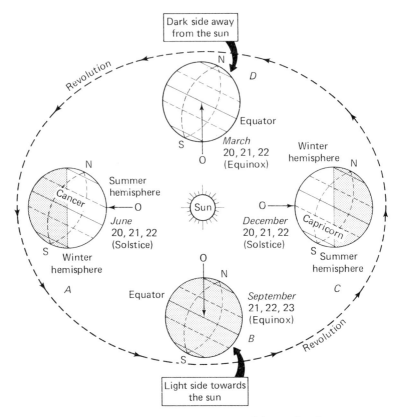

Fig. 1.4 The seasons. O = position of the overhead sun

this area passes into darkness as the earth rotates; the sun is at its highest in the southern sky at midday and at midnight it is seen to roll along the northern horizon. The opposite happens in the southern hemisphere, where it is winter. The daylight period is shorter and all the area lying within the Antarctic Circle experiences continuous darkness. If we could move along a meridian from the North to the South Pole, we would pass gradually from an area of continuous sunshine to one where the sun does not rise above the horizon. The period of daylight would contract from 24 hours to none, and at the equator it would last for 12 hours.

Three months later (21st September) the earth has moved to position *B* on Fig. 1.4 and the sun is overhead at the equator. The *terminator* (the line separating daylight and darkness) now passes through the Poles (Fig. 1.8). Everywhere on earth there is equal daylight and darkness, hence the use of the term *equinox* for this day in September and the corresponding date in March, six months later.

By 21st December the earth has moved to position *C* on Fig. 1.4; it is the converse of that at *A*. At this solstice the whole of the area within the Arctic Circle is continuously dark, while that within the Antarctic Circle experiences continuous daylight. The northern hemisphere has a short daylight period and winter, the southern a long daylight period and summer.

At the equinox in March, the earth is in position *D* on Fig. 1.4, which closely resembles *B*, with daylight and darkness of equal length throughout the world.

The Arctic and Antarctic Circles thus enclose areas which have total daylight and total darkness on their respective midsummer and midwinter days. But how do the Tropics of Cancer and Capricorn fit into this picture? The Tropic of Cancer is the latitude $23\frac{1}{2}°$ N (which is also the angle of tilt of the earth's axis). When the North Pole is tilted towards the sun in June, the sun is overhead at the Tropic of Cancer (Fig. 1.4, position *A*), but it is never overhead at any point further north. Similarly, the sun is overhead at the Tropic of Capricorn in December, but never further south. The vertical noonday sun (VNS) moves between the two tropics in the course of the year, but is overhead at the equator at the equinoxes. The angle of the sun's elevation above the horizon also varies seasonally outside the tropics, another result of the earth's revolution around the sun. These seasonal variations of the height of the sun in the sky are shown in Fig. 1.5.

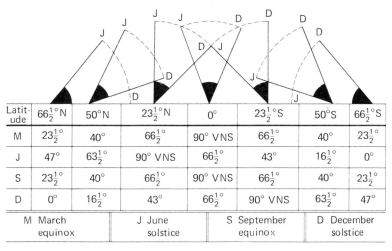

Latit-ude	$66\frac{1}{2}°$N	50°N	$23\frac{1}{2}°$N	0°	$23\frac{1}{2}°$S	50°S	$66\frac{1}{2}°$S
M	$23\frac{1}{2}°$	40°	$66\frac{1}{2}°$	90° VNS	$66\frac{1}{2}°$	40°	$23\frac{1}{2}°$
J	47°	$63\frac{1}{2}°$	90° VNS	$66\frac{1}{2}°$	43°	$16\frac{1}{2}°$	0°
S	$23\frac{1}{2}°$	40°	$66\frac{1}{2}°$	90° VNS	$66\frac{1}{2}°$	40°	$23\frac{1}{2}°$
D	0°	$16\frac{1}{2}°$	43°	$66\frac{1}{2}°$	90° VNS	$63\frac{1}{2}°$	47°

M March equinox	J June solstice	S September equinox	D December solstice

Fig. 1.5 Seasonal variations in the elevation of the noonday sun

The movements of the earth and the incidence of daylight and darkness are of vital importance for life on the earth. An understanding of the seasons is essential to an appreciation of world climates and their influence on vegetation, soil, human settlement and economic activity (Units 11 and 12).

(*b*) The Varying Length of Daylight

Fig. 1.6 shows the relative lengths of night and day at the June and December solstices. Take any line of latitude and note the proportion of it which lies

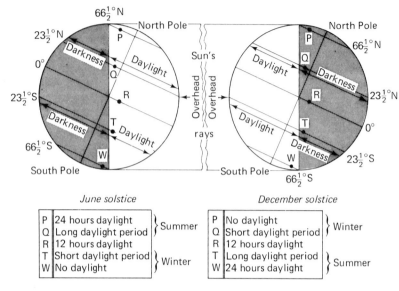

Fig. 1.6 Variation in the length of the daylight period at the solstices

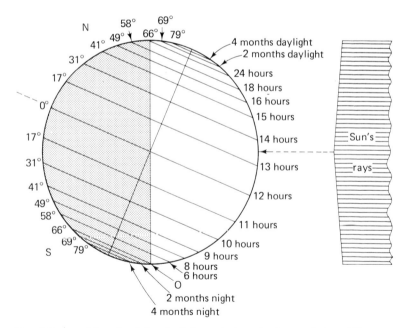

Fig. 1.7 Actual length of the daylight period at the June solstice. (The same duration of darkness at the December solstice)

within the shaded portion, representing darkness. In June, this proportion is nil within the Arctic Circle, half at the equator and the whole parallel within the Antarctic Circle.

The length of daylight varies everywhere except on the equator in the course of the year, and is longer in summer than in winter. In other words, the seasons only begin to show themselves as we move away from the equator, and they become more pronounced outside the tropics. Fig. 1.7 shows how the length of daylight varies in June, with increasing distance from the equator.

In Fig. 1.8 we can see the length of the daylight period at the equinoxes and the solstices. These *plan views* show that every parallel of latitude is cut in half

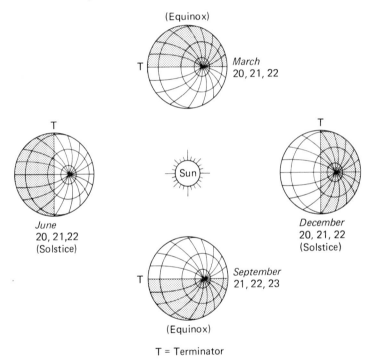

T = Terminator

Fig. 1.8 The length of the daylight period at the equinoxes and solstices. (T = terminator)

by the terminator in March and September. Notice also that in June and December the region north of the Arctic Circle rotates wholly in the light and dark halves. Compare Fig. 1.8 with Fig. 1.6. (The sun and the earth are not drawn to scale in Fig. 1.8; in fact the sun is enormously larger than the earth.)

(c) Insolation

We have just seen that the relative length of daylight and darkness varies with the seasons, except at the equator. Fig. 1.9 shows the variation in the length of

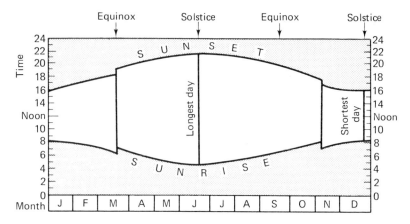

Fig. 1.9 Variation in the length of the daylight period in Britain

the daylight period in Britain. The length of daylight in summer is about twice that in winter. This means, of course, that there are also variations in the amount of heat which a place receives from the sun.

The incoming solar radiation (usually contracted to *insolation*) is the total amount of solar energy (or heat) received by the earth. All life on our planet depends upon the heat which is radiated from the sun, but the amount received and retained varies with two factors. The first is the actual number of hours in the day when the sun is above the horizon (that is, the length of daylight). The second is the angle at which the sun's rays strike the earth's

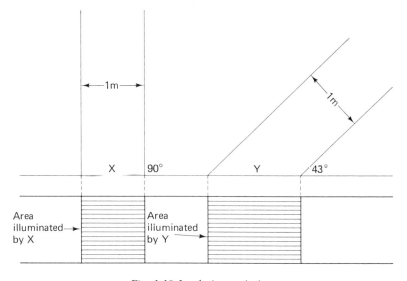

Fig. 1.10 Insolation variations

surface. You will know that it is usually warmer when the sun is high in the sky and days are longer than when it is just above the horizon and days are shorter.

In Fig. 1.10, *X* and *Y* represent two 'bundles' of solar energy, each a metre wide. Bundle *X* strikes the earth at 90° and illuminates an area 1 m². Bundle *Y*, on the other hand, strikes at the rather flatter angle of 43°, and is spread over an area almost twice as large. There is, of course, no more solar energy in *Y* than in *X*, but the *intensity* of heat delivered by *Y* is roughly half that due to *X*, because the same amount of heat is spread over a larger area. At the same

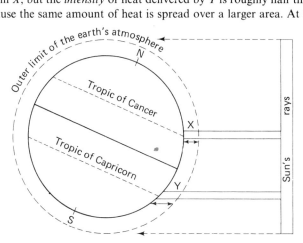

Fig. 1.11 Insolation variations at the June solstice

time, as Fig. 1.11 shows, the lower the angle of the sun's rays, the longer is their passage through the earth's atmosphere and the more heat there is lost into the atmosphere (Section 9.1). For these reasons temperatures within the area illuminated by *Y* on Fig. 1.11 are much lower than those in the area lit by *X*.

1.4 Time

The sun's position at noon (midday) is the moment when the sun is at its highest angle in the sky on that day. All places along a line of longitude

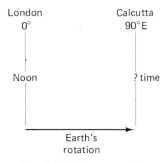

Fig. 1.12 Time conversion

experience noon at the same time. As the earth turns from west to east, places pass from dawn to morning, to noon and so to afternoon, sunset and night. At midday on the Prime Meridian (0° longitude), places to the west have not experienced noon while places to the east have done so already. To the west it is earlier than noon; to the east, it is later. For example, when it is noon in London, it is 0700 in New York (76° W) and 1800 in Calcutta (90° E).

It is easy to calculate the amount of the time change as one moves east or west of the Prime Meridian. The earth turns through 360° in the course of 24 hours, so it turns 1° in every 4 minute period. It takes 1 hour to rotate through 15° of longitude, so it is always 6 hours earlier on the meridian of 90° W than it is on the Prime Meridian, and 6 hours later at 90° E, as shown in Fig. 1.12.

(a) Time Zones

Falmouth in Cornwall lies at a longitude of 5° W, so the sun rises and sets there 20 minutes later than it does in London. To be absolutely correct, Falmouth's clocks should be set to the *local time* of 20 minutes earlier than London, but Falmouth keeps to the same time as the rest of Britain. It is obviously more convenient for the whole of the country to use the same time, and it would create a very peculiar situation indeed if every place on the earth's surface adopted the local time which was correct for its longitude. The operation of radio and television, and the running of railways and bus services alone make it necessary to have a standardized time for an extensive area.

Countries of relatively small longitudinal extent, such as Britain, can have the same time throughout their area without any serious inconvenience. However, this is not practicable in countries such as Canada, the USA and, above all, the Soviet Union, which extend over a vast range of longitude. Within the USA, eastern Maine lies 56° east of the coast of California or, in terms of

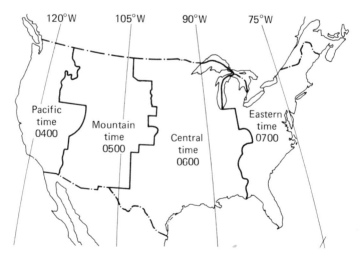

Fig. 1.13 Time zones of the USA

solar time, 3 hours 44 minutes. The Soviet Union extends through 170° of longitude or 11 hours 20 minutes in terms of time. These large countries are divided into *time zones*, each with its own particular time, earlier than that of the zone to the east, later than that of the zone to the west. Time zones appear on the map as a series of north to south strips. In the USA there are four such time zones, each an hour apart (excluding Alaska and Hawaii which have their own). In the Soviet Union there are no less than eleven time zones.

(b) International Date Line

The variations in time between different parts of the world are further complicated by the fact that different *days* exist simultaneously on the earth's surface. When it is noon on Tuesday at 0° longitude in London, time to the west is before noon and it is midnight between Monday and Tuesday at 180°

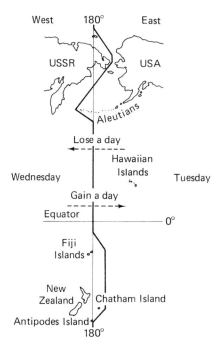

Fig. 1.14 The International Date Line

longitude. But by going eastward from 0° longitude, in which direction time is ahead of noon, it is midnight between Tuesday and Wednesday at 180°. Thus there are two times on the 180° meridian, 24 hours or a whole day apart, a state of affairs which applies whatever the time at 0° longitude.

The International Date Line was established in 1884 to solve the problems this creates. If we travel across the Date Line from east to west we jump one day forward so that Tuesday morning would become Wednesday morning and a day would be lost. Travelling in the opposite direction (that is, west to east), we would gain a day, because Wednesday morning would become Tuesday morning. The confusion which this might cause could be far greater than that which arises from time zones. Fortunately it was decided to locate the International Date Line along the meridian of 180° only where this ran across the open seas. It is diverted to avoid island groups, such as the Aleutians and Fiji.

Further Reading
Strahler, A. N.: *Physical Geography*. John Wiley (Chichester, 1969), Part 1, Chapters 1–6.

Questions
1. With the aid of diagrams, explain why, in Britain (*a*) the length of the daylight period varies, (*b*) summers are warmer than winters.
2. Using diagrams, explain the meaning of the following terms: (*a*) equinox, (*b*) solstice, (*c*) insolation, (*d*) time zone, (*e*) International Date Line.
3. Give an explanation of the following, using diagrams to illustrate: (*a*) why there are time zones in some countries but not in others, (*b*) why the sun rises in the east and sets in the west.
4. Work out the following time conversion problems (Section 1.4).
   (*a*) If local time is 1800 hours on Tuesday at 80° E, what is the local time at 100° W?
   (*b*) What is the local time at 120° E when it is noon on Friday at 120° W?
   (*c*) When the local time is 1800 hours on Sunday in Sydney, Australia what is the local time in New York?
   (*d*) When the local time is 0600 hours at 150° W, along which meridian is the time 2000 hours?
   (*e*) When local time is 0400 hours on Wednesday in Calcutta what is the local time in New Orleans?

Unit Two
The Planet Earth

2.1 How It All Began

Scientists estimate that the earth is about 4 500 million years old. The theories which attempt to explain how it came into existence are extremely complex, but all of them suggest that it originated as a high-temperature mass of gas and dust. This mass supplied the chemical ingredients for the formation of the earth's rocks. Vast quantities of gas were given off from the surface of the earth while it was cooling down, so the planet was shrouded in a thick blanket of vapour from which rain fell, only to be turned into steam when it reached the hot surface. As the earth's outer crust grew cooler, intense volcanic activity added more gas and water vapour to the atmosphere (Section 2.8). When the earth's surface was cool enough for water to collect on it, rain slowly filled up the hollower parts to form the oceans. It is thought that plant life evolved about 1 900 million years ago and began to supply oxygen to the atmosphere.

Today the earth's surface consists of about 30 per cent dry land and 70 per cent sea. The dry surface is broken up into six major land masses—North America, South America, Eurasia, Africa, Australia and Antarctica. Each is made up of rocks of varying age which form mountains, hills and plains. The sea areas are all connected but may, for convenience, be divided into four main oceans—the Pacific, Atlantic, Indian and Arctic Oceans. A layer of gas composed almost entirely of a mixture of oxygen and nitrogen surrounds the whole planet. This is the earth's *atmosphere* (Section 9.1).

2.2 The Geological Time Scale

We know very little about the earth's first 3 900 million years, mainly because most of the rocks formed in that period of time have been worn away, buried or changed into other rock types. Some areas of very old, hard rock do still exist, and these are called the *shield areas* or *cratons* (Fig. 2.5); they are surface exposures of the vast 'basement' complex which is believed to form the underlying core of each continent. The cratons have been little affected by the great changes which have taken place on other parts of the earth's surface.

Our detailed knowledge of the earth's geological history is limited to the last 600 million years, because most rocks near the earth's surface were formed during this time. Furthermore, fossilized remains of animal and plant life help in dating the rocks, and we only have these for the last 600 million years. It is possible to divide these 600 million years into a number of geological periods of varying length. Certain types of rock and fossilized remains of plant and animal life may be associated with certain periods and are found in particular areas. It is remarkable that rocks of every geological age except the Miocene can be found in an area as small as the British Isles. Table 2.1 shows their principal locations.

Table 2.1   The geological time scale

Era	Millions years ago	years duration	Period	Rock types	Principal areas	Areas affected by mountain building
Quaternary	1		Recent	Alluvium, river terraces, raised beaches	All over Britain	
	13		Pleistocene	Modification of scenery by glaciation: moraines, boulder clay	Britain north of the Thames-Severn line	
Cenozoic		12	Pliocene	Shelly 'crags'	East Anglian coast	
		12	Miocene	Absent in Great Britain	Absent in Great Britain	Alpine orogeny
	25		Alpine orogeny			Wealden anticline and minor folds in Purbeck and Isle of Wight
	36	11	Oligocene	Basalt intrusions: dykes and sills	North-west Britain; Antrim plateau	
		27	Eocene	Sands, loam, London clay	London and Hampshire Basins	
	63					
Mesozoic		72	Cretaceous	Chalk Upper greensand Gault clay Lower greensand Wealden sand and clay	West to east succession in a belt from Dorset to Yorkshire; south-east England	
	135					
		46	Jurassic	Purbeck and Portland limestone Kimmeridge clay Corallian limestone Oxford clay Oolitic limestone Lias clay	West to east succession in a belt from south Dorset to north Yorkshire	

Age (million years)	Period	Duration	Rock type	Areas	Structure / orogeny
181					
	Triassic	49	Keuper (red) marl and sandstone; Bunter Sandstone and conglomerate	Midland and Cheshire plains	Armorican orogeny
230					
	Permian	50	Magnesian limestone New red sandstone	Tyne–Notts. strip Lancashire, Cheshire, east Devon	South-west syncline, Mendip anticline, south Wales syncline (all east to west trend); also Pennines (north to south trend). Cornish granite intruded
280	Armorican orogeny				
	Carboniferous	65	Coal measures Millstone grit Carboniferous limestone	All coalfield areas Pennines, south Wales, Scottish lowlands Mendips, Pennines	
345					
	Devonian	60	Old red sandstone	Hereford, Brecon; central lowlands of Scotland; Caithness and Cheviots	Caledonian orogeny
405	Caledonian orogeny				
	Silurian	20	Wenlock limestone; shale, sandstone	Central Wales, southern Lake District, southern uplands of Scotland	Distinct north-east to south-west trend of Scottish highlands and Great Glen; also Cheviots, southern uplands, Lake District and north Wales. Granites intruded
425					
	Ordovician	75	Slate, flagstones, shale; Lake District volcanics	Snowdonia and Lake District	
500					
	Cambrian	100	Shale, slate, flagstones, grit	North Wales (Harlech Dome)	
600					
	Pre-Cambrian	3 900	Metamorphic rocks (Gneiss, Schist); some hard sedimentaries	Scottish highlands and islands; Grampians, Malvern Hills, Shropshire	

Palaeozoic

2.3   Rock Types

Many different types of rock are found on the earth's surface. The easiest way to classify them is according to the way in which they are formed.

(*a*) **Igneous Rocks** (Latin: ignis = fire)
Igneous rocks begin their life as a hot liquid called magma, deep in the earth's crust. This magma moves towards the surface as a result of internal pressures in the crust and/or because the hot liquid is lighter than its surrounding rocks. On reaching the earth's surface it cools and solidifies. Although volcanic lava probably springs immediately to mind, many other rocks are formed in this way, both on and beneath the earth's surface.

Igneous rocks may be subdivided according to their chemical composition into acid rocks, which are rich in silica, the most abundant mineral in the earth's crust, and basic rocks, which have a low silica content. Another subdivision can be made according to the size of the crystals in the rock. If the magma cools slowly, inside the crust and below the surface of the earth, it forms an intrusive and coarse-grained rock with large crystals, such as granite. If, on the other hand, it cools quickly, on the surface, it forms an extrusive and fine-grained rock which often has no crystal structure, such as basalt. It may even look like glass or be full of 'bubbles' like pumice stone.

(*b*) **Sedimentary Rocks**
Most sedimentary rocks have been laid down in beds or layers (*strata*) on the sea-floor. They are of two main types, clastic and non-clastic rocks.

(i) **Clastic rocks** consist of fragments of pre-existing rocks which are worn from the land surface and carried away and deposited in layers, usually on a sea- or lake-bed. The fragments are turned into hard rock either by a process of compression or by a natural cementing material, called *matrix*. Clastic rocks include the many varieties of conglomerate (cemented pebbles), sandstone (cemented sand), and shale or clay (compressed mud).

(ii) **Non-clastic rocks** are either chemical or organic (that is, the remains of animals or plants) in origin. They include such rocks as limestone (often made up of shell remains), coal (swamp forest vegetation compressed and changed into rock) and several mineral salts (the result of evaporation).

It is not always easy to place a particular sedimentary rock into either of these categories, as it may contain elements of both. A clay may contain fossil remains, for example, and a limestone may contain clastic material.

(*c*) **Metamorphic Rocks**
Both igneous and sedimentary rocks may be changed by heat and/or pressure from earthquakes, volcanic action or contact with igneous rocks into an entirely new type of rock, called a metamorphic rock. When a hot igneous

magma is thrust upwards under great pressure into the earth's crust, for example, the rocks already there are baked by the heat of the magma into a new type of rock.

Two common examples of metamorphic rocks are marble, which has been formed from limestone, and slate, which derives from clay, shale or volcanic ash.

2.4   The Structure of the Earth's Crust

The surface of the earth—which is not only the dry land surface but also the ocean-floor—is very uneven. But the overall difference between the top of the highest mountain (Mount Everest, 8 844 m above sea-level) and the bottom of the deepest part of the sea (the Marianas Trench, about 11 140 m below sea-level) is less than 20 km. This may seem a great difference but, as a fraction of the earth's radius (about 6 380 km) it is less, by comparison, than a wrinkle in the peel of a large orange.

Our knowledge of the internal structure of the earth comes mainly from

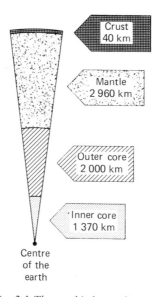

Fig. 2.1 The earth's layered structure

data collected about the speed and behaviour of earthquake waves. This evidence suggests that the earth is made up of several layers or zones—the crust, the mantle and the core. Man has only penetrated a short distance into the earth's interior, and the deepest boring is a mere 8 km.

The earth's crust is a skin of rock which is less dense (that is, lighter) than the rock of the underlying mantle. The junction between the crust and the mantle is called the M-layer or Mohorovicic Discontinuity, after the scientist who discovered it. (He found that earthquake waves speed up as they cross it.) The crust actually consists of two distinct types of rock; one makes up the continental land masses, and the other forms the ocean-floors.

(a) The Continental Crust

This is thicker and less dense (relative density = 2·7) than the oceanic crust. Its average depth is 35 km, but it may be as much as 60 km thick beneath the high mountain ranges. The upper layers are mostly granite rocks (about 90 per cent) with sedimentary rocks (about 10 per cent) on and near the surface. Very

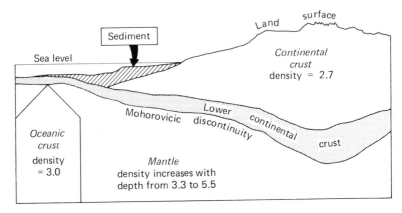

Fig. 2.2 The two kinds of crust

little is known about the lower layers of the continental crust and there is no agreement among geologists about their composition.

(b) The Oceanic Crust

This is denser (relative density = 3·0) and composed largely of basalt. It is much thinner than the continental crust, and on average is only 6 km thick. It is believed to underlie parts of the continental crust.

   These two kinds of crust meet on the sea-floor several kilometres from the coast. The junction is often obscured, however, by a varying thickness of sediment which has been worn away from the nearby land mass and deposited on the sea-floor around the coast.

2.5   The Changing Earth

The present-day distribution of land and sea over the earth's surface is familiar to us from world maps in atlases or from globes. But this distribution has not always been the same as it is today. If atlases could have been compiled at intervals of say, 100 million years, since the beginning of geological time, each one would be very different from all the others. Two separate but related theories have been put forward to explain these changes.

(a) Continental Drift

We saw in Section 2.4 that the continental crust is slightly lighter than the oceanic crust. The theory of continental drift, first put forward in 1910, suggests that the continents are like rafts 'floating' in the denser oceanic crust. The continental land masses began their existence as part of larger continents, one in each hemisphere (Gondwanaland in the southern hemisphere and Laurasia in the northern hemisphere). These broke up and the pieces drifted apart, eventually forming the continents we know today.

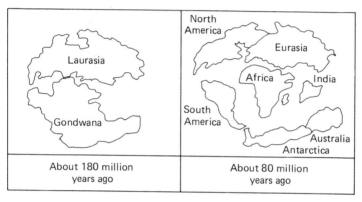

Fig. 2.3 The idea of continental drift

This hypothesis is supported by several facts. In the first place, some of the continents seem to fit together surprisingly well, almost like pieces of a jig-saw puzzle. Furthermore, several geological formations join up across this fit. Lastly, evidence of the past distribution of climatic types and previous forms of plant and animal life seems to suggest that continents now far apart, such as South America and Africa, were once joined while the continents now joined or close together, such as Europe and Africa, were once far apart.

(b) The Plate Theory

Discoveries made since 1960 about the nature of the oceanic crust have caused scientists to modify some of their ideas on continental drift. It is now thought that the earth's crust is made up of seven major plates, which are named in Fig. 2.4.

Complex movements in the underlying mantle cause movements to occur along the plate boundaries in three different ways. The plates are moving apart in some areas and this allows new material to rise to the ocean-floor from the mantle beneath. It forms long, high submarine ridges (Section 2.10(a)). The plates may collide or one may pass beneath another, and this movement causes volcanoes and mountains to form. Finally, plates are also thought to

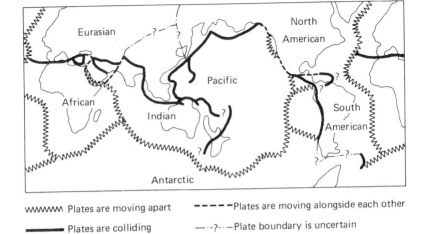

WWWWW Plates are moving apart   ‑ ‑ ‑ ‑ Plates are moving alongside each other

▬▬▬ Plates are colliding   —··?··—Plate boundary is uncertain

Fig. 2.4 The world's plates. (The continental outlines are taken to the edge of the continental crust)

scrape against one another, causing earthquakes. The plate boundaries co-incide with the *active zones* of the earth's crust, which are the areas where high mountains or ocean ridges are formed, where volcanoes erupt and earth-quakes occur.

2.6   Mountain Building

Table 2.1 shows three periods of time, each lasting several million years, during which mountains were formed. Such an event is called a mountain building period or *orogeny*.

Table 2.2   Mountain building periods

Name of orogeny	Geological time (approx.)
Alpine	25 million years ago
Hercynian or Armorican	280 million years ago
Caledonian	400 million years ago

These are by no means the only orogenies which have taken place. We know that others occurred during the vast expanse of Pre-Cambrian time, but they have left little trace in the earth's crust and so they are very difficult to date.

(a) Formation of Mountains
The formation of a mountain range may be explained simply in terms of the plate theory. When two plates move towards each other, it is likely that one

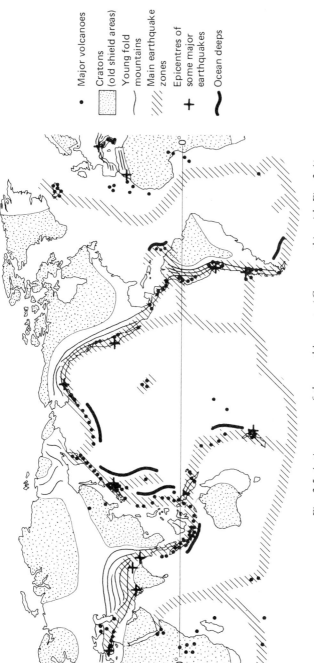

Major volcanoes

Cratons
(old shield areas)

Young fold
mountains

Main earthquake
zones

Epicentres of
some major
earthquakes

Ocean deeps

Fig. 2.5 Active zones of the earth's crust. (Compare this with Fig. 2.4)

consists of continental crust whereas the other is made up of oceanic crust. As they come together the oceanic crust, being denser, passes under the continental crust (Fig. 2.6(a)). The oceanic crust melts as it is drawn down and, because it is lighter than the mantle, it rises to the surface in a molten state to form volcanoes and igneous intrusions (Section 2.9). Sediment which has been accumulating for millions of years in the shallow water off the coast is compressed, folded and extensively cracked by the pressures generated as the plates continue to move together. The area of the plate junction eventually becomes a complex mixture of folded sedimentary rocks, volcanic lava,

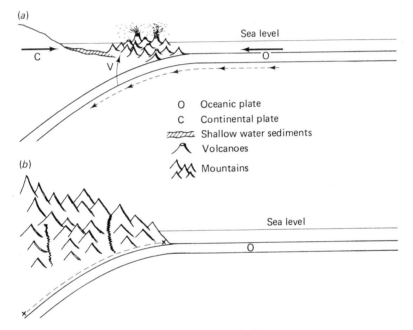

Fig. 2.6 Mountain building

igneous rocks which have moved upwards along the cracks, and metamorphic rocks formed as a result of pressure, heat or both. Those parts of the oceanic crust which have been forced downwards are less dense than the mantle, so they rise slowly after the horizontal movement has ceased, and cause the whole mountain mass to be uplifted. It is this last part of the orogeny which gives a mountain range its height above the surrounding land (Fig. 2.6(b)).

The mountains formed most recently, during the Alpine orogeny, are the highest in the world. They include the Himalayas, the Alps, the Rockies and the Andes, and they are all called young fold mountains. There are two reasons for their generally great height: first, they are still being slowly uplifted and, secondly, the processes of erosion have not been at work long enough to wear them down very much (Unit 3). The folding and cracking of the crustal rocks which accompanies a period of mountain building gives rise to a number of prominent features which we may see on the earth's surface. We shall examine the most important of these, folding and faulting.

(b) Folding

If a small carpet is placed upon a polished floor and one end is pushed, wrinkles or folds will appear. The pressure created by the collision of two plates does much the same to the sedimentary rocks on the sea-floor, and they are contorted into some of the shapes shown in Fig. 2.7. A fracture or thrust

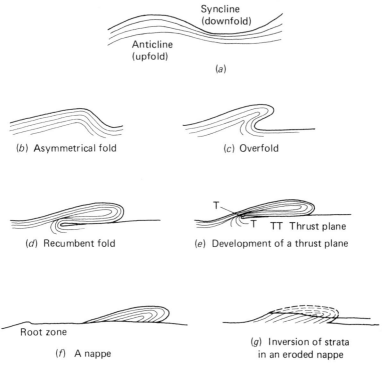

Fig. 2.7 Types of fold

plane may occur across the narrow neck of the recumbent fold, and further pressure may push the fold a long way from its root to form a *nappe*. Such extreme examples of folding may be traced for several kilometres in the Alps and Himalayas. The upper part may even have been eroded to leave only the lower part, where the sequence of the strata has been inverted, and formations like these caused early geologists much confusion (Fig. 2.7(g)).

There are several places in Britain where it is possible to see rocks folded in this way. The coastline on each side of Bude in North Cornwall is a good example, and Fig. 2.8 shows some of the Bude folding.

Fig. 2.8 Rock folding at Bude, Cornwall

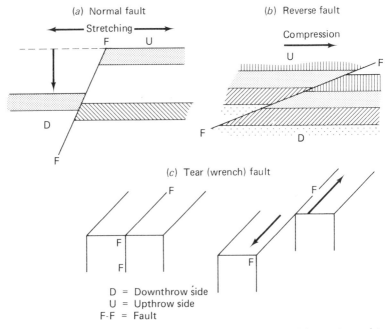

D = Downthrow side
U = Upthrow side
F-F = Fault

Fig. 2.9 Types of fault: (a) *normal fault,* (b) *reverse fault,* (c) *tear (wrench) fault*

(c) **Faulting**

A fault is a fracture in the rocks of the earth's crust, usually accompanied by movement of one or both sides of the fault. Faulting assumes several forms (Fig. 2.9). One side may simply rise or fall in relation to the other as a result of tension or stretching; this is known as a *normal fault* (Fig. 2.9(*a*)). A fault may form because of compression, and the rocks on one side may be thrust over the other; this is a *reverse fault* (Fig. 2.9(*b*)). Frequently, the relative movement between the two sides of a fault is horizontal, giving a *tear* or *wrench fault* (Fig. 2.9(*c*)).

Faults rarely occur singly and landscapes resulting from groups of faults are a major feature of some parts of the earth's surface. Such groups of faults may

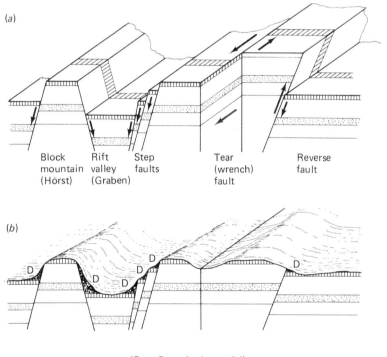

(D = Deposited material)

Fig. 2.10 Landforms resulting from faults
(a) *Diagrammatic impression of the movement resulting from faulting*
(b) *A faulted landscape*

give rise to particular landforms, of which the rift valley (or *graben*) and the block mountain (or *hörst*), are the most conspicuous and familiar features.

(i) **Rift valleys.** The stretching of the crust rocks may cause faulting and this can lead to the gradual sinking of part of the crust between more or less parallel lines of faults. The result is a rift valley. The middle valley of the river Rhine, from Basel down to Mainz, is a good example of a rift valley, but the most extensive is that which extends from Israel and Jordan, along the Red Sea, across Ethiopia, Kenya and Tanzania, to terminate on the borders of South Africa (Fig. 2.11(a)).

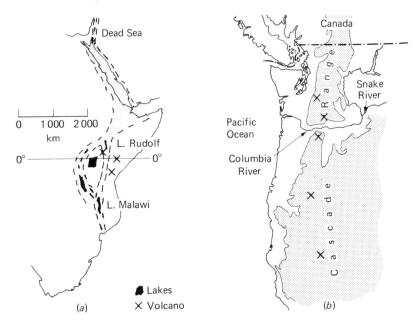

Fig. 2.11 (a) The Great East African Rift Valley
(b) A block mountain: the Cascade Range, North America

(ii) **Block mountains** are the converse of rift valleys, in that a block of the crust has been enclosed by faults, while the surrounding areas have sunk in relation to it. The Bihor mountains of Rumania, the Harz of Germany and many of the ranges of the American West are block mountains (Fig. 2.11(b)).

   Faults strongly influence the landscape in other ways. They give rise to cliff-like features or fault-scarps, although these may be worn back by erosion in a short period of time, until they are barely distinguishable. Faults also create lines of weakness in the crust, along which the broken and fragmented rocks are easily eroded. There is a tendency for rivers to follow lines of faulting; their valleys are sometimes widened and deepened to give rise to lakes. Many of the Norwegian fjords have been eroded along fault lines.
   Lastly, a fault may become a passage-way in the earth's crust along which magma can be forced towards the surface, so volcanic activity may accompany faulting. Examples of this association may be seen in the East African

volcanoes Kilimanjaro, Kenya and Elgon, which were formed near the rift valley (Fig. 2.11(a)). In the north-western USA, Mounts Rainier, Hood and Adams were formed near the block mountains of the Cascade Range (Fig. 2.11(b)).

2.7 Earthquakes

Movement along faults or plate junctions is still continuing in some parts of the earth's crust. When such movement occurs, shock waves travelling through the crust and mantle cause an earthquake when they reach the earth's surface. Earthquakes are most likely to occur near plate junctions, and it follows that their distribution is closely related to that of fold mountains and submarine ridges. We saw this in Fig. 2.5, which also shows that the shield areas seem unaffected by this earthquake or *seismic* activity.

The exact location of this movement which causes earthquakes may be anywhere in the crust or as far as 700 km down into the mantle but, wherever it is, this location is called the *focus* and the place immediately above it on the

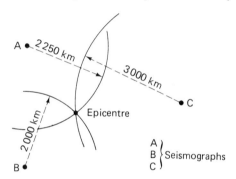

Fig. 2.12 The location of the epicentre of an earthquake

earth's surface is the *epicentre*. The position of an earthquake's epicentre and the force of the earthquake waves may be worked out by using sensitive recording instruments known as seismographs. This technique is particularly useful in the case of an earthquake below the sea-floor, when surface damage is non-existent.

(a) Earthquake Damage

There are major earthquakes almost every year and reports in newspapers or on television show the terrible devastation and damage which may be caused by them. The destruction is particularly severe if a large city is affected, as in the earthquakes in San Francisco (1906), Skopje (1963), Alaska (1964) and Managua (1972).

An earthquake may also have side effects which do more damage than the shock waves themselves. In a mountainous area, for instance, movement of the ground may generate an avalanche. In the Peruvian earthquake of 1970, millions of tons of ice, snow, rock and boulders moving at a tremendous speed—estimated at 480 km per hour—buried the town of Yungay and all its inhabitants. In Alaska in 1964 one of the most violent earthquakes ever recorded created a landslip into a fjord and the resulting waves did tremendous damage. In Guatemala in 1541, an earthquake broke down the wall of a large lake which had formed in an old volcanic crater and the deluge of water and mud completely buried the country's capital.

(b) Tsunamis (Tidal Waves)

An earthquake below the sea-floor sets up a wave on the ocean surface above which travels at speeds of up to 750 km per hour. Great loss of life and destruction may be caused thousands of kilometres from the epicentre by the effects of tidal waves, more correctly called by their Japanese name, *tsunamis*. In the deep ocean, such a wave may be several hundred kilometres long but only a few metres high. When it moves into shallow coastal water, it may rise to a height of 15 m and form a devastating wall of water which can cause great damage when it hits the coast. A special station has been set up in Hawaii to try and prevent such disasters in the Pacific; it detects and gives warning of tsunamis to coasts likely to be affected.

Volcanic eruption is a less common source of tsunamis. In 1883, the island of Krakatoa, between Sumatra and Java, was blown to dust by a vast volcanic explosion. The resulting waves rose to heights of 35 m, destroyed over 1 000 villages and killed 36 000 people.

2.8   Volcanoes

The word volcano derives from the island of Vulcano, which lies off the northeast coast of Sicily. When magma pours out or erupts on to the surface through a hole, vent or fracture in the crust, a volcano is built. Its surface shape depends largely on the chemical composition and hence the viscosity of the lava. Basic lava flows more easily than a lava with a more acidic composition (Section 2.3).

(a) Acid Lava

Acid lava becomes thick and porridge-like as it cools, and it does not flow far from the vent. The gas rising through it bursts out violently on reaching the surface of the liquid and each explosion of gas throws out fountains of lava. The lava cools as it flies through the air, and it falls on the slopes of the volcano as rounded lumps of hot but solidified lava (volcanic bombs) or as fine, dust-like fragments (volcanic ash). A volcanic cone is built up, composed of layers of ash and lava. This is called a *strato-volcano* or an ash and lava cone, and is what most people think of as a volcano. Perfect examples of this type of volcano are Mounts Etna, Vesuvius, Fujiyama, Kilimanjaro, Kenya and Shasta (see Fig. 4.5).

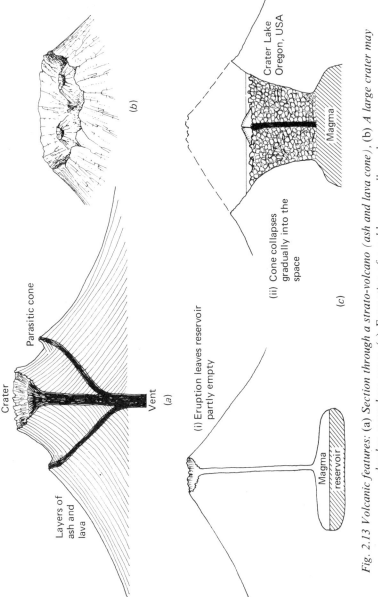

Fig. 2.13 Volcanic features: (a) Section through a strato-volcano (ash and lava cone), (b) A large crater may develop secondary cones, (c) Formation of a caldera or collapsed cone

(a) — Crater, Parasitic cone, Vent, Layers of ash and lava

(b)

(c)
(i) Eruption leaves reservoir partly empty — Magma reservoir
(ii) Cone collapses gradually into the space — Crater Lake Oregon, USA — Magma

At the top of such a cone is a hollow or crater. If the volcano is active, a great volume of gas—over 95 per cent of which is steam—rises from the crater, inside which is a red-hot pool of bubbling lava. A volcano is *dormant* if it has not erupted for some time and the lava has become solid and formed a plug, closing off the vent. It is *extinct* if it has not erupted during the time for which we have written records. If the plug is so resistant that gentle pressure from below cannot remove it, a build-up of pressure beneath it may blow the top off the volcano. Later eruptions may build smaller secondary cones in the crater. Sometimes, lava may break out sideways from the vent to build a subsidiary or parasitic cone on the flank of the main cone (Fig. 2.13).

After a long period of eruption has subsided, a large, empty space may be left in the magma reservoir beneath the volcano. The cone may slowly collapse into this space leaving a yawning hole in the surface, known as a *caldera* or collapsed cone. On the other hand, the whole of an extinct volcano may be eroded away, leaving only the plug of harder rock standing out as a high, isolated pinnacle. In the Central Massif of France, this feature is called a *puy* and is very familiar from the upstanding plugs at Le Puy (Fig. 2.14).

Fig. 2.14 A volcanic plug in Nigeria. The rest of the volcano has been eroded away

(*b*) **Basic Lava**

Basic lava flows more easily and remains fluid at low temperatures. It erupts with little explosive force and flows a long way from the vent before becoming solid. The lava often flows out from long fissures (cracks) and a number of successive flows may build up a great thickness in the form of a lava sheet. Examples of this type of volcanic activity are less well known as their scenery is not as spectacular as the acid cones. They do, however, occupy large areas of the earth's surface. In the north-west USA, the Columbia–Snake lava plain covers several thousand square kilometres to a depth of 1 500 m, while much of the north-western part of the Indian sub-continent is occupied by the Deccan lava flows. A smaller example is the Antrim plateau in Northern Ireland, famous for the unusual six-sided basalt columns of the Giant's Causeway.

A basic lava eruption from a single vent, as opposed to a fissure, gives rise to a *shield volcano* which has gently sloping, slightly convex sides, like an enormous upturned saucer. Basic lava frequently erupts from the sea-floor because the oceanic crust is composed largely of basalt (Section 2.4). The Hawaiian Islands form the upper part of a shield volcano of immense size— it is about 100 km across and 4 210 m high above sea-level—but its real base is on the sea-floor and it is over 480 km in diameter. As the sea is over 10 000 m deep, its overall height is more than 14 000 m, far higher than Mount Everest.

(*c*) **Some Famous Volcanoes**

At present there are over 500 active volcanoes, and 400 of them are in the *Pacific ring* (Fig. 2.5). A great deal is now known about the behaviour of volcanoes, and many eruptions have been very carefully studied.

In AD 79, the town of Pompeii in Italy was buried under volcanic ash after Mount Vesuvius exploded; nearby Herculaneum was buried under an avalanche of mud, a mixture of volcanic ash and the torrential rain which fell as steam from the volcano cooled in the atmosphere. The explosion of the Krakatoa eruption, when most of the island was blown to dust, was heard from a distance of 4 800 km. Some of the dust fell on to the decks of ships over 2 500 km away, several days later, and some rose high into the atmosphere and circled the earth for many months, causing brilliant sunsets. In 1912, the eruption of Mount Katmai in Alaska was heard 1 000 km away and the volcanic dust blacked out towns over 150 km distant. At Kodiak, 160 km away, the dust was 240 mm deep.

One of the best recorded and most destructive eruptions took place in 1902, on the island of Martinique in the West Indies. Mount Pelee, overlooking the town of St Pierre, split open along its side and a cloud of hot gas and dust was blasted across the town at great speed, suffocating 30 000 people almost instantly and burning everything in its path. The Mexican volcano of Paracutin has grown into a huge cone since 1943. Surtsey emerged from the sea off the coast of Iceland in 1963 and just after Christmas 1972, a nearby fissure over 3 km long opened up.

(*d*) **Hydrothermal Activity**

In some volcanic areas, hot water reaches the surface and gives rise to hydro-thermal features such as hot springs, geysers and so-called mud volcanoes.

(i) **Hot springs.** Water, often at a very high temperature, bubbles to the surface along a crack or fissure in the ground, which may have been caused by volcanic activity or may have occurred before volcanic activity took place. Hot springs are numerous in volcanic areas such as the North Island of New Zealand, Iceland and parts of California.

(ii) **Geysers** are an intermittent form of hot spring in which a jet of water is thrown into the air. Some geysers, such as Old Faithful in Yellowstone National Park, USA do this at regular intervals.

(iii) **Mud volcanoes.** If the hot water has to pass through mud or volcanic ash in its ascent to the surface, it may appear more as mud than water. It may even build a cone of mud, like a miniature volcano.

In some parts of the world, especially Iceland, hot springs have an economic importance in supplying heat, electric power and domestic hot water. Hot springs are widely reputed to have medicinal properties.

2.9   Igneous Intrusions

Extrusive igneous rocks such as lava and ash are not the only rocks which give rise to notable landscape features. Intrusive rocks such as granite and gabbro (Section 2.3) may also be found on the earth's surface, after the rocks which formerly covered them have been eroded away. The granite areas of Devon and Cornwall, and those in Brittany, were originally formed about 3 km below the surface as huge blister-like masses known as *batholiths*. Now they form areas of high ground on the surface, because the granite has been more resistant to erosion than the surrounding sedimentary rocks.

(*a*) **Dykes and Sills**

During the intrusion of a batholith the overlying rock is domed upwards, stretched and cracked. These cracks are weaknesses which help to speed up the erosive processes. Magma is forced into them from beneath to form smaller intrusions known as *dykes* (when almost vertical) and *sills* (when nearly horizontal). Such igneous intrusions often form outstanding features of the landscape because they are usually harder than the rock into which they were intruded and so resist erosion. The Whin Sill lies under much of northern England, and it gives rise to scarp-like features where it outcrops. On the west coast of Scotland, numerous dykes formed as part of a volcano in Tertiary times (Table 2.1) and they are prominent features of the coastal scenery.

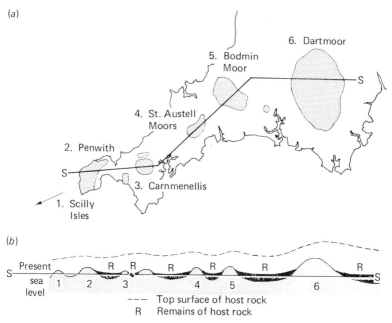

Fig. 2.15 Granite areas in south-west England
(a) Location of granite moorland. (Although these are separate on the surface,
they are probably all connected at depth)
(b) Section through the south-western peninsula (drawn along line S–S on (a))
Granite was intruded into the host rock, now mostly eroded

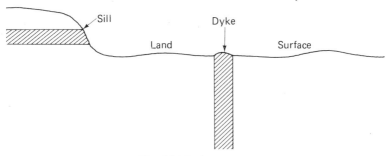

Fig. 2.16 Dyke and sill

(b) Granite Tors

Hills on granite moorlands are sometimes crowned with piles of strangely shaped, roughly rectangular blocks which may even appear to have been man-made. These are called *tors* and their block-like appearance is the result of the magma cooling and contracting. The resulting cracks are called *joints* and they are slowly enlarged by weathering (Section 3.2) to give a granite outcrop its unusual appearance. The spacing of the joints determines the size and shape of the blocks which make up the tor. Many blocks tumble down from the out-crop at the summit to cover the upper slopes of the hill with a jumbled mass of angular boulders known as *clitter*. The basalt of the Giant's Causeway has developed a similarly jointed pattern, resulting in the familiar hexagonal columns.

2.10   The Oceans

We know much less about the floor of the oceans than we do about the land surface, although oceans cover over two-thirds of the earth's surface. Pain-staking research over the past 20 years, including dredging, boring and echo-sounding, has added greatly to our knowledge, but there is still much to learn and studying the ocean-floor presents a number of major problems.

We saw in Section 2.4 that the ocean-floor consists largely of basalt. Our present knowledge suggests that the Atlantic, Indian, Arctic and Antarctic Oceans are all less than 200 million years old. They came into being when a large mass of continental crust broke up and the pieces moved apart, 'floating' on a layer of denser basalt rock (Section 2.5). As the spaces between the moving pieces grew wider, molten basalt from the underlying mantle welled up and spread out on the floor of the growing ocean. This process has been called sea-floor spreading.

(a) The Ocean-floor

A cross-section of the ocean-floor shows that a broad, shallow, gently shelving *continental shelf*, covered by up to 200 m (about 100 fathoms) of water, surrounds most of the continents (*H & R*, Section 14.1). This is made up of the same material as the continental crust, but it is covered by a thin layer of sediment eroded from the nearby land mass (Section 2.4). The real edge of the continental crust is the steep slope known as the *continental slope* at the outer (oceanic) edge of the shelf. This plunges steeply to depths of between 4 000 m and 6 000 m, where there are large areas of fairly level floor known as the

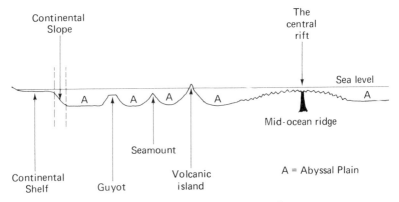

Fig. 2.17 Section across the ocean floor

abyssal plain. Many mountain-like features of volcanic origin rise from this plain. These may be simple islands or island groups, such as the Marshall, Fiji and Ellice groups in the Pacific Ocean. Sometimes the 'islands' fail to reach the surface of the ocean and they are then called *seamounts.* These underwater islands may have had their tops planed off by the action of the waves, so that they become flat-topped. These are often known as *guyots.*

All ocean-floors have mid-ocean ridges which rise to heights of 4 000 m or more above the level of the abyssal plains. These ridges mark the junctions of plates which are moving apart, and they are formed by the upwelling of basaltic material from the mantle. The higher parts of these ridges break the surface as volcanic islands, such as Iceland, the Azores, the Ascension Islands and Tristan da Cunha, which all rise from the mid-Atlantic ridge.

(b) Salinity

For hundreds of millions of years rain has fallen on to the earth's land areas and water has flowed off the land surface into the sea. Many chemicals from the rocks and from the air have been dissolved in the water and have accumulated in the seas. These chemicals have become more and more concentrated in the oceans as a result of constant *evaporation* of the ocean water, which leaves the dissolved chemicals behind. The most abundant of these is sodium chloride (common salt), which gives sea water its salty taste. On average about 3·5 per cent of ocean water is made up of dissolved chemicals, and nearly nine-tenths of these are either sodium or magnesium chloride.

(c) The Water Cycle

Every body of water on the earth's surface, from the vastness of the Pacific Ocean to the bird-bath in the garden, loses water from its surface by evaporation into the atmosphere, where it becomes *water vapour.* Water vapour makes up a variable proportion of the air all over the world. When the air is cooled, water vapour may change into rain, hail, snow, fog or cloud (Section 9.6). The water which falls on to the earth's surface eventually finds its way back into the oceans by way of streams and rivers, so the process continues all the time. This circulation is known as the *water cycle* or *hydrological cycle.*

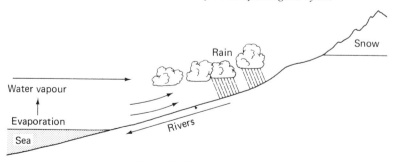

Fig. 2.18 The water cycle

(d) Ocean Currents

In every ocean there is a circulation of surface water, as shown in Fig. 10.4. This may appear to be very complicated, but the circulation can be explained simply in terms of the prevailing winds which blow the surface water along (Section 10.4). The winds create a rotation which is clockwise in the northern hemisphere and anti-clockwise in the southern hemisphere. The only exception is in the Indian Ocean north of the equator, where currents are reversed seasonally as a result of the reversal in direction of the monsoon winds. (Section 11.3(d).)

For reasons which we do not yet fully understand, an ocean current may move temporarily from its normal position. Recently the Humboldt (Peruvian) current, which usually runs northwards along the west coast of South America, moved westwards away from the coast into deeper water, severely damaging the Peruvian anchovy fishing. Happily, the current has returned to its former position, bringing with it the plankton on which the anchovies feed, and the fishing industry is thriving once again.

(e) Land Below Sea-level

We might expect that all parts of the earth's surface which are below sea-level would be covered by sea. This is largely true, but there are several exceptions to the rule. The best known area of land lying below sea-level is in the Netherlands (*H & R*, Unit 17). The Dutch have reclaimed about a third of their country from lake, marsh and the sea-floor, but all such areas which lie below sea-level need to be protected from flooding. The Netherlands is protected by a complex system of man-made dykes along much of the coast and the river banks, and natural barriers, such as extensive coastal sand dunes, also protect the low-lying land from the sea.

The Dead Sea depression in Israel and Jordan is 91 m below sea-level, and Death Valley in California is 87 m below sea-level. These are both rift valleys, and they are enclosed by very much higher ground.

(f) Changes of Sea-level

There is abundant evidence to show that the sea-level in the past has been both higher and lower than it is today, and that it is, in fact, still changing. Even in the short span of 'historic' time there is good reason to believe that the sea-level has changed a measurable amount.

(i) **Evidence.** It has been proved that Britain was joined to the rest of Europe as recently as 5000 BC. The earliest human inhabitants of our island probably walked over here from the continent. The fact that sea-level is still rising slowly around south-east England has made the construction of a river barrage across the lower Thames a matter of great urgency, to protect London from the dangers of a tidal surge. When a high spring tide coincides with a strong easterly wind, water is forced into the funnel-shaped Thames estuary producing a river-level higher than the low-lying areas of London. This creates a danger of flooding, especially in the underground railway system. A similar barrier is now being built across the mouth of the river Rhine, in the Netherlands.

Evidence for changes in sea-level is found in the large areas of almost level land, known as *platforms*, which can be seen in many parts of Britain. They are thought to have been cut by waves when the sea stood at a much higher level than it does today. The high granite areas of Devon and Cornwall show these platforms particularly clearly; they have been preserved because of the hardness of the rock in which they were cut.

There is also plentiful evidence along Britain's coasts of lower and higher sea-levels during the last million years. There are submerged forests beneath many beaches, which are exposed only rarely. They are the remains of extensive forests which once grew where today's tides rise and fall. Along some stretches of coast there are *raised beaches*, the remains of past beaches now well out of reach of the waves (Section 5.4(*b*)).

(ii) **Causes.** The changes in sea-level which were responsible for these submerged forests and raised beaches were partly the result of climatic changes during the Ice Age (Section 6.1). The climate became first colder, then warmer on at least four separate occasions; the cold periods are called *glacials* and the warm periods, *interglacials*. During the glacials, thick ice formed on some land areas. This interrupted the water cycle—because very little water was flowing back into the sea—and the sea-level dropped. During the warm interglacials much of the ice melted, the water flowed back into the oceans and sea-level rose. (Exactly how far it rose depended on the temperature during the interglacial.)

There are, however, other reasons for changes in sea-level. First, during mountain building periods there were considerable vertical movements of the crust, and large areas of sea-floor found themselves uplifted to form dry land, or even high plateaux. Secondly, a large sheet of ice constitutes a very heavy load on the continental mass, so this is forced down with a consequent rise in sea-level. Then, after the ice has melted and the load removed, the continent slowly rises again causing sea-level to fall. This process, known as *isostatic readjustment*, is still going on in several parts of the world, particularly in Scandinavia. The land is rising at the rate of about 1 m every 80 years around the northern end of the Gulf of Bothnia, and some experts believe that it will rise a further 200 m.

Further Reading

Calder, N.: *The Restless Earth*. BBC Publications (London, 1972).

Carson, R.: *The Sea Around Us*. Panther (London, 1969).

Dury, G. H.: *The Face of the Earth*. Penguin (Harmondsworth, 1970), Chapters 2–5.

Gass, I. G., Smith, P. J. and Wilson, R. C. L. (eds.): *Understanding the Earth*. Artemis Press (Horsham, 1972).

Holmes, A.: *Principles of Physical Geology*. Nelson (London, 1965), Chapters 4–12, 25–31.

Small, R. J.: *The Study of Landforms*. Cambridge University Press (London, 1970), Chapters 3 and 4.

Sparks, B. W.: *Geomorphology*. Longman (Harlow, 1970), Chapter 7.

Strahler, A. N.: *Physical Geography*. John Wiley (Chichester, 1969), Chapters 19, 20, 30, 31.

Swinnerton, H. H.: *The Earth Beneath Us*. Penguin (Harmondsworth, 1958), Chapters 7, 8, 11 and Part 3.

Tazieff, H.: *When the Earth Trembles*. Hart-Davis (London, 1964).

Questions
1. Describe the ways in which rocks may be formed, giving examples of each type.
2. What do you understand by the plate theory? What has it to do with (*a*) the formation of mountains, (*b*) earthquakes, (*c*) volcanoes?
3. Giving examples of each, say what you understand by (*a*) folding, (*b*) faulting.
4. Explain clearly the meaning of the following terms: (*a*) tsunamis, (*b*) caldera, (*c*) hydrothermal activity, (*d*) batholith, (*e*) craton, (*f*) Mohorovicic discontinuity, (*g*) nappe.
5. What is the difference between acid and basic lava? Describe and give examples of the surface features created by each.

Unit Three
The Changing Landscape

Now that we have described the earth's structure and the nature of its surface, we must examine the ways in which the surface is slowly changing. The rocks which make up the earth are constantly being broken up and the fragments are transported by water, wind or ice to be laid down elsewhere—sometimes on land, but more often on the sea-bed. Every landscape feature is subject to such change. Crags, cliffs and mountain peaks will eventually disappear, and the fragments of the rocks of which they are formed will become clay or sand on the ocean-floor. But by then earth movements (Section 2.6) may have begun to build up new chains of mountains, so that the whole process of *denudation* (the wearing away of the earth's surface) can begin again. This is the history of the earth, an endless cycle of building hills and mountains, destroying them and raising new formations from their remains.

Normally these changes, which we shall examine in Units 3–8, take place very slowly indeed. In the course of a lifetime one sees little, if any, change in the contours of the ground or the shape of the coast. Yet there are occasions when change is rapid and visible. The violent floods in Lynmouth, Devon, in August 1952, for example, brought about changes that were readily apparent. The level of a small stream and its speed and destructive power increased so much, as a result of very heavy rainfall, that flood water devastated the valley and the village at its mouth in the space of a few hours.

3.1 Denudation

A landscape at any given moment is merely one stage in the process of slow but long-continued change. There are many agents of change. Storm waves beat against the coast, causing soft cliffs to crumble beneath their attack, and the coastline will gradually recede, as it has done in parts of East Anglia. But material torn from the cliffs in this way is redistributed by waves and currents: some is spread over the sea-floor, the rest is redeposited elsewhere along the shore and across bays and estuaries. Stream water takes particles from the land's surface, carries them downstream and ultimately deposits them on the sea-floor. Frost shatters the rocks in some areas and percolating water may dissolve them. Ice may scour and scratch them, carrying away soil particles and rock fragments to deposit them on lower ground, where flowing water may carry them further in their journey towards the sea.

Denudation is the general term used to denote the whole range of processes by which the earth's crust is broken up and its materials removed, ultimately to the seas. It is convenient, however, to divide these processes of denudation into weathering, mass wasting and erosion.

(a) Weathering

Weathering is the process of breaking up or disintegration of rocks. There are, very broadly, three forms of weathering, according to whether it is accomplished by physical, chemical or biological means.

(i) **Mechanical or physical weathering** results from the action of frost, and from expansion and contraction.

Most rocks are penetrated by cracks which may be invisible to the naked eye but large enough for water to seep into them. In mountain areas there is an alternation of freezing and thawing for much of the year, and in winter in other districts temperatures frequently fluctuate above and below freezing point. The moisture in cracks in the rocks freezes and expands, then melts only to freeze and expand again. The cracks are widened until a piece of rock

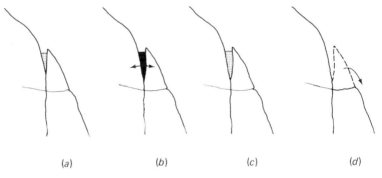

    (a)   (b)   (c)   (d)

Fig. 3.1 Frost shattering or thaw-freeze weathering: (a) *water occupies a crack,* (b) *water freezes: ice expands,* (c) *ice melts: crack is wider and water flows in further,* (d) *eventually this process detaches an angular rock fragment*

is broken from the mass. This process, known as *frost shattering* or *thaw–freeze*, is commonest in hilly and mountainous country, where the rock surface is exposed. Level surfaces are covered with a layer of angular rock fragments while steep rock faces may have an apron of angular rocks below them, known as *scree*. This is a product of long-continued thaw–freeze.

Rocks also expand in the heat of the sun, and contract again after sunset. The greater the range of temperature between day and night, the more the rocks will expand and contract. This would have little effect on a homogeneous rock; many rocks, however, are made up of a number of different minerals, each with its own rate of expansion and contraction. The exposed surface of such a rock gradually breaks up into its various components in a process known as *granular disintegration*. In the more homogeneous rocks, such as sandstone, this weathering may take the form of *exfoliation*: layers of the rock surface peel off as a result of expansion and contraction and these are in turn, broken up into smaller particles. (This process is sometimes called *onion weathering*, because it is rather like removing the skins of an onion.)

In the hot deserts the range of temperature between day and night is greater than it is anywhere else on the earth's surface (Section 11.3). It is here that rocks most readily disintegrate into the fragments which we know as sand.

(ii) **Chemical weathering.** Rain water absorbs carbon dioxide in its passage through the atmosphere, and this makes the water into a very dilute solution of carbonic acid. The acid reacts with some forms of rock, weakening the rock's structure and hastening its break-up. Limestone, for example, consists mainly of calcium carbonate which is soluble in the slightly acid rain water which percolates through it. Caves are dissolved in some limestone rocks in this way, and the network of thin joints is enlarged by solution (Section 3.2(*a*)).

Percolating water also attacks the mineral *felspar*, even in granite, reducing it to a powdery clay (kaolin), similar to that produced by the chemical action of vapours from within the earth's crust. This weakens the whole rock structure, and the loose material is easily carried away, especially by running water.

(iii) **Biological or organic weathering.** Biological factors assist and hasten the action of physical and chemical weathering. Moss holds water in contact with a rock surface, keeping it damp and helping it to disintegrate. The roots of trees and bushes may penetrate joints and cracks in a rock, forcing them open and allowing water to enter. Burrowing animals such as earthworms and even insects make holes through the soil and down to the rock below and these allow water and air to penetrate, helping to break up the rock physically and chemically.

(*b*) **Mass Wasting**
Some of the rain which falls upon the earth's surface evaporates back into the atmosphere. The rest either flows away over the surface as *run-off* or sinks into the rocks as *percolation*. Both run-off and percolation help to wear away the rocks in a number of ways which are known collectively as mass wasting.

The type of rock determines whether the water runs off or percolates. Some *impermeable* rocks such as clay and shale do not readily allow water to pass through, and much of the rainfall which runs off their surfaces flows into rivers, which may be relatively large and liable to flooding. Other rocks are *permeable*, and water can pass through them. Limestone and some of the igneous rocks, such as granite, are penetrated by joints through which water can pass. Chalk, sandstone and beds of sand and gravel are made up of grains between which are pores or minute spaces.

(i) **Soil wash** is the easiest of the mass wasting processes to understand and even to observe, for it is simply the washing of bare soil down a slope by run-off. Sometimes the water moves as a sheet, but more often it forms gullies from which the soil is washed away. Soil wash may produce bizarre land-forms, especially in unconsolidated material such as boulder clay. Larger boulders may protect the softer material beneath them, while the soil all around is washed away; the result is the formation of *earth pillars*, each with its protective cap of stone. These are short-lived features of the landscape which are destroyed when the cap falls off, but fresh earth pillars are always likely to form.

(ii) **Soil creep** acts on grass-covered slopes. The vegetation prevents soil wash, but heavy rainfall percolates into the soil and waterlogs it by filling the spaces between the soil grains. The water acts as a lubricant, allowing soil particles to move very slowly against one another. There is thus a tendency for the surface layers to creep or flow downhill. This process, known as *solifluction*, is generally too slow to be seen, but its consequences are readily apparent. Posts driven into a hillside to support a fence are often seen to lean downhill, as a result of the soil movement. The trunks of trees are sometimes pushed from the vertical, and their roots on the downhill side may be exposed by the movement of the soil. Walls built along a hillside may have soil piled up on their uphill side, but on the downhill side the soil may have been removed.

There is usually a permanent grass cover on slopes which are too steep to be ploughed. Miniature landslips occur over a long period of time, especially on clay soil, and these leave a roughly stepped surface. These steps are known as *solifluction terraces* or *terracettes*. They have sometimes been mistakenly associated with the movement of sheep and called sheep tracks. Animals do use them, but they are purely the result of natural forces (Fig. 3.3).

(iii) **Slumping.** Occasionally the movement of the soil may be more violent and sudden. A cliff face is particularly liable to slumping. The soil and rock near the top of a cliff are lubricated by rain, so that they become heavy and tend to pull away from the rest of the cliff. A crack or line of weakness develops near the cliff top and further rainfall saturates the soil, so that gravity causes a slice of the cliff face to slide downwards to the base. This process is obviously greatly influenced by the type of rock forming the cliff. Slumping is rare with hard igneous rocks, like granite, but frequent in cliffs cut in soft sedimentary rocks. Some parts of the British coast are particularly liable to slumping. In Dorset, especially near Lyme Regis and Charmouth, the cliffs are composed entirely of heavy, black Lias clay which slumps readily after heavy rain. In other areas, especially the Isle of Wight, Sussex and Kent, chalk overlies clay. Rain soaks into the chalk, but not the underlying clay, so the lower part of the chalk becomes waterlogged and heavy, causing the chalk to slump down towards sea-level.

(*c*) **Erosion**
The third process in the denudation of the earth's surface is erosion. This consists of the wearing away of the rock, principally by flowing water, but also by moving ice, the waves of seas and lakes, and by the wind. These are the four *agents of erosion*, but they are also agents of transport and deposition; they erode *because* they transport. (It is in this last respect that erosion differs from weathering, which is the break-up of the surface by agents which are themselves incapable of removing the fragments.)

Fig. 3.2 Earth pillars in boulder clay, Scotland

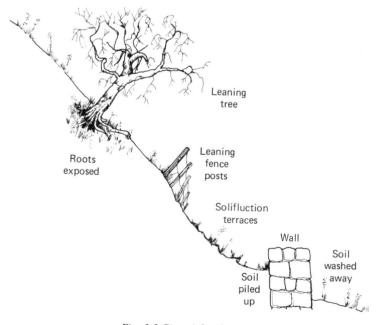

Leaning
tree

Roots
exposed

Leaning
fence
posts

Solifluction
terraces

Wall

Soil
washed
away

Soil
piled
up

Fig. 3.3 Signs of soil creep

Everything eroded and transported by wind, water and ice must be deposited somewhere. The volume of the load transported by wind and water varies with the speed of movement of the agent. A strong wind or a swift current can transport a great deal more than a gentle breeze or a slow-flowing stream. Rivers slow down as they approach lower and flatter land, and their speed is usually very slight when they enter the sea. They therefore drop more and more of their load, and the last of it sinks to the sea-bed near the mouth of the river (Section 4.4(*d*)). Most lakes tend to fill up with the sediment brought into them by rivers in the same way.

Wind also carries a load of small particles, much of which is dropped when the wind's speed of movement is reduced. It is in this way that sand dunes are formed (Section 7.3).

Only ice behaves differently, because it is not a fluid like wind or water. Ice is capable of carrying an immense load, including boulders of a size which even a river in flood could not move, and the volume of the load is not influenced by the speed of movement. Glaciers which melt in the sea deposit their load there. Otherwise, the load may be spread irregularly over the land surface when the ice melts away, leaving an uneven spread of the familiar boulder clay (Section 6.4).

The sea transports material brought to it by rivers and ice as well as fragments which it has eroded from the coast. It moves some material further out to sea and this is spread over the sea-bed. Some is carried along the coast, where it forms the familiar beaches and spits. Some even provides tools with which the waves batter the cliffs, grinding boulders to pebbles and pebbles to sand and mud (Section 5.2).

3.2   Ground Water and Topography

We saw in Section 3.1(*b*) that much of the water which falls on to the earth percolates below the surface, by means of the permeable rocks. We shall now examine the ways in which this water influences the landscape.

A rock which is permeable and underlain by an impermeable rock holds *ground water* in it; such a rock is termed an *aquifer*. It takes centuries for water to gather in an aquifer. The upper surface of the saturated part of the aquifer is known as the *water-table*. This is usually roughly parallel with the surface of the ground but it tends to move up and down with the seasons. In temperate latitudes it is lower in summer than in winter (less water percolates into the rock in summer because of the lower rainfall). When the water-table meets the surface of the ground, a spring breaks out.

In many parts of the world the water supply is derived from wells (vertical shafts sunk into the rock until they reach the water-table). The level of water rises and falls in a well, and in a dry summer it may run dry. When this happens, the level of the water-table has dropped below that of the bottom of the well.

When a well is sunk in certain types of geological structure, water may rise to the surface under its own pressure. This type of well is called an *artesian well*, from the French province of Artois where the phenomenon was first

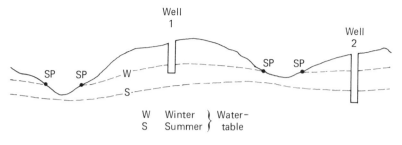

W   Winter } Water–
S   Summer } table

SP : Springs (dry up in summer)

Fig. 3.4 Movement of the water table. Well 1 dries up in summer, well 2 supplies water all year

studied. Fig. 3.5 shows the structure of an artesian well. In Australia artesian basins underlie a large part of the continent, and the water they contain may have been held in the rocks for millions of years. In recent years it has been used to water stock and irrigate land, but unfortunately the water is not being replenished as fast as it is being used. Many artesian wells have run dry and

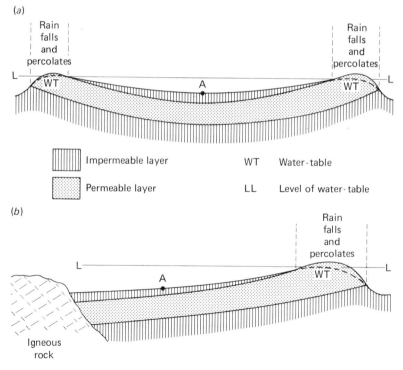

Fig. 3.5 Artesian wells: (a) *London type,* (b) *Australian type. Wells dug at A will gush*

this water, like many of the earth's natural resources, may be exhausted in the not-too-distant future.

A small artesian basin underlies London and has long been important in the city's water supply. Even in deserts there are often abundant reservoirs of ground water. Depressions in the desert surface are sometimes low enough to reach the water-table, and here an oasis is likely to exist.

(a) Limestone

As we saw in Section 3.1, limestone consists of calcium carbonate, which is slightly soluble in the rain water which percolates through it. Ground water is a major factor in the shaping of limestone landscape features. Water seeps into the rock along its joints (minute cracks and fissures), enlarges them by dissolving the rock in a process known as *solution*, and this forms a series of features which are peculiar to limestone scenery.

(i) **Limestone pavement.** The surface of exposed limestone—in parts of the Pennines, for instance—may have a corrugated appearance, because the joints have been enlarged by solution to form grooves or even small trenches, known as *grykes*. Ridges or *clints* are left between the grykes; these have been

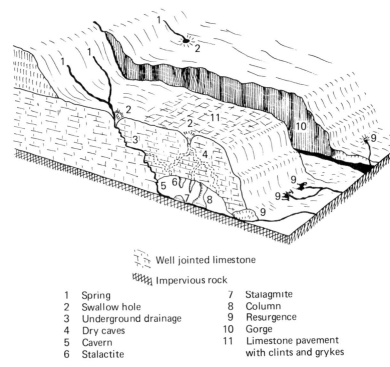

⌇⌇ Well jointed limestone

〰〰 Impervious rock

1	Spring	7	Stalagmite
2	Swallow hole	8	Column
3	Underground drainage	9	Resurgence
4	Dry caves	10	Gorge
5	Cavern	11	Limestone pavement
6	Stalactite		with clints and grykes

Fig. 3.6 Features associated with well-jointed limestone

Fig. 3.7 Limestone pavement with clints and grykes, above Malham Cove, Yorkshire

Fig. 3.8 Gaping Ghyll, a swallow hole in carboniferous limestone, near Ingleborough, Yorkshire. It is over 100 m deep

subjected to solution to a smaller degree. The result is a limestone pavement which is very uneven and difficult to walk over.

(ii) **Swallow holes.** Run-off quickly finds the vertical joints in a limestone surface, and passes down through them to lower levels. The more or less vertical crevices become enlarged until some are yawning holes. These are pot-holes or swallow holes. Sometimes a stream plunges over their rim into the dark abyss below.

(iii) **Limestone caves.** Joints in limestone may be horizontal as well as vertical, and when water moves along the horizontal joints, they are enlarged by solu-

Fig. 3.9 Stalactites and stalagmites in the Carlsbad Caverns, New Mexico, USA. This cavern is over 1 km long, 100 m high and 200 m wide

tion to form caves. Many caves are now dry, or only occupied by water after heavy rains, generally because the water has dissolved a lower passage-way for itself. Sometimes caves encroach on one another, and the intervening rock is slowly dissolved away to create a cavern of vast size (Fig. 3.9).

Stalactites and stalagmites are familiar features of limestone caves. They are formed over a period of many thousands of years by the steady drip of water from the roof of a cave. The water is highly charged with calcium carbonate (dissolved limestone), a minute amount of which is precipitated as each drop-let forms and hangs on the cave roof before it falls to the floor below. In this way, an icicle-shaped finger of limestone or *stalactite* is formed on the roof, and gradually lengthens downwards towards the floor.

As the falling drop of water strikes the floor, it breaks into smaller droplets which spread over the surrounding floor. A tiny amount of calcium carbonate is precipitated with each droplet and contributes to the building up of a thicker pillar of limestone known as a *stalagmite*. Eventually stalactite and stalagmite meet to form a pillar or column. Droplets of water trickle down its sides, making it grow even thicker.

(iv) **Resurgence.** Percolating water does not continue flowing downwards for ever. The limit set to its movement is usually an underlying impermeable layer of rock. In highly-developed limestone topography, water courses through a system of caves and eventually emerges from the hillside. This is known as a *resurgence*, as shown in Fig. 3.6.

(v) **Gorges.** Limestone terrain is often distinguished by gorges. The Cheddar Gorge in the Mendip Hills of Somerset is a famous example, and there are others in the Peak District of Derbyshire, which is part of the Pennines. Many gorges are dry. Most originated as a series of interconnected caves and caverns. These grew large and the ceiling above them became thinner until, eventually, it collapsed to reveal a gorge.

One of the world's most extensive limestone areas is in Yugoslavia. The vast plateau of the Dinaric Mountains has a profusion of all the features of lime-stone topography that we have discussed. The local name for this type of topography is *karst*, and this word is commonly used to denote the extreme development of limestone scenery. Areas like these rarely have much econ-omic value. Soils are usually thin and dry, crops do not grow well and many regions provide, at most, only rough grazing. They are often areas of great natural beauty, however, and some have been developed as resort areas. The gorges of the Tarn in southern France are a famous example, as are parts of the Pennines in England. The exploration of limestone caves (speleology or pot-holing) has become a common, though somewhat hazardous, pastime in many karst areas.

(b) Chalk

Chalk is a variety of limestone but it differs greatly from the other types in its physical characteristics and its surface features. It is found widely in south-eastern England and in north-eastern France, but in few other areas (*H & R*, Units 11 and 16). Chalk is softer and much more porous than limestone. Water can percolate into it and through it at almost any point, for it is not dependent on finding joint fissures. There is almost no run-off, and the surface of the chalk is lowered only very slowly and principally by solution of the chalk itself. Chalk tends to form hills, usually with smooth, rounded contours. Vegetation is slight—short grass, with very few trees—since there is no surface moisture, and rain is quickly absorbed.

Fig. 3.10 A chalk escarpment: the South Downs near Fulking, Sussex. Notice the differences between scarp and dip slopes, the well-developed combes along the scarp slope, the different uses to which man has put the chalk and underlying clay, and the villages along the spring line at the scarp foot

(i) **Scarp and dip slopes.** Beds of chalk are usually slightly folded, so that they form a series of synclines and anticlines. Erosion has generally removed the crest of the anticline as, for example, in the Weald of southern England. The chalk then outcrops in a ridge known as an *escarpment* or *cuesta*, with a steep scarp slope and a gentle dip slope or back slope.

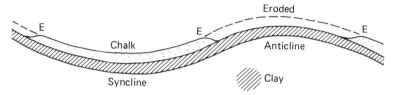

Fig. 3.11 *The formation of escarpments (cuestas) as a result of the folding of a chalk layer. E = escarpment*

(ii) **Spring line.** Springs break out at the foot of the scarp slope, where the chalk overlies impervious clay and the water-table meets the surface. A small valley or combe is often formed by the erosion of the small streams flowing out along the spring line. Human settlement has always tended to concentrate along such lines, which not only provided a water supply, but lay at the junction of two very different types of environment, the dry chalk and the damp clay.

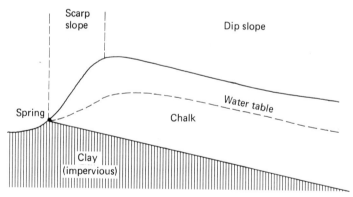

Fig. 3.12 *Drainage in chalk and clay country*

(iii) **Dry valleys** are found high up in the chalk hills and are widespread over the dip slope. They bear all the evidence of having been eroded by rivers, but in most instances the valleys do not have water in them. Their origin is one of the mysteries surrounding the formation of chalk topography, but there are several theories about their origin.

One theory holds that they were eroded during a period of much heavier rainfall than the present, when the water-table stood very high within the chalk. Springs then flowed out much further up, giving rise to streams down the slope of the chalk. As the rainfall lessened, the water-table slowly dropped and eventually passed below the level of the valley bottom, leaving it dry.

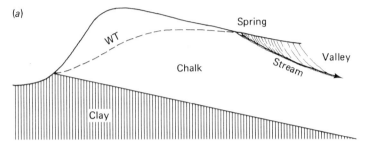

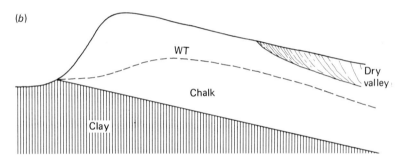

Fig. 3.13 Formation of a dry valley: (a) *valley is eroded at a time of high water-table,* (b) *valley is left dry as water-table falls*

Another explanation suggests that during the Ice Age the subsurface of the chalk was frozen, like the permafrost in the Arctic today (Section 11.5). The chalk then ceased to be permeable, melt-water ran off along the surface, and valleys were eroded.

(iv) **Gault clay** lies underneath the chalk wherever it occurs in western Europe. There is no significant percolation through the heavy clay. Most of the rainfall runs off the surface in rivers which have eroded the gault to a low-lying and only slightly undulating valley floor. The chalk scarp is thus always associated with the clay vale, and this may be clearly seen in Fig. 3.10.

Further Reading
Holmes, A.: *Principles of Physical Geology.* Nelson (London, 1965), Chapters 14, 15, 17.
Sawyer, K. E.: *Landscape Studies: An Introduction to Geomorphology.* Arnold (London, 1970), Section A.

Strahler, A. N.: *Physical Geography*. John Wiley (Chichester, 1969). Chapters 21, 22, 23.

Vallentine, H. R.: *Water in the Service of Man*. Penguin (Harmondsworth, 1967).

Questions

1. Describe the ways in which the earth's surface may be broken up by weathering.
2. What is mass wasting? Explain and give examples of the surface features formed by (*a*) solifluction, (*b*) slumping.
3. With the aid of diagrams, describe and explain the origin of features found in an area of jointed limestone. Name an area where these features may be seen.
4. Describe the surface features and drainage of an area of chalk topography. Name an area where this rock type is found.
5. (*a*) Describe the landscape shown in Fig. 3.10.
   (*b*) Explain, with the aid of diagrams, how such a landscape is formed.

Unit Four
The Work of Rivers

The greater part of the water which falls as rain runs off the surface of the earth to form streams. These unite to make rivers which in turn flow into the sea or into lakes.

4.1 A River's Regime

Most rivers do not flow steadily throughout the year; their volume of discharge varies greatly from season to season. This regular variation in a river's flow is known as its *regime* and it is, of course, heavily dependent on the climate. A river which flows down from high snow-covered mountains tends to have more water in spring and early summer, when melting is most rapid. In areas which have a dry season, such as the Mediterranean lands or regions with a monsoon climate, the level of water may be low or the rivers may even dry up for a period of months. By contrast the rainy season or the arrival of the monsoon (Section 11.3(*d*)) turns dry river beds into raging torrents. Even in Great Britain, where seasonal variations in rainfall are not great, rivers quickly respond to changes in the weather. They are liable to flooding after heavy rainfall, but the river bed may be exposed during a summer drought.

A river is said to be in flood, or in spate, when its rate of discharge approaches the maximum volume of water it can contain, even though the river may not actually overflow its bank and flood the surrounding land. Low water occurs when there is little or no water in the river.

4.2 Drainage Patterns

As small streams join to make larger ones and these in turn unite to form rivers, a river system or drainage system is formed. This receives all the run-off from a specific area, called the *basin* or *catchment area*. Each catchment area is cut off from neighbouring catchment areas by a *watershed* or *divide*, a line of high ground in which the headstreams of adjacent drainage systems rise and flow in opposite directions.

Drainage systems form an infinite variety of patterns. No two are ever identical, but they can be grouped into a number of types, each of which is closely related to a specific kind of rock or geological structure. The most important types are dendritic drainage, trellis drainage and radial drainage.

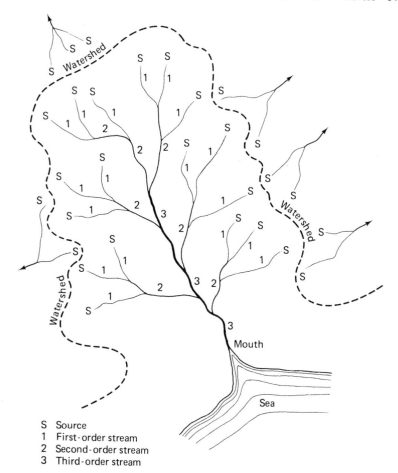

S   Source
1   First-order stream
2   Second-order stream
3   Third-order stream

Fig. 4.1 A dendritic drainage system

(a) Dendritic Drainage

This pattern of drainage tends to form over an area of relatively homogeneous rock, where there is the same degree of resistance to erosion over the whole area. The resulting drainage pattern resembles the trunk, branches and twigs of a tree, hence its name, from the Greek word *dendron*, meaning tree. (Fig. 4.1 shows a dendritic drainage system.)

The streams which make up a dendritic system are classified into first-, second-, third-order streams and so on. First-order streams are the small headstreams which rise from springs or form from run-off. Any two of these unite to form a second-order stream. Third-order streams result from the union of second-order, they join to form fourth-order streams, and so on. No increase in the order of a stream occurs when a higher-order stream is joined by one of lesser order. The largest order of stream in any system is used to denote the degree of complexity or development of the system itself. Fig. 4.1, which shows a third-order drainage basin, makes this clear.

(b) Trellis Drainage

A rectangular pattern of streams tends to develop in areas where hard and soft rocks outcrop in more or less parallel bands, such as the scarp and vale country of much of western Europe. In this type of country, the geological structure is often one of gently dipping beds, with the harder rocks giving rise to cuestas or escarpments and softer rocks to open valleys.

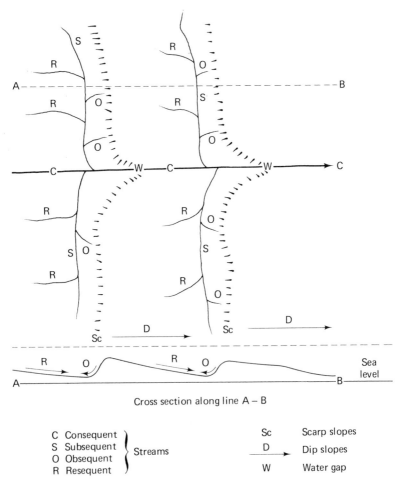

Cross section along line A – B

C Consequent	Sc	Scarp slopes
S Subsequent	Streams	D	Dip slopes
O Obsequent	W	Water gap
R Resequent		

Fig. 4.2 Trellis drainage

(c) Radial Drainage

A radial pattern of drainage, made up of a large number of rivers radiating from a central point, like the spokes of a wheel, may develop in areas which have been recently uplifted or on newly-formed volcanic areas. The Lake District in northern England displays a good example of a radial drainage pattern.

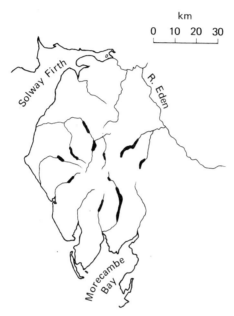

Fig. 4.3 Radial drainage in the Lake District

4.3   River Erosion

The action of rivers eroding the earth's surface, combined with mass wasting (Section 3.1), is chiefly responsible for the slow lowering of the land in most parts of the world (other than the hot deserts and the Arctic wastes). All valleys are either occupied by rivers now or were in the not-too-distant past, and in most instances these rivers have been responsible for eroding the valleys. A river erodes and deepens the valley floor, while mass wasting and weathering work on the valley sides, feeding materials into the river. The river transports this *load*, but at the same time it uses the material to erode its bed. The work of eroding the bed of a stream is accomplished in three ways: *hydraulic action*, *corrasion* and *attrition*.

(a) Hydraulic Action

The power of moving water, especially at flood-time, can do an immense amount of damage. Its erosive power, however, is largely concentrated on undercutting the river banks, so that they tend to overhang and then to collapse into the stream, which carries the material away.

(b) Corrasion
Corrasion in the actual process of wearing away the rocks. The river uses the material which it transports—its load—as tools for this purpose. The erosive power of a stream varies with its speed because this determines both the size and quantity of fragments carried in the load.

(c) Attrition
The load carried by a river varies from boulders, shifted only by the power of a river in spate, to fine dustlike particles known as *silt*. The larger particles are rolled or bounced along the stream's bed, striking one another and slowly reducing themselves to ever smaller particles by a process of attrition, until they become silt. They are then carried in suspension by the water.

The steepness of the valley sides is partly dependent on the climate of the area, because this largely determines the extent of mass wasting. There is, for example, little mass wasting in a dry climate, so the valley sides are likely to be

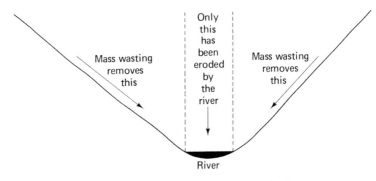

Fig. 4.4 The part played by mass wasting in shaping a valley

steep and gorge-like. In limestone country, steep cliffs may form because there is virtually no mass wasting, although simple weathering may break up the surface rocks. In a wetter climate, on the other hand, mass wasting may maintain a steady supply of material into the stream which flows in the valley bottom, and the valley sides will slope more gently.

The river's load is ultimately being transported and deposited. The coarser material, especially the larger boulders, may lie on the stream bed at times of low water and be moved only at flood stage. Even the silt, which gives a muddy or cloudy appearance to many rivers, may be deposited temporarily along the banks of a river as *alluvium*, to be picked up and taken further when the water-level rises again, until eventually it makes its way to the sea. A lake

Fig. 4.5 A New Zealand stream at low water, showing large rounded boulders on its bed. The stream can only move these in times of flood. (The volcano in the distance is Mount Egmont)

is also a resting place for silt. It may slowly fill up with silt brought down by the river flowing into it (Section 8.2).

4.4   The River Profile

The profile of a river is a section representing the slope of the river bed from source to mouth, drawn in relation to the horizontal at the river mouth. Fig. 4.6(a) shows an idealized river profile, but it may be interrupted by features along the river such as waterfalls, rapids and lakes.

We shall distinguish here between the upper, middle and lower courses of a river, but we should remember that these divisions are primarily for the purposes of description. Each part of the river passes so gradually into the next that it is impossible to establish the exact limits of each course. However, we can say that most rivers drop steeply in their upper courses and then the angle of the slope begins to flatten. The stream flows more slowly until, in the lower parts of its course, it flows across an almost level plain, the lowest part of which is known as base level. (It is to this level that the river is constantly working to erode its whole course. Normally, base level is sea-level.) Besides the changes in the gradient of the river's bed, the shape of the cross-section of its valley also varies in the three different courses. As Fig. 4.6(b) shows, there is a gradual change from the deep, steep-sided V-shape of the upper course to the very flat, plain-like valley of the lower course.

(a)

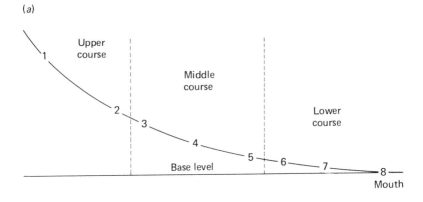

(b)

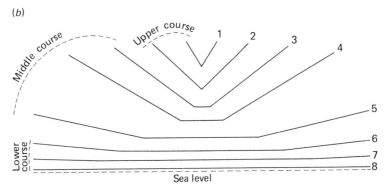

Fig. 4.6 (a) *The river profile. Numbers refer to cross-sections on* (b);
  (b) *Successive cross-sections of a river valley in the three courses*

(*a*) **Upper Course**
In hilly or mountainous country, where springs and run-off combine to form
streams, the rate of flow is swift because the land surface is usually steep.
Streams carry a large load compared with their volume, and are able to erode
their beds rapidly. Downcutting is thus their chief activity. A typical valley in
this region is narrow and steep-sided, because the downcutting of the stream
bed exceeds the mass wasting of the valley sides. The stream bed may itself be
made up of bare rocks, over which the stream cascades. The great erosive
power of stones when moved by the swift stream at flood-time may cut small,
rounded hollows in the stream bed, known as *pot-holes*. At low water
these rounded hollows may be uncovered and stones will be seen resting
at the bottom of each pot-hole. (These pot-holes should not be confused
with the pot-holes in limestone country, which we discussed in Section
3.2.)

Small streams do not contain a large volume of water, and they tend to flow around obstacles, frequently following a twisting course. As the streams deepen their beds by downcutting *interlocking spurs* are formed, the ends of which become steeper as the river goes on eroding its bed.

Fig. 4.7 Interlocking spurs on the upper course of a stream in the Lake District

As we saw in Units 2 and 3, rocks vary greatly in hardness, and this leads to sharp variations in the degree to which they are eroded. Short distances over which the river may flow smoothly are interrupted by sharper drops. If these drops are sudden a *waterfall* results, but if the drop is spread over a rather greater distance, *rapids* or *cataracts* form.

Rivers in their upper course not only deepen their beds and erode their banks; they also lengthen their valleys backwards by *headward* erosion. They bite back into the slopes above and behind their sources at the same time as their whole valley is eroded downwards, as Fig. 4.8 shows. This process is responsible for one of the more spectacular features of river development, *river capture*, which we look at in Section 4.5.

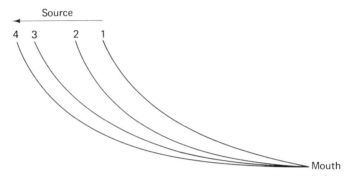

Fig. 4.8 Headward erosion. Successive profiles of the river show how the source is eroded backwards through positions 1, 2, 3 and 4 at the same time as the valley is eroded downwards

(*b*) **Middle Course**

A river contains a greater volume of water as it leaves the hills and approaches the plains which mark its lower course. This is because of the large number of tributaries which join the main stream and supply it with water. Its gradient is now more gentle, and downcutting becomes much less important. The valley floor tends to become broader and flatter in contrast to its V-shaped cross-section in the upper course (Fig. 4.6(*b*)). Indeed, the river tends to erode its banks rather than its bed, and this in turn causes it to swing in *meanders* over its plain. In the course of this slow swinging movement across the plain, the river cuts into the hills on each side and erodes the base of the slope. Low cliffs or bluffs form, where the flat valley floor meets the neighbouring hills.

(*c*) **Lower Course**

The middle course is an intermediate section between the upper and the lower. The upper course is characterized by erosion, the lower by deposition. As we have just seen, erosion in the middle course is mainly in a horizontal direction—the swinging of meanders and the undercutting of bluffs. In the lower course, erosion has given place almost completely to deposition. As a general rule, the river in its lower course is heavily laden. As its meanders slowly swing over the plain, the river erodes from one bank only to deposit on the other, with the small variations in the speed of the current and thus of the carrying power of the river.

Most rivers flood, and in the past many of them have frequently spread over their valley floor after a spell of heavy rain. Nowadays engineering works, such as dams in the upper course to control the flow of water and embankments along the river banks further downstream, may be able to confine the river to its bed even at flood stage. A river in flood is swifter than at other times, and it carries a bigger load. As its water spreads out over the flat land which borders it, in its lower course, its speed is checked and a part of its load is dropped at once. Every flood thus makes a contribution of fresh silt to the

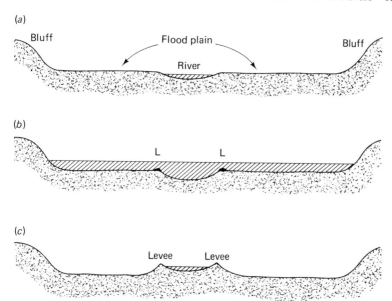

Fig. 4.9 Formation of levees
(a) *Normal river flow*
(b) *River in flood. At* L *faster moving water in the river bed is slowed down by static water over the flood plain. Deposition builds levees*
(c) *After many years of flooding, levees and river are built above flood plain level*

alluvium of the valley floor. In this way the *flood plain* of the river is gradually built up.

(i) **Levees.** When the water floods out from the river bed over the bordering flat land there is an abrupt drop in speed near the submerged bank of the river. Much of the silt is dropped here, forming a low bank or natural levee. Such natural levees only provide a slight protection against floods for the neighbouring land but, along some of the world's largest rivers, man has artificially strengthened them and raised them higher in order to keep the river within its natural bed, as far as possible.

Deposition during floods is not only responsible for the building of levees. There is also a tendency for a river to deposit silt on its own bed. This is because the bed exercises a slight frictional drag on the flow of water in contact with it, which slows it down sufficiently to make it deposit part of its load. Thus, with the building of levees and the deposition of silt on its bed, the river may come to flow wholly above its flood plain (Fig. 4.9). This is a particularly dangerous situation, as not only is the likelihood of flooding increased but after a flood the water cannot return naturally to the river. Fortunately it does not occur often, and it is only found where the load of silt is particularly heavy. It is a feature along the lower courses of the Mississippi and on the Hwang Ho in northern China, a region notorious for its devastating floods.

(ii) **Meanders.** We have seen how most rivers flow across their flood plain in broad sweeping curves, known as meanders. These slowly change their shape as a result of slight variations in the speed of the current and because of the erosion of one bank and deposition on the other. The water flows faster around the outer side of the bend, and is slowed down on the inner curve. Furthermore, currents are set up across the river which flow towards the inner bank and encourage deposition there. Thus there is erosion on the outside, compensated by deposition on the opposite bank of the river.

Fig. 4.10 Sweeping meanders on the Red river, a large tributary of the Mississippi. This picture shows the deposition on the inside, erosion along the outside of the nearest meanders and the levees along the banks, topped by a road

The curves of a meandering river tend to be accentuated and to swing. This does not just happen to a single bend in the river's course, but is occurring in all of them at once. The meander belt is in constant motion, swinging slowly to and fro across the plain, ever widening the flood plain as the meanders encroach on the higher ground which borders it.

(iii) **Ox-bow lakes.** The tendency is for all bends in the lower course to become more exaggerated, with erosion on one bank and deposition on the other. The meander thus becomes even tighter and the neck narrower. Eventually, when

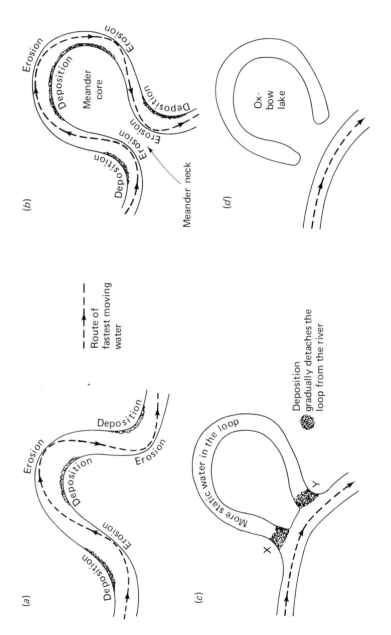

(a)

(b)

(c)

(d)

Erosion

Deposition

Deposition

Erosion

Erosion

Deposition

Route of
fastest moving
water

Erosion

Erosion

Deposition

Deposition

Meander
core

Erosion

Erosion

Deposition

Meander neck

More static water in the loop

Deposition gradually detaches the
loop from the river

X

Y

Ox-
bow
lake

Fig. 4.11 Exaggeration of a meander, leading to the formation of an ox-bow lake

the river is in flood, it may burst across the neck (between points X and Y on Fig. 4.11) to form a new and much straighter course. The former meander remains joined to the newly-formed river channel for a period, but deposition gradually takes place where the more static water within the loop meets the faster-moving water of the river. Eventually the former meander is completely separated from the river, and forms a rounded or crescent-shaped lake, known variously as an ox-bow, cut-off, mortlake or horseshoe lake.

(iv) **Braided stream.** The gradient is so gentle in the lower courses of some rivers that, at low water, the river may divide into a number of streams which reunite and, often enough, redivide and reunite again. This network of branching and converging channels may be clearly seen at low water on some rivers. The smaller channels are continually shifting as a result of the river's greater speed and volume at flood-time, and this presents many problems. Crossing the river is often difficult and cultivating the land on the river banks may be even more so, because of the frequent changes in the channels.

(*d*) **Deltas**

Despite the abundant deposition which occurs on levees and over the flood plain in the lower course of a river, a great deal of silt nevertheless reaches the sea. It is either deposited at the mouth of the river, or it is carried out to sea or redistributed along the coast. Its fate is determined largely by the amount of movement in the water at the river mouth. If there is very little tidal rise and fall, and currents are slight, the water near the river's mouth is likely to be still and this encourages the deposition of silt as soon as the river enters the sea. The silt forms large flat banks which are separated by channels, kept clear by the movement of the river's water towards the sea. This is a *delta*, named after the Greek letter of the same name, which has a triangular shape.

The Mediterranean Sea is almost tideless, and all the large rivers which flow into it have developed deltas; those of the Nile, Po and Rhône are the most familiar. The Gulf of Mexico is similarly tideless, and here the Mississippi has developed a very extensive delta. Other rivers with large and complex deltas are the Niger, in Africa, and the Ganges, Irrawaddy and Mekong in Asia. We suggest that you study these deltas on an atlas.

Some deltas, notably that of the Nile, leave a smoothed or rounded coastline and are known as *arcuate* deltas. This is due to a slight current which carries silt along the coast, drawing it out in spits and bars (Section 5.3(*c*)). Where there is no such movement in the water, the delta may advance into the sea as if it were a partially submerged system of levees. The result is a *bird's foot* delta, typified by that of the Mississippi.

Deltas are not only found where a river enters the sea. The still water of a lake leads to the deposition of silt and the formation of a *lacustrine* delta. A similar feature may even form where a swift stream flows into a large, flat-bottomed valley. In such cases a bank of silt, sand and even gravel may be formed, shaped like half of a flattened cone. This is an *alluvial cone* or *fan*. Occasionally such cones grow to immense sizes and a series of them may even

Fig. 4.12 The Mississippi delta looking south towards the Gulf of Mexico. Notice the flatness, the deposition and the pattern of distributaries

merge with one another to produce a gently sloping bank at the foot of a mountain range. In California a series of cones or fans, emerging from valleys of the Sierra Nevada range, has pushed the Sacramento and San Joaquin rivers across to the other side of the valley.

(e) The Estuary

Many rivers have no visible delta but enter the sea by way of a funnel-shaped opening, known as an estuary. The Thames estuary, the Humber and the Bristol Channel are good examples in the British Isles. An estuary is the result of several factors, which include the shape of the sea-floor, the strength of the tidal flow and the distance to which the tide flows inland. These conditions ensure that not much silt is deposited at the river mouth, so that a delta does not form. Even so, there is always some deposition, and mud-flats or sand-banks are often formed. They are sometimes exposed at low tide and are always hazardous for navigation. The mud-flats in the Thames estuary and the Bristol Channel are conspicuous: they are, in fact, deltas whose proper forma-tion has been prevented by the movement and depth of water in the estuary.

Almost all estuaries are tidal, and many have a very large tidal range, which means that the flow of water in and out is rapid. Channels are thus kept rela-tively clear of deposition. This in turn allows ships, with or without the aid of the tide, to sail up to the head of the estuary, which has become a common site for large ports. London, Glasgow, Hamburg and Bordeaux are familiar examples.

4.5   River Capture

In Section 4.4(a) we referred to headward recession (that is, the extension backwards of the source of the stream), in the process of which one river sometimes invades the basin of another. The first river's catchment area is increased while the neighbouring catchment area is correspondingly reduced, and sooner or later the river cuts back into the course of the neighbouring stream and abstracts its water. This is river capture, or river piracy.

In Fig. 4.13 the headward erosion of tributary X causes it to meet river B. The upper part of B is diverted into X, leaving the remainder of B as a shortened or beheaded river. The exact point of the capture is known because

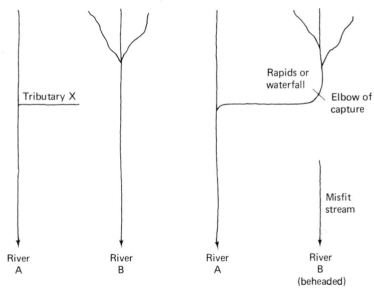

(a) Stage 1   (b) Stage 2

Fig. 4.13 River capture

of the sharp bend, called the *elbow of capture*. For a short distance there may even be a steep gradient in the course of stream *X*, which has done the capturing, marked by rapids or a waterfall. Meanwhile *B* has become a small river, disproportionately so in comparison with its valley, which was eroded when it was a much larger stream. *B* is now known as a *misfit stream*. There are many examples of river capture in Britain, and Fig. 4.14 shows a familiar example.

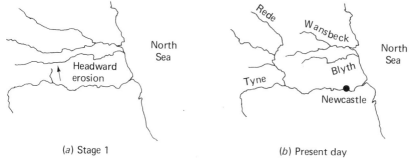

(a) Stage 1   (b) Present day

Fig. 4.14 *River capture in Northumberland*

4.6   The Changing Sea-level

A change in the level of the sea considerably modifies the shape of river valleys flowing into it. A rise in sea-level inundates the lower parts of a valley to form a *ria* (a process known as *drowning*, which we shall describe in Section 5.4).

The changes brought about by a drop in sea-level—a process known as

Fig. 4.15 *Rejuvenation terraces along the river Severn. Each of the flat platforms at different heights marks a former level of the river's flood plain*

rejuvenation—may be prominent features of the new valley. The lower sea-level increases the speed of flow of the whole river so that its erosive power is increased. It begins to cut downwards and incise its bed into the former valley floor. Nowhere is this more clearly seen than in the river's lower course. Meanders are cut deeply into the flood plain, and sometimes into the underlying rock, to form *incised meanders*, such as those along the lower course of the river Wye. A new, lower flood plain may be formed by the slow widening of the meander belt, but remnants of the former flood plain may be left as flat platform-like features above the edge of the new flood plain. These are rejuvenation terraces.

Further Reading

Dury, G. H.: *The Face of the Earth*. Penguin (Harmondsworth, 1970), Chapters 3–8.

Greswell, R. K.: *Rivers and Valleys*. Hulton Educational Publications (Amersham, 1964).

Holmes, A.: *Principles of Physical Geology*. Nelson (London, 1965), Chapters 18, 19.

Sawyer, K. E.: *Landscape Studies: An Introduction to Geomorphology*. Arnold (London, 1970), Section A.

Sparks, B. W.: *Geomorphology*. Longman (Harlow, 1970), Chapters 5, 6.

Strahler, A. N.: *Physical Geography*. John Wiley (Chichester, 1969), Chapters, 24, 25.

Questions

1. Give an account of the ways in which river erosion takes place.
2. Why does river deposition go on mostly in the lower course? Name the principal features which result from this and, with the aid of diagrams, explain how any two are formed.
3. Write an essay on *River Capture*.
4. With the aid of annotated diagrams say what you understand by (a) trellis drainage, (b) interlocking spurs, (c) levees, (d) deltas.
5. Describe the nature of the river and its valley (a) in Fig. 4.5 and (b) in Fig. 4.10. Explain the differences between these two illustrations.

Unit Five

The Work of the Sea

The waves of the sea attack the coast, where the land meets the sea, and they erode the land in a number of ways. The sea transports the eroded materials, building fresh land with some of them. A great many landforms result from this combination of erosion and deposition. Erosion usually gives rise to cliffs, deposition to flat coastlands and beaches, together with spits, bars, sandbanks and other features, many of which develop below sea-level.

5.1 Waves and Erosion

Waves can be one of the most powerful and destructive of all the agents of erosion. They are formed by the wind blowing over the surface of the sea. The size and energy of a wave depends partly on the strength of the wind, but also on the distance of open water over which the wind blows in building up the wave. An open sea coast facing thousands of miles of ocean, over which onshore winds can build up immense waves, is likely to be severely eroded and to be characterized by towering cliffs. The coast of a sheltered estuary, where only small waves can develop, is far less prone to erosion. In the course of a storm the wind may develop waves of exceptional power and destructiveness, especially if it is blowing onshore (that is, from the sea). Such storm waves may erode cliffs extensively, and can cause more destruction to the beaches and promenades of coastal resorts in the course of an hour than normal wave action can do in many years.

As a wave moves from the deeper sea into shallower coastal waters, its crest

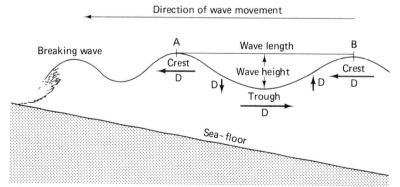

Fig. 5.1 Movement of a sea wave. Arrows (D) show the direction of movement of water particles in the wave

continues to move forward under the impulse of the wind, while the water a few metres below the surface is slowed by its frictional contact with the sea-floor (Fig. 5.1). This continues until the upper part of the wave 'overtakes' the lower and the crest topples over or *breaks*, in a mass of white, foaming water. This water—the *swash*—rushes up the beach and then runs more slowly back into the sea, as the *backwash*.

We shall distinguish between the effect of waves on a sandy or pebble beach, and on the steeper cliffs. The beach may, of course, be backed by cliffs, in which case both phenomena can be observed at the same place, according to the stage of the tide.

(a) The Beach

The effect of waves on a beach is governed by several factors. The most important of these are the steepness of the beach itself, the material—sand, shingle, large pebbles—of which it is made, and the height and frequency of the waves. The first two factors are not likely to change very much on any one particular beach, but the height of the waves (that is, the vertical distance between their crests and the preceding or following troughs) and their frequency (the number of waves per minute) are of vital importance in shaping the beach. Large waves, with a frequency of 12–15 to the minute, are created by strong storm winds. Such waves crash down almost vertically on to the beach, giving rise to little swash, but a very powerful backwash, which drags much of the beach material out to sea. These are *destructive waves*. (Bathing is particularly dangerous under such conditions.)

However, if the waves are much less frequent, say 5–8 to the minute, they tend to spread up the beach when they break. They have a powerful swash, and tend to wash material—both the rock material of which the beach is composed and other material which has got into the sea—up the beach and deposit it there. These are *constructive waves*.

Every beach shows the marks of the latest phase in its long struggle with the sea. A beach may have been lowered by destructive waves, or a bank of shingle or *berm* at the upper tidal limit may show that the most recent activity of the waves has been constructive.

(b) Cliffs

Waves have enormous destructive power as they hit the land, and they can cause cliffs to crumble and recede. The mechanics of wave erosion are complex, and depend not only on the height and frequency of the waves but also on the hardness of the coastal rocks. Much of the coast of eastern England, for example, is made up of soft glacial deposits or boulder clay, and this is easily eroded by the storm waves of the North Sea. This coast has been worn back in places by as much as 3 km during the period since the Roman occupation of this country (this is an average of nearly 2 m a year). It is unlikely that the towering granite cliffs of Land's End have undergone any significant change at all in this time.

We saw in Section 3.1 that almost all rocks are penetrated by cracks or

Fig. 5.2 Rapid coastal erosion in soft glacial deposits south of Lowestoft, Suffolk

joints which are gradually enlarged by weathering and erosion. The pressure of the waves beating against such rocks not only erodes them by its sheer power but also forces water into the fissures, causing a sudden compression of the air which they contain. The pressure exerted by the air with each breaking wave slowly enlarges each crack, weakening the structure of the rock and hastening its erosion. This is known as *hydraulic action*.

At the same time the waves are armed with cutting tools (the stones and pebbles derived from the cliffs by previous erosive action), which are hurled against the rock at the base of the cliff. This undercuts the cliffs and ultimately leads to their collapse. The corrasion or abrasion of the cliffs resembles the erosive action on a river's bed and banks, but it is often a great deal more violent. As corrasion is going on, the pebbles and rocks are themselves subjected to the same process of *attrition* as they continually knock against each other and are gradually reduced in size. Angular stones become smoothed and rounded pebbles, and the rocky waste is ultimately ground so fine that it can be removed and taken out to sea by the destructive force of the waves. The attrition of beach materials can even be heard. In a heavy sea on the Chesil Beach in Dorset, for example, the backwash of each wave drags pebbles down the beach with a loud rattling noise.

All these processes slowly wear away a cliff, causing it to move slowly inland. This is *cliff recession*. People who live near the coast are accustomed to cliff falls, especially during severe winter storms and after a period of heavy rainfall, and to the tendency for the value of property close to the cliff to decrease.

5.2   Erosional Features of the Coast

As the cliff-line recedes it leaves a number of erosional features, some 'of them conspicuous and scenic features of the coastline.

(a) Abrasion Platforms

Fig. 5.3 shows a *wave-cut platform* or *abrasion platform* at the foot of the cliffs. The cliff-line formerly stood at the seaward edge of the platform, but gradual erosion of the cliff has caused a recession to its present position. You will see that the gullies in the platform, eroded along the lines of weakness, lead to indentations in the cliff. The present platform extends from high-tide mark down to below the low-tide level. There may be *reefs* or patches of rock out beyond low-water level, which are only exposed at low tide. These are also part of the wave-cut platform, formed as the sea slowly encroached on the land.

Fig. 5.3 Wave-cut abrasion platform, Falmouth, Cornwall

(b) Arches, Stacks and Caves

These picturesque features of the coast all originated in weaknesses in the cliffs—faults, joints or merely beds of relatively soft rock—gouged out by the erosive and hydraulic action of the waves. A weakness extending across a projecting area of cliff may first be hollowed out to form caves and, as these approach one another from each end of the line of weakness, a tunnel or arch is formed. In time the ceiling of the arch collapses, weakened from below by wave action and from above by weathering. The result is a *stack*, an upstand-

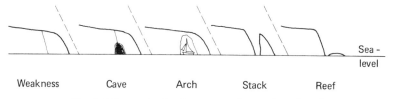

Fig. 5.4 Stages in the formation of a stack and reef

ing mass of rock such as the Old Man of Hoy, shown in Fig. 5.5. This, in its turn, is attacked by waves from all directions. It is narrowed to an unstable pillar of rock and, ultimately, it is destroyed, leaving a *reef* which is only visible at low tide.

Fig. 5.5 The Old Man of Hoy, Orkney, a stack 140 m high

Occasionally a cave is formed when a line of weakness extends inland from the cliff. Erosion is frequently very active at the inner end, owing to the hydraulic pressure created by the waves. This tends to weaken the roof of the cave and, in time, the roof collapses at the inner end and a *blow-hole* is formed. Sea water may be ejected up through the hole when waves build up pressure in the cave below, especially during a storm. But a blow-hole is a short-lived landscape feature. The forces which created it eventually destroy the whole roof of the cave, and it becomes a minor indentation of the coast.

(c) Capes and Bays

A cliff-line is only likely to be straight for a considerable distance if it is built of the same type of rock and has no significant weaknesses in it. The chalk of the Sussex coast produces such a coastline: it has given rise to the line of cliffs known as the Seven Sisters, near Beachy Head.

But coastlines are usually very uneven, with alternating headlands and bays. Bays are formed, either from bands of relatively soft and easily eroded rock, or from the presence of jointing on a large scale, which opens the rock up to the forces of weathering and erosion. The result in both cases is differential erosion as the weaker parts of the coast become bays and the harder parts headlands. The exact shape of a coastline is thus heavily dependent both on the presence of alternating beds of relatively hard and soft rock and on the angle which these make to the general line of the coast.

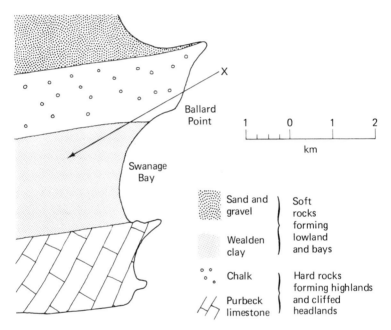

Fig. 5.6 The geology of the Swanage coast. (The arrow shows the direction in which Fig. 5.7 is seen)

The Purbeck region of Dorset is a museum of coastal landforms. There are beds of hard and soft rock—chalk and limestone on the one hand, and sand and clay on the other, lying in a west-to-east direction. On the east-facing coast of Purbeck the chalk and the Portland limestone run out to sea to form headlands (Fig. 5.6), and the chalk headland is continued in some impressive stacks. There is a broad, sweeping bay between them, where the Wealden clay reaches the coast, and the seaside resort of Swanage lies on this.

On the south coast, the Portland limestone lies parallel to the coast. A few miles to the west the geological sequence is the same but the beds of limestone and clay are much narrower than in the Swanage area. All the beds have been

Fig. 5.7 Ballard Point and Swanage Bay

folded and tilted here so that they dip at a steep angle. The limestone beds tend to constitute a line of cliffs—a wall, as it were, protecting the softer clay which lies to the north of them. But here and there, notably at Lulworth Cove, the sea has breached the rampart formed by the limestone and eroded a rounded bay in the area of softer clay, backed by a high chalk cliff. Several such coves can be seen on the map in varying stages of development (see also Map 2, page 263).

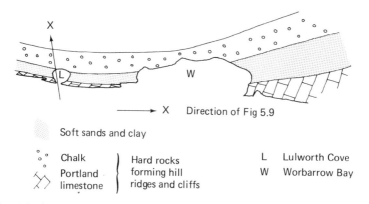

Soft sands and clay

°° Chalk	Hard rocks	L Lulworth Cove
°° Portland	forming hill	W Worbarrow Bay
⟨⟩ limestone	ridges and cliffs	

Fig. 5.8 The geology of the Lulworth coast. (The arrow shows the direction in which Fig. 5.9 is seen)

Fig. 5.9 Lulworth Cove, Dorset

5.3   Coastal Deposition

Material brought down by the rivers and eroded from the cliffs is continually being moved by the sea. The waves may stir up sand on the sea-floor, especially during storms when the movement of the water is more violent. After a storm the sea is often discoloured with sediment, which may be carried in suspension for several days before it is deposited again. The coarser eroded material moves along the coast, mainly by a process known as *long-shore drift*, where it builds up as a number of beach forms, both permanent and temporary.

(*a*) Longshore Drift

This is the movement of the coarser, heavier material along the coast by wave action. More often than not, waves approach a beach obliquely, as shown in Fig. 5.10, at an angle which depends largely on the direction of the wind. A pebble is thus thrown obliquely up the beach by the swash of a wave, but tends to be pulled back more directly by the backwash, since here the force of gravity down the beach slope is the principal influence. In Fig. 5.10 a pebble at *A* is thrown to *B*, falls back to *C*, is thrown by a later wave to *D*, is washed back to *E*, and so on. In this way, assuming that wind and wave direction do not change significantly, the pebble in question moves along the beach, probably gradually becoming smaller by attrition in the process. A sharp change in wind direction may reverse this movement, and the pebble will travel slowly back towards *A*.

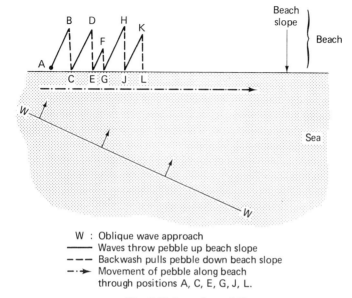

W : Oblique wave approach
——— Waves throw pebble up beach slope
– – – Backwash pulls pebble down beach slope
– · ➤ Movement of pebble along beach
       through positions A, C, E, G, J, L.

Fig. 5.10 Longshore drift

Longshore drift can sometimes be quite violent. A seaside resort may lose much of its beach as the result of a violent storm. It is, in any case, likely to be faced with the slow movement of material from one end of a beach to another. This movement can be partially checked by building *groynes* (low barriers of wood or concrete) at intervals along the beach and at right angles to the coast from above high-tide level to below the low-tide mark. Beach material nevertheless moves within each of the spaces between groynes, so that we find sand and shingle banked up high against one side of a groyne, while on the other side it has been scooped away.

(*b*) Beach Formation

(i) **Bay-head beach.** Material eroded from the cliffs tends to be carried, principally by longshore drift, towards the head of the bay that forms between each pair of headlands. This gives rise to a *bay-head beach*, and these are found in profusion around the more westerly coasts of the British Isles. The composition of these beaches varies according to the composition of the neighbouring rocks and the local marine life. They will consist of rock fragments from the cliffs along each side of the bay, which have been reduced in varying degrees to shingle and sand. They are also likely to contain a proportion of shell fragments, derived from sea creatures, which may sometimes make up more than half the total beach material. Lastly, the beach will, unhappily, contain man-made materials—glass, tins, cinders, slag and the waste from buildings—not to mention matter which has been washed up from the sea—oil, wood and the fragments of ships which have been lost at sea.

(ii) **Storm beaches.** The upper part of a beach usually lies well above normal high-tide mark. The material of which it is composed could only have been deposited there by storm waves breaking at high tide and throwing beach material well above high-tide mark, so building up that part of the beach that the sea does not normally reach. A succession of storms, perhaps over a long period of time, may build up a beach well above high-tide mark, or even a succession of such beaches. These are *storm beaches*.

Fig. 5.11 A recurved spit across the Mawddach estuary, Cardigan Bay

(c) Bars and Spits

(i) **Bars.** A bar is a submerged, or largely submerged, bank of sand or silt, consisting of eroded material which has been resorted and transported by the waves. A *harbour bar* may occur near the mouth of a river, which is generally where river silt is deposited.

(ii) **Spits.** A spit, on the other hand, is composed of beach material which has been transported along the coast by the process of longshore drift, until its course is interrupted by a bay or estuary. The deposit then tends to be drawn out across the opening in the coastline, partially closing it. There are numerous spits around the British Isles. They partially close the estuaries of the rivers Dovey and Mawddach on the west-facing coast of Wales. There are several spits in the Solent and Southampton Water, and the Humber is also partially closed by the hook-shaped spit known as Spurn Head. The end of a spit may be curved by strong winds from another direction, to form a *recurved* spit.

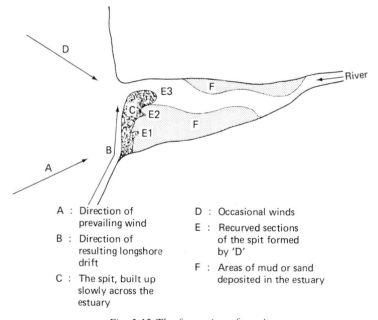

A : Direction of prevailing wind

B : Direction of resulting longshore drift

C : The spit, built up slowly across the estuary

D : Occasional winds

E : Recurved sections of the spit formed by 'D'

F : Areas of mud or sand deposited in the estuary

Fig. 5.12 The formation of a spit

Storm waves throw material up on to the spit. Blown sand is held there by vegetation, so that it grows higher as well as longer. Silting goes on rapidly in the sheltered water behind the spit (*F* on Fig. 5.12). The sea-floor is turned to marsh which is converted into rough grazing land, sometimes with the help of man.

(iii) **Nehrung and haff.** A spit rarely closes an estuary completely. The tidal movement is usually powerful enough to keep a channel open between the end of a spit and the opposite shoreline, but there are exceptions. Tidal rise and fall in the Baltic Sea is very slight, and the discharge of some of the rivers is very small. Here a spit, known locally as a *nehrung*, up to 80 km in length and 3 km wide may seal off a bay to form a lagoon, or *haff*. Access to the haff is only possible by breaching the nehrung. Some of these spits have become crowned with enormous sand dunes, occasionally rising as high as 70 m above sea-level.

(d) Sand Dunes

Some areas of low coast are backed by tumbled heaps of wind-blown sand, but they only occur where certain conditions are met. There must be a large sandy beach, a strong prevailing wind blowing onshore, and the area behind the coast must not be so high or steep that sand cannot be blown over it.

Wind can carry the sand far inland. Dunes may encroach on agricultural land and may even overwhelm houses, as has happened, for example, along parts of the north coast of Cornwall, at Gwithian and Perranporth. Dunes can usually be fixed or stabilized by planting vegetation, either coniferous trees or the tough marram grass, which develops a complex root system and binds the sand together. Nevertheless, the Culbin Sands on the Moray Firth in northern Scotland are still active, despite attempts to fix them. The most extensive area of wind-driven *coastal* dune sand in Europe (there are larger areas of *desert* sand in Arabia and North Africa) is the Landes of south-western France. This vast area of about 15 000 km² and extending for nearly 500 km along the coast has been stabilized by planting conifers, which are also an important source of turpentine.

5.4   The Changing Sea-level

We saw in Section 2.10 and 4.6 that the level of the sea has undergone a number of significant changes in relation to the land. Sea-level sank during the glacial periods of the Ice Age, as water was taken from the oceans to form ice on the land. The level rose during the warm interglacials, though it fluctuated greatly. Now, in north-western Europe, it is continuing to rise slowly, and the coastline bears plentiful evidence of the changes of level which have occurred during glacial and postglacial times.

(a) Drowned Coasts

Since the most recent movement has been the rising of sea-level, the coast of the British Isles shows signs of *drowning*. The rias of Ireland, Wales and south-western England are drowned river valleys. The fjords of western Scotland as well as those of Norway are glaciated valleys which have similarly been drowned.

The shape of any drowned coastline depends on the grain of the land. If the hills and valleys generally lie at right angles to the coast, deep tidal inlets, such as those in south-western Ireland, are likely to result from a rise in sea-level. This is known as a *discordant* coast (Fig. 5.14(a)). Where the mountains and

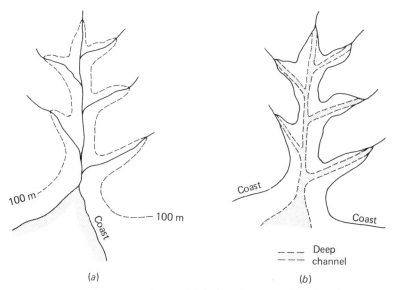

Fig. 5.13 *The formation of a ria:* (a) *before drowning,* (b) *after drowning*

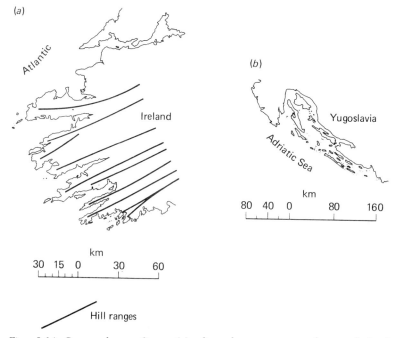

Fig. 5.14 *Drowned coastlines:* (a) *discordant coast, south-west Ireland,*
(b) *concordant coast, Yugoslavia*

hills are aligned parallel to the coast, however, drowning is more likely to produce chains of offshore islands, each of them elongated in the direction of the coast. The Frisian Islands and the Dalmatian Coast of Yugoslavia are examples. Such a coastline is *concordant* (Fig. 5.14(*b*)).

Obviously a drowned coastline is not likely to have much coastal plain, because it will have been submerged by the sea, but it may possess a wealth of deep, natural harbours. This is true of all the coastlines we have just mentioned. One ria, Milford Haven in South Wales, has been chosen as a port for giant tankers despite its rather remote situation, because submergence has produced there an unusually great depth of water (see *H & R*, Unit 12).

(*b*) Emergent Coasts

The effect of a drop in sea-level is the opposite of what we have just described. When sea-level falls estuaries and creeks tend to be narrowed, because the sea does not occupy them to as great a depth as before emergence, and a low coastal plain is formed from what had once been the shallow sea-floor.

Features arising from both submergence and emergence are apt to be short-lived when the rocks are soft, as in eastern and south-eastern England. They are quickly destroyed by erosion, or are covered up and hidden by deposition. But evidence that the sea once stood higher than it is today is better preserved in the harder rocks of western Britain. There are *raised beaches* along some parts of the coast, as much as 30 m above the present level of the sea. The most extensive beach in south-western England and Wales is at a height of about 3 m. It is exactly what its name suggests—a beach, sometimes with sand and shingle, now hardened into a conglomerate, lying above the reach of the

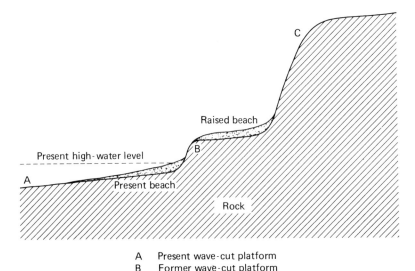

A   Present wave-cut platform
B   Former wave-cut platform
C   Raised cliff line

Fig. 5.15 Section across an emergent cliffed coast, showing raised beach

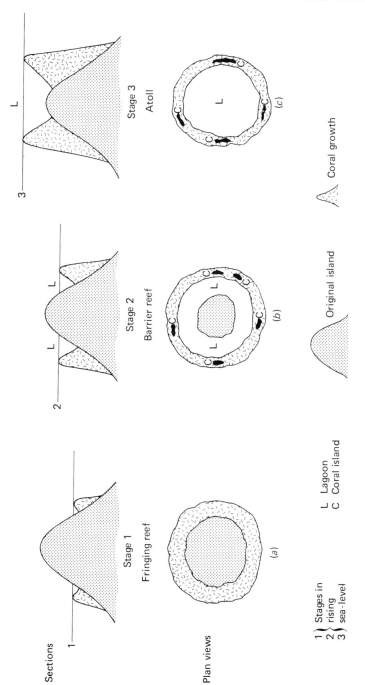

Fig. 5.16 The progression in the forms of coral growth

Sections

Stage 1
Fringing reef
(a)

Stage 2
Barrier reef
(b)

Stage 3
Atoll
(c)

Plan views

1 ⎫ Stages in
2 ⎬ rising
3 ⎭ sea-level

L Lagoon
C Coral island

Coral growth

Original island

waves except in unusually severe storms. It lies on a wave-cut platform (Section 5.2(*a*)) and may be backed by a raised cliff-line, as Fig. 5.15 shows clearly. It usually ends in a low cliff on its seaward margin, below which lies the present beach and wave-cut platform.

All the features of present-day beaches, such as cliffs, stacks, caves and arches can be found in association with raised beaches, especially in areas of very hard rock, such as the west coast of Scotland and parts of the Cornish coast.

5.5   Coral Coasts and Islands

In some parts of the world, particularly between the tropics, a form of coast-line occurs which may be termed a *biological* coast. It is made up entirely of the skeletons of living and dead coral polyps, which are small sea creatures. The coral can only live in seas with a temperature above 21 °C. This limits it to an area of the sea bounded by latitudes 30° N and S. Even here it is rarely found on western coasts, where there are often cool currents (Section 10.4). Coral must also have some natural sunlight, and this limits the polyps to a maximum depth of about 55 m. Furthermore, the water must be clean and free of silt, so coral will not live near a delta or the mouth of a large, silt-laden river.

Colonies of coral polyps give rise to three distinct forms, fringing reefs, barrier reefs and atolls. The *fringing reef*, as shown in Fig. 5.16(*a*), is a strip of coral ranging in width from a few metres to several kilometres, which fringes the coast and is covered by a very shallow depth of water.

The *barrier reef* (Fig. 5.16(*b*)) is similar but it is separated from the coastline by a tidal channel which may itself be many kilometres in width. The most famous example is the Great Barrier Reef of Australia which extends, with very few gaps, over a distance of 1 600 km along the coast of Queensland.

An *atoll* (Fig. 5.16(*c*)) is also a reef, ring-shaped and enclosing only a deep lagoon, with no land mass or island within it. Many such coral atolls are to be found in the Pacific Ocean, among them such familiar islands as Bikini, Eniwetok, Kwajalein and Midway.

Further Reading

Carson, R.: *The Sea Around Us.* Panther (London, 1969).

Cotter, C. H.: *The Physical Geography of the Oceans.* Hollis & Carter (London, 1965).

Dury, G. H.: *The Face of the Earth.* Penguin (Harmondsworth, 1970), Chapters 9–11.

Gresswell, R. K.: *Beaches and Coastlines.* Hulton Educational Publications (Amersham, 1964).

Holmes, A.: *Principles of Physical Geology.* Nelson (London, 1965), Chapters 23, 24.

King, C. A. M.: *Beaches and Coasts.* Arnold (London, 1959).

King, C. A. M.: *Oceanography for Geographers.* Arnold (London 1962).

Sawyer, K. E.: *Landscape Studies: An Introduction to Geomorphology*. Arnold (London, 1970), Section B.

Small, B. W.: *The Study of Landforms*. Cambridge University Press (London, 1970), Chapter 12.

Sparks, B. W.: *Geomorphology*. Longman (Harlow, 1970), Chapters 5, 6.

Steers, J. A.: *The Coastline of England and Wales*. Cambridge University Press (London, 1964).

Steers, J. A.: *Coasts and Beaches*. Oliver & Boyd (Edinburgh, 1969).

Strahler, A. N.: *Physical Geography*. John Wiley (Chichester, 1969), Chapters 27, 29.

Questions
1. In what ways does the sea erode the coast? Give examples of the processes which you describe.
2. Describe, with the aid of diagrams, the ways in which waves may alter the shape of the coastline.
3. With the aid of clearly annotated diagrams, describe and explain the formation of: (*a*) stacks, (*b*) abrasion platforms, (*c*) sand spits.
4. Why are some coastlines much straighter than others? Give examples of each form of coast that you mention.
5. Write an essay on *Beaches*.
6. Describe and explain how a change of sea-level influences the shape of the coastline.
7. (*a*) Describe the coast shown in Fig. 5.5.
   (*b*) Explain how this coast may have been formed.

Unit Six

The Work of Ice

Large areas of the earth's surface have been shaped by ice. Much high ground has been eroded by ice to produce the sharp peaks and crests of mountain ranges such as the Alps, the Himalayas and the Rockies. But a great deal of the material worn from the mountains has been carried away by moving ice and laid down on the lowlands, covering the rocks beneath, diverting the drainage and profoundly influencing the character of the soil. We shall, therefore, study the work of ice as an agent of destruction and as a creative force.

6.1 The Ice Age

On several occasions in the course of earth's 4 500 million year history the climate has grown sufficiently cold for ice to cover large areas of its surface, perhaps for tens of thousands of years at a time. Such an event is called an *Ice Age* and there were Ice Ages both in Pre-Cambrian and Permo-Carboniferous times (Table 2.1). The Ice Age which has left most evidence of its presence was the most recent one which began just under 2 million years ago. It is known as the *Pleistocene Ice Age* and during its lifetime the climate became colder for at least four prolonged periods, but grew appreciably warmer between the cold periods.

(a) Glacial Periods

In each glacial period the snow line (that is, the lowest level of permanent snow) moved slowly down the mountain sides, as the climate gradually grew colder and the snow lay longer, at lower levels, during the year. On high ground the snow cover grew ever thicker as less of each winter's fall melted away during the following summer, and this snow gradually became compacted into hard ice. Under the influence of gravity the ice began to move slowly downhill, gathering in the valleys to form *glaciers*, which in turn moved down the valleys towards the lowland. As conditions became colder the glaciers spread out over the plains, joining with one another to form *ice-sheets*. In Europe the ice-sheets extended as far south as 50° N, thus covering much of England and the North European Plain (Fig. 6.1(*a*)). In North America they spread over the whole of Canada and a great deal of the Midwest of the United States (Fig. 6.1(*b*)).

Eventually, after each advance of the ice, the climate grew warmer again and the ice slowly melted away around its margins until the ice-sheets had disappeared. A totally different landscape was revealed from that which had been covered by the spreading ice many centuries before, because the ice

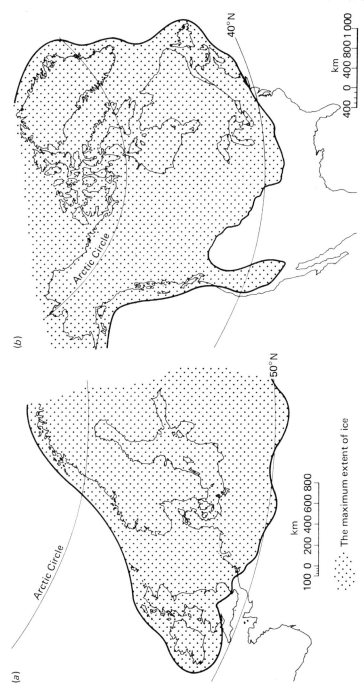

Fig. 6.1 The extent of ice during the Ice Age: (a) *Europe,* (b) *North America*

had eroded the land in some places, and deposited the eroded material to make a new land surface in others.

(b) Changes in Sea-level

The formation of these vast ice-sheets led to changes in sea-level. Each glacial period was accompanied by a drop in the level of the sea because the water cycle was interrupted (Section 2.10). Most of the precipitation fell as snow which remained 'locked' in the form of ice for many centuries, whereas evaporation continued from the surface of the seas in order to provide more snow. The result was a gradual fall of nearly 100 m in sea-level. Each glacial period ended when the temperature gradually became warmer, the land ice melted, water returned to the oceans and the sea-level rose again. The temperature was not the same in each of the warm *interglacial* periods, however, and the extent to which the oceans filled up was different in each interglacial.

As we saw in Section 5.4, this rise and fall of the sea-level has had an important influence on the formation of coastal features.

(c) Ice-sheets Today

The most recent Ice Age, which began nearly 2 million years ago, may not have ended yet. It is true that ice-sheets have disappeared almost entirely from Europe and that glaciers are found only in the highest mountains, but ice-sheets can still be found elsewhere. Greenland and the Antarctic continents are largely covered by enormous sheets of ice which, at their centre, reach thicknesses of up to 3 km. There is a smaller ice-sheet in Iceland, and fragments of vanishing ice-sheets in Alaska and Norway. If all these were to melt, sea-level would rise sufficiently to inundate London and most coastal lowlands.

On the other hand, some geographers believe that the ice has melted as much as it is going to do and that we are heading for another cold glacial period, another advance of the ice-sheets. The climate of northern Europe did, in fact, begin to get colder in the mid-sixteenth century. For a period of almost three centuries the world experienced a cold spell which has come to be called the Little Ice Age. Then, rather more than a century ago, it became generally warmer again. Glaciers in the Alps, which had been extending ever further down the valleys, began to melt and they are still retreating very slowly.

6.2   Ice Erosion

As a mass of ice—a glacier or an ice-sheet—moves over the land surface it erodes the rock, breaking away and removing parts of it. It does this in three ways. In the first place, the mass of an advancing glacier 'bulldozes' all that lies in its path. The ice carries this load forward, either on the surface or embedded in the ice itself. Secondly, pieces of rock along the margins of the slow-moving ice become frozen into the ice mass. As the mass moves it 'plucks' out these pieces and carries them away. Lastly, the most important method of ice-erosion is by *corrasion*. Fragments of rock become frozen into the ice, and as the ice drags these along they scrape and gouge the surface over which they move.

There is also a very active *frost-shattering* process along the margin of the ice, where temperatures may rise above freezing during one part of the year or during the day, but will fall below during another season (Section 3.1(*a*)). Large quantities of rock fragments thus fall on to the ice, to be carried away and used as tools in the process of corrasion.

All these erosional forces acting together have carved out a landscape which we recognize as *glaciated* or *alpine*. We shall consider the landscape features produced by ice erosion in the next section.

Fig. 6.2 Glaciated scenery in the Lake District, showing a tarn (a corrie with a lake), a corrie without a lake, arêtes, a glacial valley and lacustrine deltas

6.3   Landscape Features Produced By Ice Erosion

(*a*) **Corries**

Corries are hollows—sometimes described as armchair-shaped depressions—on the flanks of a mountain. The largest of them may be more than a kilometre across, and some contain a shallow lake or *tarn* on the 'seat' of the depression. Corries are common features of all glaciated mountain areas. (The word corrie is a Scottish term; in Wales they are known as *cwms* and in France as *cirques*.)

The formation of a corrie begins when a snow patch in a slight hollow or depression—often on the north or north-east facing slope of a mountain—lingers through the summer (Fig. 6.3(*a*)). The next winter's snow is added to this patch so that it grows thicker, and eventually the snow is compacted under its own weight to form a mass of ice (Fig. 6.3(b)), which slides downhill, under the influence of gravity, and immediately begins to exercise its powers of erosion.

The thicker snow and ice in the middle of the patch moves faster than that on each side. A crack may open up towards the upper edge, as shown in Fig. 6.3(c). This is known as a *bergschrund*, a German word meaning mountain crack. Each summer, melt water drips into the bergschrund, and contributes to frost-shattering along the upper edge of the slowly developing corrie. This process in turn supplies angular masses of rock to the bottom surface of the mass of ice, where they are used as tools of corrasion.

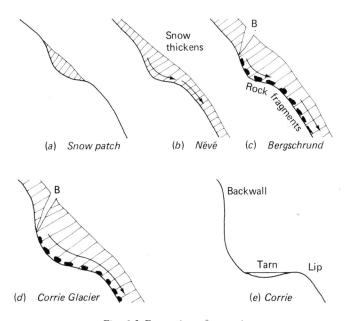

Fig. 6.3 Formation of a corrie

The process of erosion accelerates. The patch of snow and ice grows thicker as the hollow is deepened, and the erosional powers of the corrie glacier are increased until the typical armchair shape is scooped out (Fig. 6.3(d)). Ultimately, the return of warmer conditions and the melting of the ice reveals the corrie (Fig. 6.3(e)): its steep back wall, its 'arms' on each side, sometimes a lip made up of deposited material or even of solid rock, and a small lake or tarn in the hollow behind the lip.

Corries on opposite sides of a mountain may cut back towards each other. In extreme cases this leads to the formation of a steep *pyramidal peak*, such as the Matterhorn on the borders of Switzerland and Italy. Corries on the same side of a mountain or a pair of corries which are formed on exactly opposite sides of a mountain may also encroach on one another, until only a steep-sided and often narrow ridge known as an *arête* (Fig. 6.2) separates them. Striding Edge on Helvellyn in the Lake District is a well-known example.

(b) Glaciated Valleys

A corrie may be only the upper end of a glaciated valley. Ice and snow from several corries and mountain slopes eventually slide down into the valleys. The ice and snow become thicker and more compacted and the pressure of accumulating snow, combined with the force of gravity, forces the ice to move slowly down the valley. It has become a glacier. The erosive power of the glacier increases with the thickness of the ice and its speed of movement.

Fig. 6.4 South Sawyer glacier, Alaska, with two of its many tributaries. This photograph, taken in summer, shows the large expanses of snow on the mountain tops, known as névé field. In winter snow probably covers the entire rock surface. It is likely that corries are forming in several places. The dark stripes on the surface of the glaciers are moraines

The speed of glacial flow is dependent on many factors including fluctuations in the climate, the shape of the valley sides and the steepness of the valley floor. Ice near the middle of the glacier moves faster than that which is in contact with the floor or the sides of the valley because this contact slows down the glacial movement. But even the fastest glacier moves extremely slowly; its speed can only be measured in metres per year.

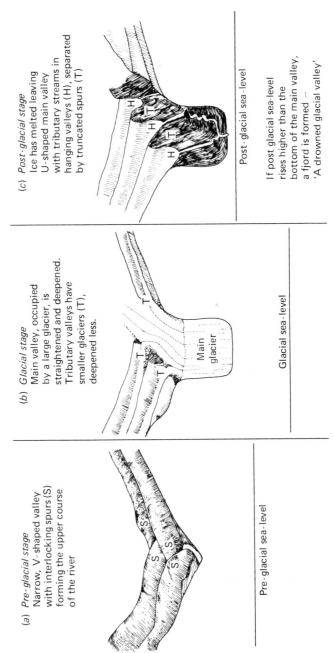

(a) Pre-glacial stage
Narrow, V-shaped valley with interlocking spurs (S) forming the upper course of the river

Pre-glacial sea-level

(b) Glacial stage
Main valley, occupied by a large glacier, is straightened and deepened. Tributary valleys have smaller glaciers (T), deepened less.

Main glacier

Glacial sea-level

(c) Post-glacial stage
Ice has melted leaving U-shaped main valley with tributary streams in hanging valleys (H), separated by truncated spurs (T)

Post-glacial sea-level

If post glacial sea-level rises higher than the bottom of the main valley, a fjord is formed — 'A drowned glacial valley'

Fig. 6.5 The formation of a glacial valley

(i) **Ice-falls.** The surface of a glacier is far from level. Pressures within the ice and the uneven nature of the valley floor cause *crevasses* to form. Sometimes the valley floor itself becomes steeper, and this is reflected on the surface of the ice in an ice-fall, a jumbled mass of fractured ice, with deep crevasses and steep ice pinnacles, called *seracs*.

(ii) **U-shaped valleys.** The erosive power of a glacier is concentrated on the floor of the valley. This is deepened and, after the ice has melted away, it is often seen to be U-shaped and very steep-sided. The famous Lauterbrunnen Valley in Switzerland is often cited as a typical glaciated valley, but it is really too perfect an example. Not all valleys will show the features of glacial erosion as well as this one.

(iii) **Truncated spurs and hanging valleys.** A flowing stream can twist and turn as its valley curves, but a glacier is much less agile. It cannot readily change its direction, and the interlocking spurs typical of the upper course of a river, which we saw in Section 4.4(*a*), tend to be cut off or *truncated* by the glacier in its search for the straightest and most direct course. This results in two more features of glaciated valleys, *truncated spurs* and *hanging valleys*.

Fig. 6.5 shows a valley before, during and after glaciation. You can see how the spurs projecting between tributary streams and in the upper course of the valley in its pre-glacial stage have been truncated by the movement of the ice. After the ice disappears, steep cliffs are left, rising above the new valley floor (Fig. 6.10). Before the onset of the ice, tributary streams joined the main river at the same level. During the glacial periods, however, the main valley was occupied by a much larger glacier with far greater erosive powers than the smaller glaciers in the tributary valleys. When the ice melted, the main valley was found to be greatly overdeepened while the tributary valleys had been eroded to a much lesser extent. Thus each tributary became a *hanging valley*, and the stream which discharged from it dropped by a cascade or waterfall to join the main streams.

(iv) **Alps.** An overdeepened or U-shaped valley does not always destroy all the outlines of the pre-glacial valley. The steep sides of the new valley are sometimes topped by the remains of the more gently sloping sides of the pre-glacial valley. These shelves or shoulders are called *alps* in Switzerland, and they play an important part in the human geography of mountain areas (*H & R*, Unit 3).

(v) **Roches moutonnées** are large masses of rock which have been smoothed and polished by the movement of the ice on their upstream side, whereas the downstream side is rough and irregular, from the constant plucking action of the ice. Deep scratches, often parallel to one another, may still be visible on the surface of the rock. These are *striations*, cut by the movement of rock fragments held firmly in the grip of the ice.

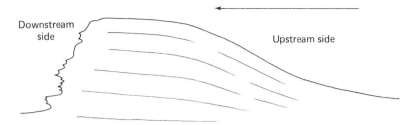

Fig. 6.6 A roche moutonnée. (Arrow show direction of ice movement)

(vi) **Crag-and-tail.** Some obstacles in the path of the moving ice prove to be too hard for glaciers or ice-sheets to erode completely. A plug of hard volcanic rock, for example, may resist the erosive power of the ice. The Castle Rock at Edinburgh is a familiar example. Its upstream side was worn by the ice as it attempted to demolish this obstacle in its path. On the downstream side (that is, the lee of the rock) there was not such pressure from the ice. Material being carried by the ice was dropped here and, in Edinburgh, formed the gentle ascent of the Royal Mile. This phenomenon is known as *crag-and-tail*. It is a common feature of glaciated valleys and lowlands, although few can match the scale and impressive character of the Edinburgh example.

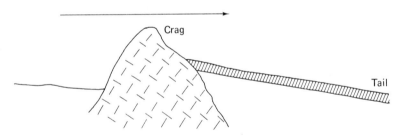

Fig. 6.7 Crag-and-tail. (Arrow shows direction of ice movement)

(c) **Fjords**

Fjords are drowned glaciated valleys; they are found along the coasts of Norway, Alaska and British Columbia, southern Chile, New Zealand and South Greenland. They were formed in these places because only in these high latitudes did valley glaciers actually reach the coast, eroding the deep valleys which became fjords as the sea-level rose. This process is still continuing today on parts of the coast of Greenland, where the snouts of glaciers break off and float away as icebergs. Fjords display all the typical features of glacial valleys, including steep sides, truncated spurs, hanging valleys and, sometimes, alps. The fjord sides rise from the calm water of an arm of the sea and this gives them a peculiar beauty, which has made the more accessible fjord coasts great tourist attractions.

Fig. 6.8 Milford Sound, a fjord on the coast of South Island, New Zealand

6.4   Glacial Deposition

A glacier carries away by far the greater part of the material which it has eroded from the land surface and deposits it, often a long way from where the rock originated. The surface of a glacier is often littered with this material, which is known as moraine. It occurs in bands along the edge of the glacier (*lateral moraine*) and, for every tributary that has joined the main glacier, there will be a strip of *medial moraine* as well, as shown in Figs 6.4 and 6.9. There is also much *englacial* material within the depths of the glacier, eroded from the rock over which the ice moves. All this material, which the ice has

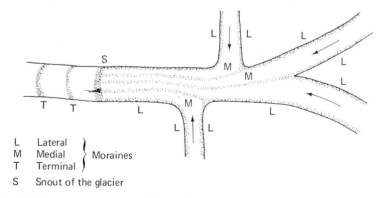

L   Lateral ⎫
M   Medial ⎬ Moraines
T   Terminal ⎭
S   Snout of the glacier

Fig. 6.9 Moraines associated with a valley glacier. Compare this with Fig. 6.4

torn away from the earth's surface and transported away, must be deposited somewhere eventually. When the ice melts, the material is laid down on the floor of the glacial valley, on the lowlands or in the sea.

As the glacier leaves the confines of its valley the ice spreads out and joins up with ice from other valley glaciers to form an ice-sheet, as we described in Section 6.1(a). It may spread over a vast area and carry with it incalculable quantities of rock waste derived from the highlands. But a glacier or ice-sheet can only survive as long as the temperature remains low enough for ice to exist. As soon as the moving ice reaches a point where it can melt, streams begin to form on or within the ice. The melting water forms tunnels under the glacier until it emerges at the margins of the ice as swift, turbulent streams carrying an immense amount of rocky waste.

(a) Moraines
Without ice to support and carry it, much of the rocky material is dropped as soon as melting occurs.

(i) **Lateral and medial moraines.** When a glacier melts within the confines of its valley, the lateral and medial moraines, formerly on the surface of the glacier,

Fig. 6.10 The snout of a glacier in Jasper National Park, Alberta, Canada. This glacier is merely the remnant of a much larger predecessor which was responsible for forming the truncated spurs and hanging valleys, still containing glaciers. Deposits of lateral moraine are clearly visible along the valley sides and there is terminal moraine in the foreground

are deposited as long heaps of rock waste along the length of the valley floor. The deposits are still known as lateral and medial moraines. Their presence disrupts the appearance of the flat valley floor that we normally associate with a U-shaped glacial valley.

(ii) **Terminal or end moraines.** The slow rise in temperature which causes the ice to melt is not a steady, regular process. It appears to happen very unevenly, the climate becoming warmer for, say, three or four centuries, and remaining at that temperature for several more centuries before beginning to grow warmer again. This has resulted in very irregular melting of the glacier snout or ice-sheet, and the deposition of a bank of material, known as end or terminal moraine, at each still-stand of the ice.

(iii) **Fluvio-glacial action.** The shape and composition of all the landscape features resulting from the deposition of glacial material is determined by fluvio-glacial action (the action of the torrents of melt water which issue from the melting ice). The coarser materials, including gravel and even large boulders, are deposited close to the ice margin, forming the end moraine. The streams sift out the finer materials and carry them a considerable distance from the ice margin before depositing them. There is usually a large, gently sloping area known as the *outwash plain* beyond the end moraine, made up of gravel, sand and fine clay, successively.

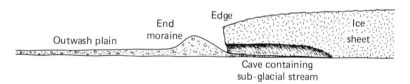

Fig. 6.11 Formation of an end moraine and outwash plain

The Jutland peninsula in Denmark has a broad belt of end moraine as its backbone, and there is a large expanse of outwash material on its outer or western side. This region was once infertile heathland, but reclamation during the last 120 years has turned much of it into productive farm and forest land (*H & R*, Unit 19).

(*b*) **Glacial Drift**
The belt of end moraine and outwash deposited at each still-stand may be as much as 50 km in breadth or as little as 5 or 10 km. Usually a much larger area of glacial drift (that is, all the material laid down directly by the ice or by fluvio-glacial action) is deposited between the end moraine and the retreating margin of the ice. The end moraine is created when climatic conditions remain unchanged for a long period; the line of melting changes little and englacial material continues to be dropped along approximately the same line. If, on the other hand, the climate gradually gets warmer, the margin of

the ice will slowly retreat and leave a cover of glacial till or boulder clay as it does so.

The composition of boulder clay varies widely, as its name suggests. It contains rock fragments of all sizes which are dumped on the land surface when the ice melts. If the proportion of stones and boulders is high, the deposit is not a fertile soil. When it is mainly clay, it makes very productive agricultural land. The high, natural fertility of parts of Scandinavia, such as the eastern side of the Jutland peninsula, the Danish islands and southern Sweden, is the result of boulder clay which was deposited behind the Great Baltic End Moraine.

(c) Other Depositional Features

There are several other features of a glacial or boulder clay plain which are produced by the deposition of englacial materials.

(i) **Erratics** can sometimes be found among the glacial drift. These are masses of rock which are large enough for their character, composition and origin to be determined. They provide valuable evidence about the direction of movement of the ice-sheets. In East Anglia one may find pieces of red granite from Shap Fell in Cumbria and, along the north-east coast of England, fragments of larvikite, a characteristic Norwegian rock, are found in the boulder clay.

(ii) **Drumlins** are oval-shaped heaps of boulder clay which vary considerably in size but are usually found in groups or 'swarms'. Geographers are uncertain as to how they were formed, but they probably originated in the deposition of a mass of englacial material beneath an ice-sheet. As the ice moved, the heap of boulder clay was smoothed and rounded. Some boulder-clay areas have no drumlins at all while drumlin swarms are common in others, for example, in northern Ireland, central Scotland and parts of northern England. Their axes are roughly parallel, thus denoting the direction of movement of the ice. Drumlins produce a landscape which is sometimes called *basket-of-eggs* topography.

(iii) **Eskers** are long ridges of glacial sand and gravel, rather like embankments, and they may extend for long distances across a glaciated lowland without regard for the local relief. The origin of these features is also uncertain but they may be related to deposition within or at the mouth of a cave or tunnel in the edge of a rapidly retreating ice-sheet. Sometimes an esker widens into a rounded platform, before again contracting to its usual ridge-like profile. This is called a *beaded esker*. Finland is noteworthy for its eskers, and the one known as the Saupauselka today carries a railway, elevated safely above the level of the damp and lake-studded plain.

(iv) **Loess or limon.** This is a very fine-grained soil with a texture like flour, which is sometimes found along the outside edge of an area of glacial

Fig. 6.12 The Punkaharju esker, Finland, winding through lakes formed on the uneven surface of glacial drift

outwash. It is usually a pale brown or buff colour. It is supposed that wind, blowing over an expanse of glacial drift during the cold, dry conditions usually accompanying the retreat of an ice-sheet, removed the finer clay particles and deposited them outside the glaciated area, often over great distances. There are large areas of such soil in both Europe and North America. It is always well drained and fertile, and was often the earliest soil to be ploughed and cultivated.

6.5 Glacial Lakes

Lakes are a common feature of all glaciated landscapes, and they contribute greatly to the beauty of many mountain areas. Glacial lakes may be produced by both erosion and deposition, and it is not always possible to say which has been the more important element.

The powerful erosive action of ice can scoop out hollows in the rock. We have seen how a shallow tarn may come to occupy a depression formed in the floor of a corrie. The ice may deepen part of a glaciated valley floor in a similar way, especially if the rock is relatively soft or has been weakened by faults. The result of this type of erosion is a long narrow lake, sometimes known as a *ribbon* or *finger lake*. The lakes in the Trossachs in Scotland are finger lakes, as are those of the northern Appalachian Mountains in upper New York State. Intensively glaciated areas of very hard rock, such as the Laurentian Shield of Canada, northern Sweden and Finland, and even the extreme north-west of Scotland, are strewn with lakes, most of them quite small, occupying hollows gouged out by ice action.

On the other hand, the deposition of a moraine across a valley may cause a lake to be impounded behind this 'barrier'. The Italian Lakes—Maggiore, Como, Garda—were formed in this way, at the lower end of valleys which opened from the Alps (*H & R*, Unit 20). It is not always clear to what extent such lakes are due to the dam created by the moraine, and to what extent to a depression actually hollowed out by the movement of the ice. Whatever their mode of formation, these lakes are also known as ribbon or finger lakes, because they occupy parts of the floor of a glacial valley.

Lakes may also form on the surface of a boulder clay plain. The glacial material was usually deposited far from evenly, and lakes naturally formed in the hollows and depressions. Finland and the states of Michigan and Minnesota in the USA are strewn with this type of lake.

Fig. 6.13 shows a type of lake called a *kettle hole*, formed when an ice-sheet was melting. A large compacted mass of ice was buried in the glacial drift or boulder clay, which on melting left a rounded hollow, known as a kettle hole, which gave rise to a lake. In time a system of drainage may develop on the

(a)   (b)

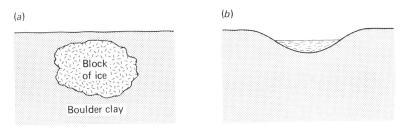

Fig. 6.13 Formation of a kettle hole

ground moraine, linking several of these lakes together like beads on a string. Such small lakes are sometimes called *paternoster lakes.*

Lastly, a glacial lake may sometimes form in the mountains, where thick ice remains in the main glacial valley after the thinner ice of a tributary valley has melted. The former holds back melt water in the latter to form a lake. The most famous example of such a lake is the *Marjelen See*, in Switzerland, held back by the Aletsch glacier. There are many other lakes of this type in Iceland.

6.6   Glaciation in the British Isles

As the climate grew colder at the onset of the first glacial period in the British Isles, the snow grew progressively thicker on the higher ground and lasted for much of the year on the lower. Thick ice began to form in the valleys and glaciers started to move towards the lower ground. Eventually, during the coldest part of the glacial period, much of the country was covered by ice. Then, equally slowly, the climate became warmer. The ice melted first from the lowlands, leaving behind a vast spread of glacial drift. Finally, the ice over the mountains melted away. The glacial period was over and temperatures may even have been higher than before the onset of the ice.

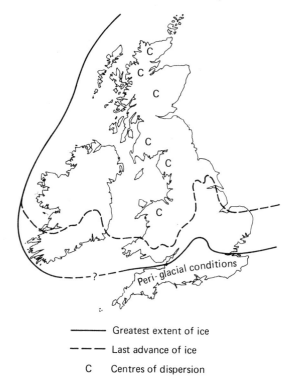

Peri- glacial conditions

——— Greatest extent of ice

– – – Last advance of ice

C   Centres of dispersion

Fig. 6.14 Glaciation of the British Isles

This sequence of events took place four times, but temperatures during the coldest part of each of these glaciations varied greatly. The glaciation with the greatest extent of ice was the third, during which an ice-sheet covered all of Ireland and Great Britain, roughly as far south as the Thames Valley and South Wales. South of this line there was not a continuous sheet of ice, but conditions were similar to those of the tundra of northern Canada or Siberia today. Such conditions are called *peri-glacial* (that is, on the edge of the ice).

Further Reading

Dury, G. H.: *The Face of the Earth*. Penguin (Harmondsworth, 1970), Chapters 12–15.

Gresswell, R. K.: *Glaciers and Glaciation.* Hulton Educational Publications (Amersham, 1964).

Holmes, A.: *Principles of Physical Geology.* Nelson (London, 1965), Chapters 20, 21.

Sawyer, K. E.: *Landscape Studies: An Introduction to Geomorphology.* Arnold (London, 1970), Section C.

Sparks, B. W.: *Geomorphology.* Longman (Harlow, 1970), Chapters 12–14.

Strahler, A. N.: *Physical Geography.* John Wiley (Chichester, 1969), Chapter 26.

Swinnerton, H. H.: *The Earth Beneath Us.* Penguin (Harmondsworth, 1958), Chapters 21, 22, 23, 24.

Questions

1. Using annotated diagrams, explain how a corrie is formed. Name an area where examples of this feature may be seen.
2. Describe and explain the features which result from glaciation in a mountain valley.
3. Why have changes in sea-level been closely associated with glaciation? Describe and explain the features which result from changes in sea-level.
4. With the aid of diagrams, describe and explain the formation of: (*a*) pyramidal peaks, (*b*) arêtes, (*c*) roches moutonnées, (*d*) crag-and-tail, (*e*) striations.
5. What surface features result from glacial deposition? Draw annotated diagrams to explain how these features are formed.
6. (*a*) Describe the landscape shown in Fig. 6.4.
   (*b*) Explain how such a landscape is formed.

Unit Seven
The Work of Wind

The wind is an agent of erosion and transportation like flowing water and moving ice, but it is very much more limited. Wind has immense power: it can flatten houses, destroy crops and uproot trees. But wind alone has little influence on shaping the surface of the ground, because it is only able to move small dry particles. If the land has a cover of vegetation it is adequately protected against the erosive power of the wind. Thus the wind is only effective as an agent of erosion and transportation where the surface is made up, in part at least, of loose dry particles, and where there is little plant cover to protect it from the wind.

7.1 The Formation of Sand

The conditions necessary for wind erosion are only met in two types of area—in most deserts and along parts of the world's coastline, where there is usually a belt of sand close to the edge of the sea (Section 5.3(*d*)).

Roughly a quarter of the land surface of the earth is occupied by desert, where the generally arid climate (that is, one with a very low rainfall) prevents the growth of an extensive vegetation cover. A desert is not necessarily just an area of drifting sand, like that shown in Fig. 7.2. There is, of course, a great deal of sand, but most of it is around the desert margins. As one moves from the edge of a desert towards the centre, one passes from an area covered mostly by sand to one of pebbles and loose stones. The centre of the desert, especially the Sahara, the Western Australian Desert and the Gobi Desert in Mongolia, may contain extremely rugged mountains, but it is generally made up of bare rock. In desert conditions the rock is broken up into ever smaller fragments by the alternate expansion and concentration of exfoliation, until ultimately it is reduced to sand (Section 3.1(*a*)).

Around the coasts, sand is continually being formed as the sea batters the rocks of the coastline. As we saw in Unit 5, the rocks are gradually reduced to ever finer particles and the sea transports them and accumulates them in the form of beaches. Another constituent is usually added to sand formed in this way, derived from finely broken-up shells and the skeletons of sea creatures. The sand of a coral island, for example, consists wholly of particles of coral.

7.2 Wind Erosion

(*a*) Types of Erosion
Wind uses sand as the agent of erosion, in three main ways—*deflation*, *abrasion* and *attrition*. These three processes are not really separate and

distinct. They are carried on at the same time whenever the wind has a supply of loose, sand-like materials to transport.

(i) **Deflation.** A strong wind can transport very coarse sand, lifting it from the ground and propelling it for great distances. Fine dust-like particles can be whirled into the air and may even be carried right across a continent by the wind before they touch the ground again. Deflation is thus the dispersal of sand and dust particles by the wind. It is experienced on the beaches or coastal sand dunes of the British Isles where it scoops out hollows known as *blow-outs*. But the main effects of deflation can be seen in the gigantic depressions that have been created in the Sahara Desert by the scooping action of the wind. The Qattara Depression, for example, now lies more than 120 m below sea-level.

(ii) **Abrasion.** The movement of particles, especially the coarse, hard particles which we call sand, gradually wears away the rock with which it comes into contact. This is *abrasion*, and it is a kind of slow sand-blasting. Paint may be

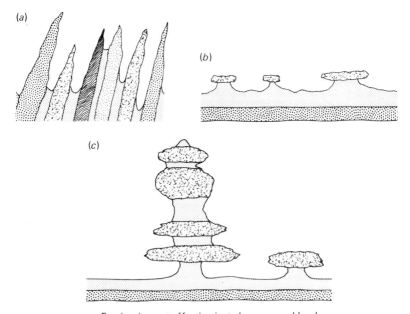

Erosion is most effective just above ground level

Fig. 7.1 Features resulting from wind erosion
(a) *Yardangs: these features of differential erosion may be 7 m from crest to furrow*
(b) *Zeugen*
(c) *Pedestal or mushroom rocks: erosion is most effective just above ground level*

stripped from buildings near the coast by abrasion, but it is in desert environments that the abrasive power of wind is greatest, notably on bare rock surfaces.

(iii) **Attrition.** The coarse particles are not lifted more than a few millimetres from the surface except by a very strong wind. They flow very close to the ground, constantly knocking against one another, breaking under the impact and being reduced to even smaller sizes. This is *attrition*.

(b) Features Produced By Wind Erosion

The erosive power of the wind is always greatest close to the ground, because the larger particles—those with the greatest abrasive power—are never lifted very far above it. There is also a marked difference between the wind's erosional effects on hard and on soft rock.

Bare rock surfaces are etched by the effect of sand-blasting into shapes which depend on the original rock structure. Vertical beds of rock of varying hardness will be carved into a series of ridges and furrows known as *yardangs* (Fig. 7.1(a)), while horizontal strata are eroded to form *zeugen* (Fig. 7.1(b)). Pedestal rocks are an extreme form of the zeugen and may be over 30 m high (Fig. 7.1(c)). The softer rocks are deeply eroded and a narrow stalk produced. Erosion is at its most vigorous at a metre or so above the ground, depending on the strength of the wind.

7.3   Wind Deposition

The power of the wind to transport the particles which are made available to it by deflation, abrasion and attrition largely depends on its speed. Strong winds may produce a *sandstorm*, in which coarse particles are whirled along close to the ground, or a *dust storm*, when finer materials are carried high into the sky, sometimes darkening the sun, and transported immense distances in the higher atmosphere. The sand of the sandstorm, however, is quickly deposited as the wind strength drops, to await the next storm before it is carried forward again.

(a) Sand Dunes

When the wind drops the sand which it is carrying, it forms dunes which are continually shifting and changing their shape. Coastal dunes have no regular pattern, but the dunes of the desert fall into a number of distinct types. These depend mainly on wind strength and direction, and on the presence of obstacles to the free movement of the wind on the desert floor.

(i) '**Sand-sea.**' The sand-sea, known as *erg* in the Sahara, consists of large areas of patternless, undulating dunes whose surface has been rippled by the wind. These areas of sand usually occur where the wind does not blow from a constant direction.

Fig. 7.2 Rolling areas of sand dune in the American desert. The ripple marks on the sand may be clearly seen over much of the surface

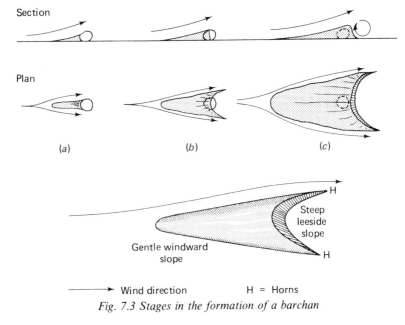

Fig. 7.3 Stages in the formation of a barchan

(ii) **Crescentic dunes or barchans** result from a steady wind-flow, without significant changes in direction. The stages in the formation of such a dune are shown in Fig. 7.3. An obstacle, such as a boulder or even a patch of pebbles, obstructs the free flow of the wind, thus reducing its speed and its carrying power. Deposition occurs on the windward side of the obstacle and the sand then piles up until the dune achieves a shape which offers the least resistance to the flow of the wind. Particles of sand are carried up the gentle windward slope of the dune and tumble over on to the calmer leeward side, where an eddying motion of the air tends to maintain a steep slope. At the same time, wind is deflected around the sides of the growing dune, where its frictional contact with the sand slows the wind down slightly. Sand is deposited there in the form of long, pointed *horns*, following the direction of the wind and thus giving the dune its characteristic crescent shape.

A barchan will last as long as the wind direction remains unchanged, and it will be growing larger all the time. It may even move very slowly forward as sand is blown up its windward slope, over the top and down the steep leeward slope. Such dunes may be up to 800 m across and as much as 40 m high. Although single, isolated barchans may develop, especially in the Atacama Desert of Chile and Peru and the deserts of the American South-west, a system of many overlapping barchans is more likely to form.

(iii) **Longitudinal or seif dunes** are long, high ridges of sand lying roughly parallel to one another. They sometimes attain immense sizes—hundreds of kilometres in length and a hundred metres or more in height. Some have a level even crest, others a series of high 'peaks', like a mountain range in miniature. There may be smooth sand or even bare rock between these dunes.

The formation of seif dunes has never been adequately explained. It seems likely that they were shaped by a prevailing wind from one direction, interrupted by occasional cross-winds. Seif dunes are fully developed in the deserts of Libya in north Africa, Thar in India and in the Western Australian Desert.

(iv) **Loess or limon** differs from sand in its very much finer texture, the result of the process of attrition (Section 6.4(*c*)). There is no evidence that wind-borne transport of such material is taking place today, except on a small and local scale, but vast areas were covered with loess in the past. The loess region of north-western China is larger than France, and in some parts of it the loess has accumulated to a depth of over 300 m. There are also extensive loess deposits of glacial origin (see Section 6.4(*b*)) in Europe and North America, but here the climate is moister and much loess has been removed by river erosion.

(*b*) The Expanding Desert

Wind-transported sand now covers considerable areas of the earth's surface. Archaeologists have shown that the Sahara Desert covers a greater area to-day than it did at the time of the Roman Empire, and it is still expanding. Several years of continuous drought along the desert margin, in Mauritania,

Senegal, Mali, Niger and Chad have recently lowered the water-table, killed the vegetation and produced conditions that have enabled the desert to take over. There has been nothing to prevent the encroachment of the sand. It has now overwhelmed areas which were inhabited and cultivated a century ago.

Man is fully as capable of creating a desert as nature. The surface layers of the soil are naturally fixed and held in place by vegetation. If you destroy the vegetation, the soil particles can dry out and blow away. This is most likely to happen in a region of low rainfall, such as the Russian steppe or the American prairie, but it can also occur in a region as moist as England. The peaty soils of part of the Fenland of Cambridgeshire and Lincolnshire and the chalky soil of Salisbury Plain have been blown away in dust storms. The most extreme case of such soil erosion by wind has been in the United States, where a large area in the states of Kansas and Oklahoma was reduced to a *Dust Bowl* because the tough, grassy cover was destroyed and the soil exposed to the drying wind which is always blowing on the High Plains. (We shall discuss man's contribution to soil destruction by *soil erosion* in Unit 12.)

7.4   Water in the Desert

No desert is completely rainless, but rain usually falls in the form of highly irregular and infrequent storms. They may occur only once in several years, but they may be extremely violent. Some of the rain water is absorbed by the sand or percolates through joints and cracks in the rocks, but the rain is usually so torrential that much of it runs directly off the surface, since there is neither vegetation nor soil to trap it and slow down its movement. Torrents quickly form and erode a number of distinctive desert landscape features.

(a) Wadis
Wadis are deep, steep-sided valleys, probably eroded by storm run-off over a period of thousands of years. The water rushing down the wadi is armed with the abundant sand and loose stones of the desert floor, and it is a powerful agent of erosion and transportation. Eventually the water evaporates and the torrent becomes smaller and more sand-laden until it turns into a river of liquid sand, and then dries up.

The floor of the wadi is usually a flat expanse of dried mud, sand and boulders. Its sides are steep because few agents of weathering are ever active enough to wear them back. The wadi thus provides a welcome shelter from wind and sun in the fierce desert environment, but it would be rash to stay for too long on the floor of a wadi. A distant storm can turn it into a raging torrent in a matter of minutes.

Some wadis are so deep that it has been questioned whether they could be solely the work of infrequent storms. Some geographers have suggested that, in common with several other desert features, wadis may have been largely formed at a time when rainfall was much heavier there than it is today.

(b) **Inselberg**

The bare rock surface may be broken by isolated, steep-sided mountains to which the German name *inselberg* has been given. It is generally assumed that they have acquired their characteristic smooth, rounded shape partly as a result of erosion in an arid climate, but very little is known about the processes involved. One thing, however, is certain: their rounded, wind-smoothed features are mere remnants of more extensive areas of high ground. They are entirely made up of one rock type, usually a hard sedimentary rock, such as sandstone, or a homogeneous igneous rock, such as granite. They may have been formed when the climate was wetter than it is in today's deserts.

(c) **Buttes or Mesas**

Similar residual hills are formed from horizontally bedded sedimentary rocks, with vertical joints along which erosion can take place. Isolated flat-topped, steep-sided hills are left, each skirted by scree and surrounded by low-lying desert. These *buttes* or *mesas* are found mostly in the deserts of Algeria and the American South-west.

Fig. 7.4 A group of mesas in the Arizona desert, USA. The horizontal bedding is clearly seen and erosion along the vertical joints is especially apparent on the central mass. The level of their tops conforms with the plateau surface in the distance to suggest that they were all part of a much more extensive plateau at one time

(d) Playas and Bolsons

The desert floor has many hollows and depressions. The torrents which follow the rare desert storms rush into such basins, laying down a sheet of mud, which dries out under the sun to give a fairly smooth, dusty surface. This is covered by water whenever it rains. Such short-lived 'lakes' are called *playas* or *bolsons*.

(e) Basins of Inland Drainage

Little of the rain which falls in a desert ever flows back to the sea. It ends up in a wadi or a playa, from which there is no outlet, and the water lies there until it evaporates into the atmosphere. A playa is part of a *basin of inland drainage*. If you study an atlas you will see that most of the world's desert regions consist of basins of inland drainage. The most famous examples are the Great Basin of the western United States, the Dead Sea, Lake Chad on the southern margin of the Sahara, and Lakes Eyre and Torrens in Australia. All these basins are fed by rivers, but no water ever flows out of them.

(f) Exotic Streams

Nevertheless, rivers do flow across some of the world's largest deserts. They rise in moist regions outside the desert and cross it to reach the sea, and they are called *exotic streams* for this reason. They lose much water by evaporation, but their volume is such that they are able to survive and reach the coast. The Nile, for example, draws its water from the mountains of Ethiopia and the highlands of East Africa and flows across the Sahara Desert to the Mediterranean. The Colorado river rises in the Rocky Mountains and once crossed the desert plateaux of the American South-west to reach the Gulf of California. Now man takes so much water from the Colorado to supply the towns of southern California, to irrigate the land along its banks and to fill reservoirs for hydro-electricity that the river no longer reaches the sea. The river which was powerful enough to erode the Grand Canyon now disappears somewhere near the Mexican frontier, and the distributaries of its former delta have completely dried up.

(g) Oases

An oasis is a small area of a desert where water is available, either at the surface or in shallow wells. Small as desert rainfall is, enough falls over a period of tens of thousands of years to percolate into the rocks and form substantial underground reserves. This supply may be augmented by water falling in distant mountains or on the fringes of the desert and moving into the desert region itself if there is a suitable underlying *aquifer* (Section 3.2). Some of the water may even have survived in the rocks from a distant period when the desert had a much moister climate.

In parts of the Sahara water lies in abundance quite close to the surface, and enormous reservoirs have been tapped in the course of oil drilling in Libya. Near the Kufra oasis, underground water is sufficient for the large-scale cultivation of fodder crops for sheep rearing. In Australia there are a number of basins, known as *artesian basins*, in which the water may be forced to the surface by its own pressure when a bore-hole is put down to reach it (Section 3.2).

The oasis of romantic fiction is in realiyt most often a large area, sometimes hundreds of square kilometres, within which the water-table lies close to the surface and can be reached by means of shallow wells. Deep-rooting trees, especially the date palm, can reach the water, and the supply is abundant and regular enough to sustain agriculture and even support a town. The water may rise to the surface in springs; more often it has to be reached in wells. Excessive use may lower the level of the water so that mechanical power must be used to pump it to the surface.

Further Reading

Dury, G. H.: *The Face of the Earth*. Penguin (Harmondsworth, 1970), Chapter 16.

Holmes, A.: *Principles of Physical Geology*. Nelson (London, 1965), Chapter 22.

Sawyer, K. E.: *Landscape Studies: An Introduction to Geomorphology*. Arnold (London, 1970), Section D.

Sparks, B. W.: *Geomorphology*. Longman (Harlow, 1970), Chapter 11.

Strahler, A. N.: *Physical Geography*. John Wiley (Chichester, 1969), Chapter 28.

Questions

1. Why is wind most active as an agent of erosion in a dry climate? What desert landforms result from wind erosion?
2. Why is sand abundant in parts of every desert? What other types of surface may be found?
3. Using carefully annotated diagrams, describe and explain the formation of the desert features resulting from deposition.
4. Write an essay on *Water in the Desert*.
5. Describe and explain the ways in which each of the following desert landforms originate: (*a*) pedestal rock, (*b*) mesa, (*c*) barchan, (*d*) wadi, (*e*) playa.
6. (*a*) Describe the landscape shown in Fig. 7.4.
   (*b*) Explain how this landscape may have been formed.

Unit Eight
Waterfalls, Lakes and Gorges

Waterfalls, lakes and gorges are all mainly associated with river erosion, but they may also be formed by a combination of any of the agents of denudation. All three may be relatively short-lived features of the landscape, but they are nearly always spectacular while they exist.

8.1 Waterfalls

A waterfall is a steep, even precipitous drop in the course of a river. It occurs where there is an obstacle to the formation of a smooth river profile, such as a barrier of hard rock. A waterfall is always in the process of destroying itself, because of the river's constant attempts to make its profile smooth and regular. The erosive powers of the river are concentrated on the barrier rock over which the water falls, and this rock is constantly being eroded.

The form of a waterfall is determined largely by the geological structure of the region. When there is a bed of more or less horizontal hard rock overlying

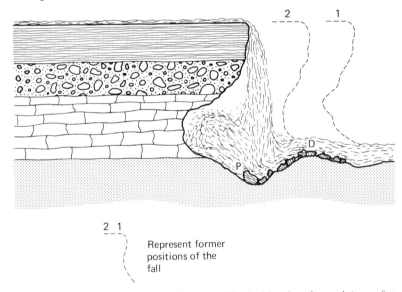

Represent former positions of the fall

Fig. 8.1 A waterfall caused by a horizontal bed of hard rock overlying softer rocks. The force of the falling water erodes the plunge pool (P) and undercuts the hard rock, which collapses. D = debris from such a collapse

a softer and more easily eroded rock, a fall is formed as illustrated in Fig. 8.1. In waterfalls of this type, such as Niagara Falls and Victoria Falls, the water has a powerful abrasive and scouring action at the base of the fall and the bed of the stream is deepened there, forming a *plunge pool*. The erosive power of the water also wears away the softer bed of rock, undercutting the fall so that the unsupported 'lip' periodically collapses into the pool below, causing the fall gradually to work its way upstream. This usually produces an ever-lengthening gorge below the falls. The gorges created by the river Niagara and by the Zambesi below the Victoria Falls are among the most spectacular in the world.

Fig. 8.2 Alexandra Falls, North-west Territory, Canada. The horizontal strata are visible in the steep sides of the gorge below the fall

The river may, on the other hand, flow across a vertical belt of hard rock—an igneous dyke, for example. Here the fall is likely to become more gentle, and will gradually turn into a cataract or rapid.

Many other landscape features can give rise to waterfalls. A fault may create a steep slope over which a river may plunge. In glaciated areas a stream may drop steeply from the lip of a corrie, or a torrent may fall from a hanging valley to the floor of an over-deepened glacial valley (Unit 6). The recession of a cliffed coastline can lead to the formation of hanging valleys, with the probability of a small waterfall developing from each. Some of the most

(a)

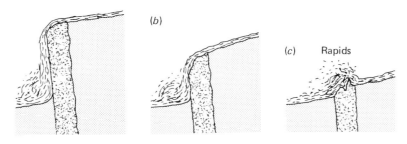

Fig. 8.3 Stages in the removal of a waterfall formed by a hard vertical bed. The fall is slowly lowered until it tumbles over rapids

spectacular falls occur where a river flows over the edge of a plateau. The highest falls in the world such as the Kaieteur Falls, over 200 m high, occur around the margin of the plateau which occupies the interior of Guyana and neighbouring areas of Venezuela and Brazil in South America.

8.2   Lakes

Lakes are also temporary features of the earth's surface. They are bodies of water which occupy hollows or depressions in the surface of the land masses.

(a) Formation of Lakes

Most lakes receive their water from the rivers of the surrounding land. The load carried by the river is dropped when it enters the lake, and even the smallest lakes can usually show the formation of deltas, miniature replicas of the larger deltas formed when rivers enter the sea.

Since lakes are fed largely by the rainfall of the surrounding region, their level may rise and fall with the seasons. Some, such as certain lakes in North Africa and Australia, contract to a few pools of water or even dry out during the dry season. Most lakes have an outlet by which they discharge to the sea, but in the *lakes of internal drainage*, the water evaporates from their surface (Section 7.4).

(b) Types of Lake

Lakes can best be classified according to the origins of the depressions or hollows in which they lie.

(i) **Earth movements.** Movements of the earth's crust may form basins which sometimes contain lakes. Faulting, especially the formation of a rift valley, produces elongated depressions, and the Rift Valley of East Africa today contains a number of lakes. The largest of these are Lakes Tanganyika and Malawi (Section 2.6).

(ii) **Volcanic action.** Lava flows sometimes obstruct the natural drainage, and lead to the formation of a lake. The Sea of Galilee was formed in this way, but the barrier which created it is being slowly eroded away by the river Jordan.

Fig. 8.4 Crater Lake, Oregon, USA. This lake occupies the caldera formed by the collapse of the volcano, Mount Mazama. The small island is a subsidiary cone

Water often collects in the caldera or crater of an extinct volcano (Section 2.8). The Crater Lake in Oregon is probably the largest and best known of this type.

(iii) **Solution and mining.** Rock below the surface can be taken away, either by mining or by the solution and removal of soluble minerals. The land surface sometimes collapses above shallow coal, iron or salt mines, and the resulting hollows fill with water to form 'flashes'. Such lakes are common in the Cheshire saltfields and in the coalfields of Lancashire and Upper Silesia, in Poland.

(iv) **Glacial lakes.** Most of the hundreds of thousands of natural lakes in the world today owe their origin to the work of ice (particularly during the last, or Pleistocene glaciation). We have already discussed glacial lakes in Section 6.5.

(v) **Coastal lakes** are sometimes formed when arms of the sea are cut off by the formation of spits or bars (Section 5.3).

(vi) **Other types.** Lake basins may form in other ways. A landslide may close a valley, causing water to be held back in a lake. This is usually very short lived because the rising water behind the landslide is likely to overflow and erode the dam holding it back. Small lakes, or ox-bows, form in the course of a river's meandering (Section 4.4(c)). Wind deflation in a desert may produce a depression large and deep enough to contain at least a temporary lake. There are, lastly, the thousands of man-made lakes, from giant reservoirs to ornamental ponds in gardens and parks.

8.3   Gorges

Gorges are deep, steep-sided narrow valleys formed when the downcutting action of a river is much more vigorous and rapid than the weathering of the sides of the valley. Any factor or set of factors which concentrates the river's erosive power along a particular section of its course is likely to lead to the formation of a gorge.

We met one example of this in Section 8.1. When a river tumbles over a waterfall, such as Niagara Falls, the river's power of erosion is concentrated in the plunge pool and the fall recedes, leaving a gorge to mark the course of its

Fig. 8.5 One of the many deep, steep-sided gorges in the arid American south-west, eroded by the Colorado river and its tributaries

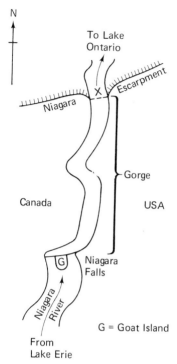

Fig. 8.6 The Niagara gorge. About 9 000 years ago the falls plunged over the Niagara escarpment at X, since when it has receded 11 km

recession. The gorge of the Niagara river now extends for 11 km below the falls.

A glacial overflow channel which assumes the form of a gorge may be cut by the sudden rush of water escaping from a lake which has been held back by an ice barrier. Melt water from the ice feeds the lake, the water level rises and the lake eventually overflows, quickly cutting a deep channel.

There are, of course, other ways in which a gorge can be formed. A series of faults may guide the course of a river and, since downcutting along the line of the fault is relatively easy, a gorge may result. Occasionally the roof of an underground drainage system may collapse to reveal a gorge, especially in the limestone country of Derbyshire and the Mendip Hills of Somerset (Section 3.2). Cheddar Gorge may have formed in this way.

Further Reading

Cotton, C. A.: *Landscape*. Cambridge University Press (London, 1955), Chapters 5, 11.

Questions

1. Explain the different ways in which waterfalls and rapids are formed.

2. Lakes are common in a glaciated landscape. Describe the ways in which they may be formed.

3. Describe and explain the factors, other than glaciation, which may give rise to lakes.

4. How do gorges form? What is the relationship between the shape of the gorge and climate?

5. (a) Describe the landscape shown in Fig. 8.2.

   (b) Explain how this landscape has been formed.

Unit Nine
The Weather

In this Unit we shall be concerned with the measurement of certain elements which together make up the earth's weather. We shall also be looking at the mechanics of the atmosphere, particularly the reasons for the day-to-day variations in the weather experienced in Britain and north-western Europe. This is the study known as *meteorology*. In Units 10 and 11 we shall be discussing the world's pattern of climates, which is the corresponding study of *climatology*.

9.1 The Atmosphere

The earth is surrounded by an envelope of gas called the atmosphere which extends outwards from the earth's surface, becoming gradually thinner, until it ceases to exist. The atmosphere has no precise upper limit, but 75 per cent of it is less than 11 km from the earth's surface, 90 per cent lies below 16 km and 97 per cent is below 27 km.

(a) Constituents

The atmosphere is a mixture of gases, about 78 per cent of it consisting of nitrogen and 21 per cent of oxygen. The remaining 1 per cent is made up of carbon dioxide, hydrogen and other gases. There are also two further constituents, water vapour and dust, which are both of great importance in determining the weather.

Water vapour is the result of *evaporation* (the process by which liquid is changed into vapour) from water surfaces on the earth. There is a strict limit to the amount of moisture which the atmosphere can hold, and this limit is set mainly by the temperature of the air. (We shall investigate this in more detail in Section 9.5.)

The dust is spread unevenly through the lower layers of the atmosphere. It is made up of volcanic dust, the dust stirred up by desert storms, carbon from factory and other chimneys, and even particles of salt left in the air when droplets of spray evaporate from the oceans.

(b) Temperature

The temperature of the atmosphere varies greatly at the earth's surface but at the upper levels it falls at an average rate of about 1 °C for every 100 m of ascent, whatever the temperature is at ground level. (We shall be discussing this more fully in Unit 10.) This decrease of temperature with increasing altitude is known as the *lapse rate*. There is a level, known as the *tropopause*,

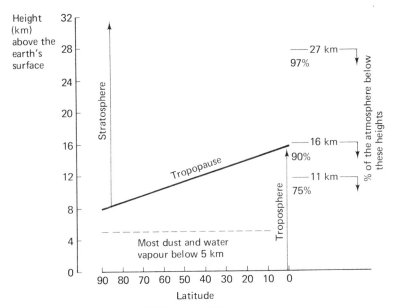

Fig. 9.1 Divisions of the atmosphere

at which this regular temperature change ceases; it occurs at a height above the earth's surface which varies from about 16 km at the equator to about 8 km at the poles. Above the tropopause the temperature ceases to fall with increasing altitude. The atmosphere is thus divided into two layers—the troposphere lies below the tropopause and the stratosphere lies above it.

The stratosphere is very much colder than the lower atmosphere, and this arrangement of temperatures demonstrates the very important fact that the earth's atmosphere is heated from *below*. Heat energy from the sun enters the atmosphere as *short-wave radiation*, which does not heat the air through which it passes. Only about 45 per cent of this energy reaches the earth's surface, and 10 per cent of this is reflected back into the atmosphere from snow and water surfaces (Fig. 9.2). Thus only about a third of the total solar energy entering the atmosphere actually warms the earth's surface. This heat is then passed back into the atmosphere from the earth's surface as *long-wave radiation*, heating the lower atmosphere.

9.2   Weather and Climate

The daily weather forecast tells us what to expect in the next 24 or 48 hours. It indicates the probability of rain, frost or strong winds, and it suggests the likelihood of sunshine or cloud. No two days ever have exactly the same weather, because weather changes from hour to hour and from place to place. We cannot know with any degree of certainty whether next Saturday will be dry for a game of football or next Sunday sunny enough for a picnic. But we can be certain that there will be no frost if it is midsummer or that we shall not be troubled by excessive heat if it is January. This emphasizes the difference

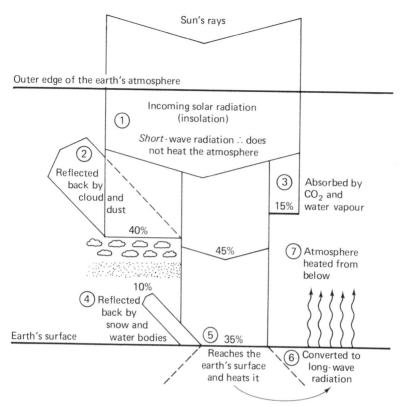

Fig. 9.2 *The earth's atmosphere is heated from below*

between weather and climate. *Weather* consists of the day-to-day changes in atmospheric conditions which we can only predict for a short time ahead. *Climate* is a more general statement of atmospheric conditions, for it is an expression of the *average* weather conditions we can expect to experience. Climate can be regarded as *average weather*. It has been said that climate is what you expect but weather is what you get.

The weather in Britain and north-western Europe is notoriously unpredictable. It often departs widely from the theoretical climatic norm because a number of factors, including the latitude, the distribution of land and sea, ocean currents and variations in atmospheric pressure, affect these countries. (We shall explain this more fully in Section 9.11 and in Unit 10.)

But not all parts of the world have such uncertain weather as Britain and north-western Europe. The day-to-day pattern of the weather is much more predictable along the equator, within the polar circles and in the hot deserts. In these parts of the world the weather does not show the wide variations which we experience, so it is possible to predict it with greater accuracy.

There are a number of measurable characteristics which determine the probable weather anywhere in the world. There are seven main *weather elements*—atmospheric pressure, temperature, humidity, precipitation, wind, visibility and sunshine—and we shall examine them in Sections 9.3–9.9. They are regularly measured and recorded at hundreds of weather stations, and the data obtained are used to produce weather maps, which explain and forecast the weather for the coming hours and days.

9.3   Atmospheric Pressure

The atmosphere exerts a considerable though slightly varying pressure on the earth's surface and everything on it. The pressure is, in fact, the weight of the column of air which extends from the ground to the outermost layers of the atmosphere. (We are not conscious of this pressure on our bodies, because we have compensating internal pressure.)

Atmospheric pressure decreases with altitude (Fig. 9.3) so the measurement of atmospheric pressure can be used as a means of determining height above sea-level. It is sometimes used for this purpose in climbing but, most importantly, it is the chief means of determining the altitude of aircraft. Reduced

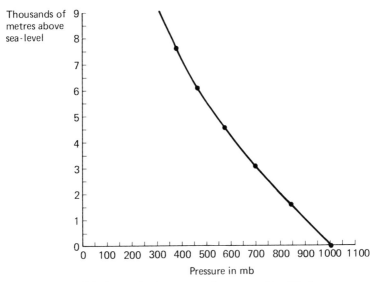

Fig. 9.3 Atmospheric pressure decreases with altitude

atmospheric pressure makes bodily exercise difficult. Athletes accustomed to the higher atmospheric pressures of lower altitudes find it very difficult to perform at such places as Mexico City (2 300 m) or Denver, Colorado (1 613 m). This is because a lungful of air at these altitudes contains a great deal less oxygen than it would closer to sea-level. When mountaineers climb at high altitudes they often carry oxygen with them to supplement that which is contained in the rarefied atmosphere. The cabins of high-flying aircraft have to be pressurized so that passengers stay alive and comfortable during the flight.

(a) Barometers

Atmospheric pressure is measured by a *barometer* which means, literally, weight-measure. There are two patterns in general use, the fortin or mercury barometer and the aneroid barometer.

(i) **The fortin or mercury barometer** consists of a vertical glass tube, about a metre in length, which is sealed at one end and filled with mercury. The open

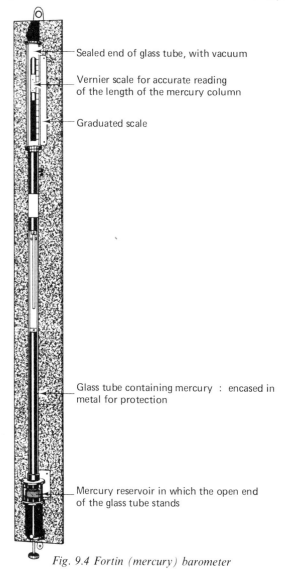

Sealed end of glass tube, with vacuum

Vernier scale for accurate reading of the length of the mercury column

Graduated scale

Glass tube containing mercury : encased in metal for protection

Mercury reservoir in which the open end of the glass tube stands

Fig. 9.4 Fortin (mercury) barometer

end of the tube is then placed in a bowl of mercury. The mercury is held in the tube by the pressure of the atmosphere on the surface of the mercury in the bowl. Mercury is used because its silvery colour is easily visible, and also because it is the heaviest known liquid. (Water could be used but the tube would have to be over 11 m high.)

As the pressure of the atmosphere changes on the exposed surface of the mercury in the bowl, so the mercury in the tube responds, rising higher in the tube when pressure is higher and sinking lower when pressure falls. The height of the mercury is measured either in inches or, more often nowadays, in millimetres. The average atmospheric pressure is about 760 mm or 29·92 in of mercury. Another unit of measurement, the millibar (mb), is often used. A millibar is a thousandth part of a bar, which is equivalent to 750·1 mm. The pressure in the United Kingdom rarely goes outside the limits of 950–1 050 mb.

The fortin barometer is accurate, but cumbersome and awkward to transport. It could not be used conveniently on an aircraft or a mountaineering expedition, so a more compact and easily portable instrument containing no liquid is used.

(ii) **The aneroid barometer** is used widely, particularly in homes. The needle of the barometer is operated by a small box, from which the air has been

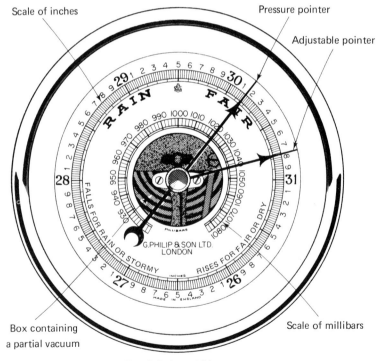

Fig. 9.5 Aneroid barometer

partially extracted. Changes in atmospheric pressure cause the corrugated surface of the box to move, and this movement is transferred through a system of levers and springs to a pointer or needle which moves, like the hand of a clock, in front of a circular dial on which the scale of pressure units is printed.

The words on the face of the household barometer cannot be regarded as a correct assessment of the weather, either present or to come. But the variations in pressure shown by this instrument can tell us a great deal about the weather. What matters most is the direction in which atmospheric pressure is changing. As a general rule, a rising barometric pressure is likely to indicate improving weather, and a falling barometer the likelihood of rain. The barometer should be tapped gently every day to take up the slack in its linkage system, and the pressure noted. The pressure trend can be seen on the instrument by using the adjustable pointer. The change over the ensuing hours can then be observed.

(iii) **The barograph** is an aneroid barometer in which the linkage system is connected to a pen, not to a pointer. The pen traces a continuous line graph on a revolving drum (Fig. 9.6) which is operated by clockwork. It usually takes a week to make one complete turn, so a single graph records the changes in atmospheric pressure at the recording station over a period of a week.

Fig. 9.6 Barograph

130   The Weather

(b) Maps of Atmospheric Pressure

The barometer or barograph can tell us a great deal about the weather in one place, but it cannot give the pattern of weather over a larger area or forecast the changes that are likely to take place. The simultaneous recordings of many stations are necessary for this. If the recordings are numerous enough they will yield a *surface*, like the surface of the ground, with depressions and high areas. Just as the uneven land surface can be portrayed by means of *contours* (Section 13.6), so the variations in atmospheric pressure can be represented by *isobars*. Isobars are lines of equal pressure, and they are drawn on a map in just the same way as contours. Fig. 9.7(a) and (b) shows the stages in the preparation of such atmospheric pressure maps. These maps are of two kinds.

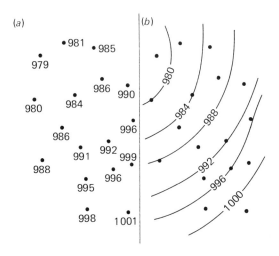

Fig. 9.7 *How isobars are drawn:* (a) *pressure in mb at a number of weather stations,* (b) *resultant isobars drawn at 4 mb intervals*

(i) **Weather charts** are produced daily, or even more frequently, for many parts of the world. They represent the actual weather conditions that are being experienced over a large area, which may be a country or even a continent, at the time when the chart is printed.

(ii) **Atlas maps.** Pressure at any place varies from hour to hour. The average pressure at one season may differ greatly from that at another, so it is necessary to have maps of average pressure for a month, a season or a year, in order to study the pattern of world climate. Such maps are often printed in atlases.

The uneven surface of the earth raises a serious problem when it comes to compiling pressure maps. As we saw in Section 9.1(b), even a small variation in altitude is reflected in a change in atmospheric pressure. Before being plotted on a map readings taken from all the barometers used have to be reduced to what they would be if the barometers were all at one level, that is, sea-level.

9.4   Temperature

(a) Thermometers

The instrument most often used for measuring the temperature of the air is the thermometer. This consists of a sealed glass tube with a bulb at one end, in which there is either mercury or spirit. The fluid expands and contracts with changes in temperature, and so rises and falls in the tube. A scale is attached to the tube, and the temperature can be read in degrees Fahrenheit (°F) or Centigrade (sometimes called Celsius) (°C). The Centigrade scale has always been used in continental Europe, but in England and the United States it has been the practice to use the Fahrenheit scale, except for scientific purposes. The British Meteorological Office has now changed to the Centigrade scale.

It is sometimes necessary to convert a temperature from one scale to the other. The following formula will serve this purpose

$$°C = \frac{5(°F - 32)}{9}.$$

(i) **Stevenson screen.** The thermometers used at weather stations are usually kept in a Stevenson screen, a white-painted louvred box standing 1 m above the ground, which allows the free passage of air but excludes the direct rays of the sun. (It houses several other weather instruments as well.) The screen should be sited in an open space, away from trees and buildings, with its hinged opening facing north so that the sun cannot shine on to the instruments as they are being read.

(ii) **Maximum and minimum thermometers** are used to record the highest and lowest temperatures during a period of 24 hours. (This is the most practical way of representing temperature conditions in the course of a day.) There are two patterns of such thermometer in general use.

One of these instruments consists of two separate thermometers, one filled with mercury and the other with spirit. The mercury-filled thermometer has a constriction near the base of the tube, which prevents the mercury from contracting back into the tube as the temperature drops. This leaves the upper end of the mercury column to register the highest temperature reached. The other thermometer contains spirit, with a small indicator floating in it. As the temperature falls this is pulled down in the tube, where it remains to mark the lowest temperature reached. At the end of the observing period both thermometers have to be reset by shaking them gently.

The other type of maximum and minimum thermometer, known as Six's thermometer, consists of a U-shaped glass tube with a sealed bulb containing creosote at each end. The bulb at the minimum end is filled, while that at the

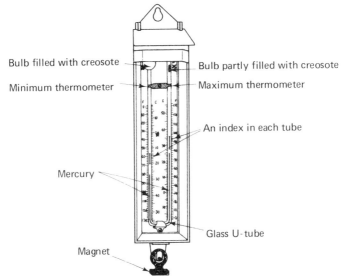

Notice that the scale of the minimum side is inverted and that, at any time, the mercury in both arms of the U-tube should show the same temperature.

Fig. 9.8 Six's maximum and minimum thermometer

maximum end is only partly filled. Between the creosote at each end, occupying the lowest part of the U-tube, is a string of mercury. As the temperature rises the creosote in the filled bulb expands and pushes the mercury towards the partly filled bulb; as the temperature falls the liquid in the filled bulb contracts and the weight of liquid in the other bulb pushes the mercury column back. As the mercury moves in each direction, it pushes a small metallic index ahead of it. When the mercury reaches the limit of its movement in either direction, the index is held there by a small spring to show the daily maximum and minimum temperatures. A magnet supplied with the instrument is used to return each index to touch the mercury, after the daily readings have been taken.

(*b*) **Average Temperatures**
An average daily temperature is obtained by adding together the maximum and minimum temperatures and dividing by two. Average monthly temperatures are obtained by adding the daily averages for the month in question and dividing by the number of days in the month. But a monthly average obtained from a single year's observation can be misleading because, in one year, we may have a very cold April or a heatwave in July. Thus the average temperature for any particular month is obtained by averaging the monthly average for at least 30 years. The result is the *mean monthly average temperature*, which is quoted in this and other books when describing the climate of particular places.

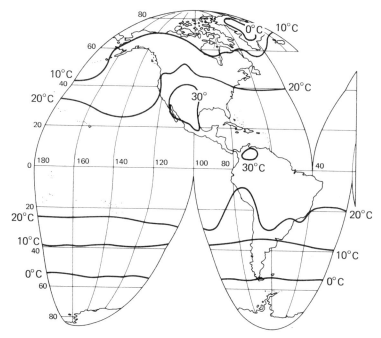

Fig. 9.9 July isotherms, based on mean monthly average temperatures reduced to sea-level

(c) Temperature Maps

Temperatures can be thought of as forming a surface, like pressure. This surface can be mapped by plotting the observing stations with their individual temperatures and by drawing in *isotherms*, or lines of equal temperature (Fig. 9.9). But temperature readings are also influenced by the altitude of the recording station, so temperatures must be reduced to sea-leve! by using the factor of 1 °C per 100 m.

9.5   Humidity

Evaporation goes on constantly from all water bodies on the earth's surface, and water vapour permeates the lower atmosphere. This moisture in the atmosphere is known as *humidity*. The amount of water vapour that the air can hold depends on its temperature: warm air can hold more moisture than cool, and hot air very much more than warm. The amount of water vapour in the air varies from day to day, even from hour to hour, as well as from place to place. When a mass of air is holding its maximum content of water vapour, it is said to be *saturated*. Humidity is measured by expressing the amount of water vapour in the air at a particular time as a percentage of the volume of moisture which that body of air could hold if it were saturated and *relative humidity* is expressed as a percentage. Air with a 50 per cent relative humidity would thus have just half the moisture which it is capable of holding.

(a) Relative Humidity

A high relative humidity—anything over 80 per cent—makes the atmosphere oppressive and enervating. Body moisture is not evaporated as it would be if the relative humidity were lower, and conditions become decidedly uncomfortable. India at the onset of the monsoon (Section 11.3(*d*)), the central and southern United States in summer and equatorial regions throughout much of the year have such conditions, which can become intensely unpleasant, especially to those accustomed to a cooler and drier climate.

The amount of water vapour which can be held in the atmosphere depends on the temperature, as we have seen. If an air mass is cooled its relative humidity increases until, ultimately, it becomes saturated. The temperature at which this happens is known as the *dew point* of that particular air mass. If the temperature is further reduced, the result is some form of condensation, either water particles forming mist or cloud, or water droplets which fall as rain or, if the temperature is low enough, as hail or snow. It is important to know the relative humidity of an air mass when assessing the likelihood of precipitation (Section 9.6).

(b) Measuring Relative Humidity

A hygrometer is the instrument for measuring relative humidity. The most widely used type is the *wet and dry bulb thermometer*, which is usually kept in the Stevenson screen, and it consists of two thermometers. The dry bulb records the air temperature in the usual way while the wet bulb is completely covered with an absorbent cloth, which is kept permanently wet by a wick linking it to a container of water. The temperature as recorded by the wet bulb thermometer is always lower than that of the dry bulb, because heat is lost when water evaporates from the wet cloth around the bulb. The rate of evaporation, and hence the amount of heat lost, is higher in dry air than in moist, so that the difference between the two temperatures can be used to calculate the relative humidity, using tables supplied with the instrument.

Table 9.1 shows part of such a relative humidity table. If the dry bulb temperature is 25 °C and the wet bulb temperature is 19 °C, the *depression* of the wet bulb is 6 °C. Table 9.1 shows us that the relative humidity in this case is 54 per cent.

9.6   Precipitation

We saw in Section 9.5 that the temperature of an air mass may cool to a point known as the dew point, when some of its water vapour begins to condense. The more the air mass is cooled below the dew point, the more water vapour will condense. *Precipitation* is the collective name given to the various forms of water which result from the condensation of water vapour in the atmosphere, and it may take many forms. It can be seen as a small cloud of minute water

Table 9.1 Relative humidity table

Dry bulb readings (°C)	Depression of wet bulb (°C)													
	0·5	1·0	1·5	2·0	2·5	3·0	3·5	4·0	4·5	5·0	5·5	6·0	6·5	7·0
−5	85	71	58	44	30	17	4							
4	87	73	61	48	35	24	12							
3	88	75	64	52	40	29	18	7						
2	89	77	67	56	45	34	24	14	3					
1	90	79	69	59	49	39	30	20	10	1				
0	90	81	71	61	52	44	34	25	16	7				
+1	90	81	73	64	55	47	38	29	20	13	4			
2	91	82	73	64	57	49	41	33	24	17	9	1		
3	91	83	74	65	57	49	43	36	28	21	14	7		
4	92	83	75	67	59	51	43	35	32	25	18	11	4	
5	92	84	76	68	61	53	46	38	31	24	21	15	8	2
6	92	85	77	70	62	55	48	41	34	27	20	14	12	6
7	93	85	78	71	64	57	50	44	37	30	24	17	11	5
8	93	86	79	72	65	59	52	46	39	33	27	21	15	9
9	93	86	80	73	67	60	54	48	42	36	30	24	18	12
10	93	87	81	74	68	62	56	50	44	38	33	27	21	16
11	94	87	81	75	69	63	58	52	46	41	35	30	24	19
12	94	88	82	76	70	65	59	54	48	43	37	32	27	22
13	94	88	83	77	71	66	60	55	50	45	40	35	30	25
14	94	89	83	78	72	67	62	57	52	47	42	37	32	27
15	94	89	84	78	73	68	63	58	53	48	42	39	34	30
16	95	89	84	79	74	69	64	59	55	50	43	41	37	32
17	95	90	85	80	75	70	65	61	56	52	47	43	39	34
18	95	90	85	80	76	71	66	62	57	53	49	45	40	36
19	95	90	86	81	76	72	67	63	59	54	50	46	42	38
20	95	91	86	81	77	73	68	64	60	56	52	48	44	40
21	95	91	86	82	78	73	69	65	61	57	53	49	45	42
22	95	91	87	82	78	74	70	66	62	58	54	50	47	43
23	96	91	87	83	79	75	71	67	63	59	55	52	48	45
24	96	91	87	83	79	75	71	68	64	60	57	53	49	46
25	96	92	88	84	80	76	72	68	65	6!	58	54	51	47
26	92	92	88	84	80	76	73	69	66	62	59	55	52	49
27	96	92	88	84	81	77	73	70	66	63	59	56	53	50

particles on your breath on a cold morning. It forms on the inside of the window when the temperature outside the room is very much colder. It may condense on to the ground as *dew* or *frost*. It forms mist and fog in the lower atmosphere, and it gives rise to cloud, rain, hail, snow and sleet throughout the troposphere.

The air must be cooled before any of these types of precipitation can form, and this can happen in several ways. An air mass may be forced to rise to cooler levels, for example when it blows across a range of hills. It may blow over land or sea at a lower temperature or it may meet air of different temperature and relative humidity, and the warmer—and lighter—of the two is forced to rise over the cooler, thereby becoming cooler itself. Air may blow from warmer into cooler latitudes, and the earth's surface may itself radiate heat, so that the air in contact with it is cooled. Each of these processes may lead to some form of precipitation.

(a) Dew
The ground loses heat by radiation on the still, sometimes cloudless nights which follow warm, sunny days. Air which remains in contact with the ground for a prolonged period in such conditions becomes cooled below its dew point, and the water vapour condenses on grass and other vegetation as dew.

(b) Frost
The same process may happen in winter at a temperature below freezing point. Water vapour then condenses directly into ice crystals, forming *hoar frost* on the leaves of plants. Occasionally dew forms and is then further cooled below freezing point, sometimes by radiation. Rain which has fallen on to a road may be frozen by a drop in temperature. The result in both these cases is *glazed frost*, made up of a layer of very clear ice. It is sometimes called *black ice*, because it is difficult to see on road surfaces; it is a particularly dangerous form of precipitation.

The air temperature may drop slightly below freezing while the temperature of the ground remains above, owing to its internal warmth. No visible hoar frost appears under these circumstances, and there may, in fact, be too little water vapour in the air for frost formation. But the fact that the air temperature is below freezing point may have a serious effect on plant life, so it is for this reason that *air frost* is frequently mentioned in weather forecasts.

(c) Rain and Snow
Air which rises higher in the atmosphere is normally cooled in the process. Condensation takes place if the temperature falls below the dew point, and billions of tiny water droplets or ice crystals gather to form a *cloud* (Section 9.6(d)). Initially the droplets are too small to fall against the resistance of the surrounding air. Eventually a disturbance in the atmosphere may cause the small droplets to be thrown together and form drops which are large enough to overcome the atmospheric resistance and to fall as rain. The size of rain drops varies enormously. The minute drops which occur as drizzle are only just large enough to fall, whereas those which form in thunderstorms are often very large.

If the dew point in a particular air mass is below freezing point, the water vapour condenses directly in the form of minute ice crystals. The result is the growth of snow flakes. If the snow falls through a layer of warmer air, it may partially melt and reach the ground as *sleet*.

The cooling of the atmosphere which leads to rain or snow usually happens in one of the three ways illustrated in Fig. 9.10.

(i) **Relief rain.** Fig. 9.10(a) shows that when a stream of humid, onshore air (A) meets a line of hills or mountains, or even the cliffs of a coastline, it rises to pass over the obstacle and is cooled in the process (B). The air temperature falls below dew point, clouds form and precipitation may follow on the *windward side* (C). If it is cold enough, snow may form on the crest (D). The air sinks, growing warmer as it does so (E), and this *leeward side* is a dry area called a *rainshadow* (F).

The windward side of a mountain range always has more rain than the leeward side. Thus the west coast of Scotland has a higher rainfall than the east, Lancashire is wetter than Yorkshire, and Norway is wetter than Sweden.

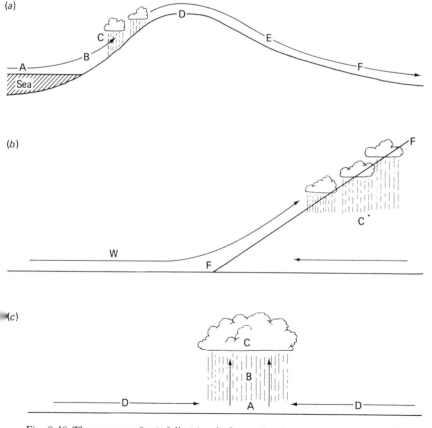

Fig. 9.10 Three types of rainfall: (a) relief rain, (b) frontal rain, (c) convection rain

(ii) **Frontal rain.** Warm moist air usually comes into contact with cooler, drier air during the passage of a depression (an area of low atmospheric pressure). The line separating the two air masses is known as a *front* (*F–F* on Fig. 9.10(*b*)). The warmer and moister air (*W*) rises when it meets the cold, dry air (*C*) along the front. In doing so the warm air is cooled and, since it is moist (that is, it has a high relative humidity), clouds form and rain falls when cooling is below the dew point. This is *frontal rain*, and it makes up a large part of the rainfall which the British Isles and north-western Europe experience. We shall be discussing the mechanics of a depression in fuller detail in Section 9.11.

(iii) **Convection rain.** As we saw in Section 9.1, the land surface is heated directly by the rays of the sun. Land within the tropics or even, in summer, in middle latitudes, becomes intensely hot (*A* in Fig. 9.10(*c*)). The air which is in contact with the warm surface becomes heated, expands and becomes lighter, and therefore tends to rise (*B*), drawing cooler air in to take its place (*D*). This *convectional* rise of the air may become very rapid and can extend upwards to heights of 10 000–12 000 m. The air cools as it rises, water vapour condenses and clouds form (*C*). The immense extent of this rise means that there is a correspondingly greater range in the cooling of the air mass. Vast amounts of moisture condense and enormous cumulonimbus clouds may tower to great altitudes (Section 9.6(*d*)). The turbulence and the large amount of moisture in such clouds lead to exceptionally heavy rain, which we sometimes call *thunder rain*.

(iv) **Hail.** The rapid uprush of air which gives rise to cumulonimbus clouds and convection rain may reach such great heights that water droplets which form at a lower level are carried up by the air to cooler altitudes, where they freeze as small pellets of ice. Such small ice drops may then fall and moisture may collect on them. They may be swept up again, to freeze and fall, until at last the convectional flow of the air weakens and allows the resulting *hailstones* to reach the surface of the earth.

Thus a hailstone usually consists of several concentric layers of ice. The larger the hailstone, the more times it has alternately begun to fall and been carried back up again by the upward rush of air. The largest hailstones occur where the convectional rush of air is most vigorous, and they may reach immense sizes. Hailstones the size of golf balls are not unusual in the strongly heated interiors of the larger mid-latitude land masses, such as the interior of North America. Hailstorms can be extremely damaging, destroying crops, breaking window glass or the roofs of houses and even killing animals which have not been able to shelter from them.

(v) **Thunder and lightning.** Lightning is another and equally frightening aspect of the towering cumulonimbus clouds. It is caused by an electrical discharge either within the cloud or between the cloud and the ground, visible as a lightning flash which may be destructive if it strikes the ground. The *thunder* clap following the flash is caused by the rapid expansion and contraction of the air as a result of heat generated by the passage of the lightning. The rumblings which accompany and follow a thunder clap are echoes, either within the clouds or between a cloud and the ground.

(vi) **Measurement of rainfall.** Rainfall is measured in millimetres as the depth to which the water would have accumulated if it had fallen on a level surface and neither evaporated nor drained away. In practice, the instrument used to measure rainfall is a *rain gauge*. This consists of a metal or plastic outer case, over which fits a flanged funnel 127 mm in diameter; the funnel leads to a collecting vessel. The water is poured out regularly into an appropriate glass measuring cylinder, graduated to read to the nearest millimetre. Sometimes, although the collecting vessel is wet, the amount of water is too small to measure: this is recorded as a *trace*. The rain gauge should be sunk into the ground so that the rim of the funnel stands 305 mm above ground level. It must be carefully sited, well away from trees, buildings and rock outcrops, so that rain may enter the funnel freely from any direction.

Daily rainfall totals are added to give a monthly total, and the monthly figures added for the total annual rainfall. But in the study of climate the *average monthly rainfall* and the *mean annual rainfall* are usually quoted. These figures are obtained by averaging the monthly and the annual figures for a period of at least 30 years. Rainfall maps are drawn in the same way as pressure maps (Section 9.3(*b*)) and temperature maps (Section 9.4(*c*)). Lines of equal rainfall, known as *isohyets*, are constructed by plotting the location of the observing stations with their individual rainfall totals and drawing the isohyets.

(*d*) Clouds

As we mentioned at the beginning of Section 9.6(*c*), clouds consist of immense numbers of minute water droplets or ice particles which are too small to overcome the density and resistance of the air to fall to the ground. Clouds take many forms, and each type is characteristic of certain atmospheric and weather conditions. Indeed, certain types of cloud belong so regularly to particular types of air mass or to specific parts of a depression that they can be used, within limits, to forecast the weather for the next few hours.

These cloud types have descriptive names. Thus *cirrus* is a delicate feathery or fibrous cloud which indicates fine weather, and *cumulus* is a heaped-up cloud, like masses of cotton wool, sometimes towering to immense heights. *Stratus* clouds lie in layers or sheets, often covering the whole sky. Some of them can be qualified as *alto* (high) or *nimbus* (rain), while others combine the qualities of two of the three major types, so we can distinguish ten major cloud types in all. The sky may be partly or entirely covered by a single cloud type—cumulus on a fine summer afternoon, stratus on an overcast winter day. On the other hand, two or even three different types of cloud may be visible at different heights at the same time. (Study these cloud types in the sky until you can recognize and describe them.)

Fig. 9.11 Cloud types
(a) *Altocumulus: patches of fleecy, white cloud with blue sky between. Distant cloud appears more continuous because of low angle of observation* (b) *Cumulus: white, fleecy patches of cloud, set against a background of blue sky*

(c) *Cumulonimbus: a tall, towering cloud on a flat base. Convection currents may be seen carrying cloud up to great heights where strong winds may draw out the top of the cloud into the shape of an anvil. Heavy rain, hail, thunder and lightning are likely*

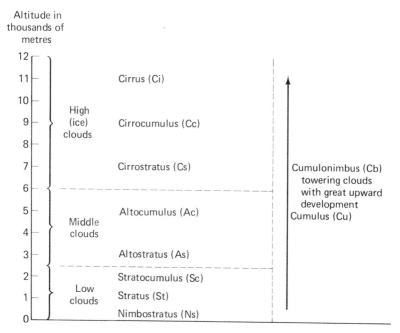

Fig. 9.12 *Classification of clouds by height. The standard abbreviations for each type are shown in brackets*

(e) **Fog**

We have seen that condensation occurs not only high in the atmosphere, but also in the lower levels, when the air close to the ground is cooled. The result is *mist* or *fog*. We commonly distinguish between these two with fog being thicker than mist. In fog, according to the International Meteorological Code, visibility is less than 1 km whereas, in mist, visibility is between 1 and 2 km. Fog is described as either *radiation* fog or *advection* fog, according to how the air mass has been cooled.

(i) **Radiation fog.** A clear warm day, such as we may have in early or late summer, is often followed by a still clear night. There is no cloud to restrict the loss of heat from the earth's surface, so the land cools rapidly after sunset, as does the air which is in contact with the ground. In calm conditions, the lowest layers of the atmosphere may temporarily be cooler than those above. This unusual circumstance is known as a *temperature inversion*, because it is the reverse of the normal situation. If the lower air is chilled so that its temperature falls below its dew point, condensation takes place in the form of fog. This is known as *radiation fog*, because it results from the radiation of heat from the earth's surface.

If the surface of the ground is uneven, a low-lying mass of cold, heavy air produced in this way may flow down the slopes and collect in valleys and hollows. Fog often forms and lies in patches on lower ground. Sometimes the cold in such low-lying areas is sufficient for frost formation. This tendency of radiation fog to concentrate in valleys often makes motoring extremely dangerous and difficult, and the icy patches which sometimes occur add to the hazard.

(ii) **Advection fog.** Radiation fog occurs in still air, but advection fog forms when a moist air mass passes over a cooler land or ocean surface and is cooled by the contact. This occurs regularly in some areas. There is a current of cold water off the west coast of nearly every major land mass, between the latitudes of 35° and 45°. Warm humid winds frequently blow across these cool water bodies and as they are cooled, fog forms. Such fogs are frequent off the coast of California and they are likely to occur around the British coasts in summer, when a warm south-westerly wind is chilled by the cool surface of the sea. Warm air from the Gulf Stream moves over the cold Labrador Current off the coast of Newfoundland also, and the result is banks of dense and dangerous sea fog in a much-used shipping lane.

9.7 Wind

Wind normally results from differences in atmospheric pressure, for air moves from high-pressure areas to areas of relatively lower pressure. We saw in Section 9.3(b) how variations in atmospheric pressure lead to the formation of a surface or *gradient*. On a physical surface water flows down a slope towards the hollows and low points. The surface formed by variations in atmospheric pressure is similar: air (wind) flows down the slopes, and the steeper the slopes, the faster the wind.

(a) Wind Direction

Wind direction is registered by means of a *weather* or *wind vane*, a device with a pointer which rotates freely and is forced by wind strength to point *into* the wind. A weather vane should be mounted as far from the ground as possible, as wind direction close to the surface is greatly affected by buildings and trees.

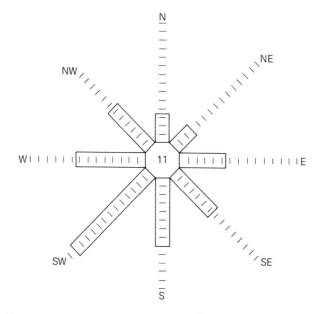

Fig. 9.13 A wind rose for March 1972, based on six-hourly observations. The frequency of calms is given in the centre

A wind is always named after the direction *from* which it blows. Wind direction is usually noted at regular intervals, several times a day at weather stations, and the frequency of the wind from each direction is recorded. This information can be easily expressed in a diagram known as a *wind rose*, in which lines are drawn from a central point, proportionate in length to the frequency of the wind from the corresponding direction. The frequency of calms, that is, occurrences of no wind, is shown by the figure at the centre of the rose. The wind is described as *veering* if its direction changes in a clockwise manner, for example, starting at south and moving through south-west and west to north-west. When the wind changes direction in the opposite way, it is said to be *backing*.

Table 9.2 The Beaufort Scale

No.	Descriptive term	Sea criterion	Land criterion
0	Calm	Sea like a mirror	Smoke rises vertically
1	Light air	Ripples formed on water but without foam crests	Wind direction shown by smoke drift but not by wind vane
2	Light breeze	Small, short waves. Crests look glassy but do not break	Wind felt on face, leaves rustle, wind vane moves
3	Gentle breeze	Larger waves with breaking crests. Slight foam with scattered white horses	Leaves and small twigs in constant motion. Wind extends a light flag
4	Moderate breeze	Waves become longer. More frequent white horses	Raises dust and loose paper. Small branches move
5	Fresh breeze	Moderate, longer waves. Many white horses. Some spray	Small trees sway. Small waves form on inland water
6	Strong breeze	Large waves with extensive white foam crests. Spray more extensive	Large branches in motion, whistling in telegraph wires. Umbrellas used with difficulty
7	Near gale	Sea heaps up, waves break and white foam blows in streaks. Spray very extensive	Whole trees in motion. Difficult to walk against the wind
8	Gale	High waves of greater length. Crests break and foam is blown more densely	Breaks twigs off trees. Impedes progress of walkers
9	Strong gale	High waves with dense foam. Wave crests begin to topple and roll over. Spray may affect visibility	Slight structural damage occurs. Chimney pots and slates removed
10	Storm	Very high waves with long overhanging crests. Large patches of foam and much spray. Visibility impeded	Seldom experienced inland. Trees uprooted and much structural damage occurs
11	Violent storm	Exceptionally high waves. Sea completely foam-covered and spray is dense. Visibility difficult	Very rarely experienced inland. Widespread damage to buildings and trees
12	Hurricane	Enormous waves. Sea completely foam-covered and driving spray seriously affects visibility	

(b) Wind Speed

Wind speed was one of the earliest elements of weather to be regularly measured and recorded. This was because of its immense importance to sailors, who needed a standard system of recording wind. In 1805 Admiral Beaufort devised a system of referring to wind strength, using a set of numbers from 0 to 12. Each number on the *Beaufort Scale* had a simple, descriptive term which all seamen could understand, and a similar scale was soon devised for use on land (Table 9.2). This is still the basis of weather description and forecasting, and gale warnings broadcast on the radio may refer to 'force 8 winds'.

Fig. 9.14 Cup anemometer

The instrument used for measuring wind speed is called an *anemometer*. At a weather station it should be set up 10 m above the ground and well clear of roof tops. Two types of anemometer are in regular use. The more common is the *cup anemometer*, where three or four cups are fixed to bars on a rotating spindle. The wind turns the cups and thus the spindle, which is geared to a measuring device. The speed of rotation of the cups is proportional to that of the wind, but the instrument has several major disadvantages. It tends to overestimate the speed of the wind. Strong gusts also force the cups to turn rapidly, but the gust may have died down long before the momentum built up by the rotating cups subsides. The *tube anemometer* is a more sensitive instrument. An open tube is built into the end of a wind vane, which turns so that the opening is always facing into the wind. The wind blows through this tube into a sensitive measuring device which records the changes in its speed and also in its direction, usually on a graph on a rotating drum.

9.8   Visibility

Visibility is the distance at which certain objects can be clearly seen and distinguished. It varies greatly with the amount of moisture and dust in the atmosphere: the air is usually much clearer after rain has washed the dust particles from it, for example. Good visibility is of immense importance in motoring, boating and flying, so weather reports regularly contain a statement of any abnormal visibility.

9.9   Sunshine

The number of hours of sunshine experienced in a day, a month or a year is important chiefly as a measure of the attractiveness of a particular town, especially if it is a holiday resort. The duration of sunshine can, of course, be measured by direct observation with the help of a wrist-watch but it is normal to use a *sunshine recorder*, of which the Campbell-Stokes pattern is the best known. This consists of a solid glass ball which focuses the sun's rays on to a strip of sensitized and graduated paper, where they burn a trace. The paper is read and changed daily. The duration of sunshine is usually expressed as either the number of hours of sunshine per day, month or year, or as a percentage of the maximum possible sunshine in the same period.

9.10   The Daily Weather Chart

(a) Weather Recording
The instruments and methods we have described so far are those used at most weather stations throughout the world. Weather stations are not only maintained by the Meteorological Office but also by the Navy and Air Force, by many local government authorities, by other public and private bodies and by interested amateurs. In addition, weather conditions are observed by naval and merchant ships at sea and by nine internationally organized *Ocean Weather Ships*, which maintain their station in the Atlantic and transmit hourly weather readings. At least two weather ships are required to man each station, and the British weather ships, based at Greenock on the Firth of Clyde, each spend 24 days on location, followed by a period in harbour.

In addition to the information supplied regularly by a vast number of weather stations, the Meteorological Office is able to use the methods developed in recent years to probe the higher atmosphere. This is done by means of balloons and weather satellites. Balloons are sent up from weather stations at sea and on land, they record meteorological conditions mechanically and report back to the surface by radio. Weather satellites rise a great deal higher than balloons, and among the recordings which they transmit to earth are photographs of the cloud cover.

The end-product of all this recording is a vast stream of information which flows into the Meteorological Office at Bracknell in Berkshire. Much of it is received, recorded and processed by computers, and from it emerges the daily and the long-range weather forecasts as well as other forms of weather information required by air lines, ships, the armed forces, trawler fleets and many other organizations.

(b) The Weather Map

The Daily Weather Chart is the best known and most important publication of the Meteorological Office. It gives detailed daily information about conditions in the North Atlantic and western Europe, in four separate maps which give weather information for intervals of six hours. You can subscribe to the Meteorological Office for these, and they are often displayed in public buildings, technical colleges and schools.

The basic information on the weather chart is the distribution of atmospheric pressure, because it is this which determines the pattern of weather. Isobars and fronts are shown on the chart, together with the principal weather reporting stations, and standard symbols are used to express the weather elements experienced at each.The form of precipitation—whether rain, heavy rain, sleet or snow—is indicated. The degree of *cloudiness* is expressed as the fraction (in eighths or *oktas*) of the sky which is covered. The words 'sky obscured' mean that the degree of cloudiness could not be estimated because

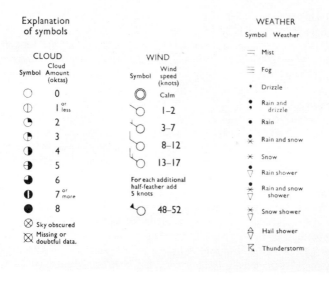

Fig. 9.15 Weather symbols used on the Daily Weather Chart

at the time of observation it could not be seen because of fog or mist. *Wind direction* is represented by an arrow, and its *speed* by 'feathers' affixed to it; above 2 knots, each feather represents ten knots of wind speed and a half-feather five. *Temperature* is given in degrees Centigrade for the stations at which they were recorded. In addition to the information given for each

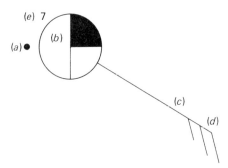

Fig. 9.16 The station model: (a) *weather (precipitation),* (b) *cloud cover in oktas,* (c) *wind direction arrow,* (d) *wind speed feathers,* (e) *temperature in °C*

station, the barometric pressure at each station may be worked out from the isobars. The weather charts on pages 156–60 represent typical weather situations and the range of symbols used to express them.

9.11   The Weather in Britain and North-western Europe

The Daily Weather Chart will show a sequence of low-pressure areas—*depressions* or *lows*—which form over the North Atlantic and move eastwards across the British Isles and north-western Europe. They are separated by ridges of high pressure, which may sometimes expand into *anticyclones* or *highs.*

(a) Depressions

It is not clearly known how a depression comes into existence. An explanation put forward early this century by two Norwegian weather observers named Bjerknes, father and son, is still popular because of its basic simplicity. Their theory starts with the assumption that, in the world-wide circulation of the atmosphere, tropical air moves towards the poles and polar air towards the equator. These two strongly contrasted air masses—the one warm and moist, the other cool and dry—meet along a line which has somewhat misleadingly come to be called the *polar front.* This is the key to the sequence of events which culminates in a fully developed depression.

Fig. 9.17 illustrates the formation of a depression. In the first stage, the warm and cold air masses in the northern hemisphere blow respectively from the tropic and the pole, but they have not yet come into contact. Then, in the second stage, a wave or kink develops in the polar front and two separate

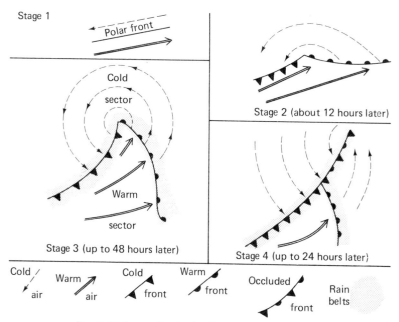

Fig. 9.17 *Stages in the development of a depression*

fronts begin to form, with warm tropical air rising over the cool arctic air in the more forward front, while in the other the arctic air burrows under the tropical air. At this stage, frontal rain begins to fall because the humid air rises and is cooled and condensation takes place. While this is happening, the developing pressure system is moving towards the east at a speed which ranges from 16–80 km per hour. The average speed of movement of the centre of the depression is about 40 km per hour. (But the speed of movement of the system has nothing to do with the speed of the winds which compose it. These can be mere breezes or they may rise to hurricane force.)

In the third stage the whole circulating system has grown very much larger and may now measure as much as 2 500 km in diameter. Barometric pressure at the centre has become lower, and the depression is said to have *deepened*. At the same time the fronts of stage two have developed into contrasted warm and cold fronts. The warm air is forced to rise along both of these fronts with the resulting formation of a rain belt.

The cold front, lying towards the rear of the depression, travels faster and gradually catches up with the warm front. Eventually they coalesce to form an *occluded front*, and in stage four we see that the cold front has literally lifted part of the warm front off the ground. The depression is beginning to die as an active weather system. Barometric pressure in the centre rises, and the depression is said to have 'filled'. The life of such a depression may be anything up to two weeks and, during its existence, the whole system moves several thousand kilometres at varying speeds in a generally easterly direction.

A depression is represented on a weather chart by a pattern of isobars. These are roughly circular and concentric, and are usually drawn at intervals of 4 mb. The lowest pressure is in the centre, and air moves down the barometric gradient towards the area of lowest pressure, although it does not take the straightest and shortest route. The rotation of the earth causes any moving

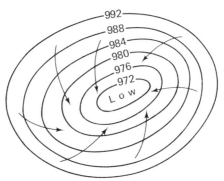

Fig. 9.18 The isobar pattern of a depression

body of air to be deflected to its right in the northern hemisphere, and to its left in the southern. This phenomenon establishes a rotating wind system which is anti-clockwise in a depression in the northern hemisphere and clockwise in the southern.

(b) Anticyclones

Anticyclones are areas of high atmospheric pressure and, as such, they are the converse of depressions. The air in the centre of an anticyclone is gently sinking, getting warmer as it does so and moving outwards from the centre near the ground surface, towards the edge of the anticyclone. Rain rarely occurs in an anticyclone, and such a *high* may remain stationary for several days, giving a period of settled weather. An anticyclone may even remain stable for two or three weeks, blocking the movement of other atmospheric

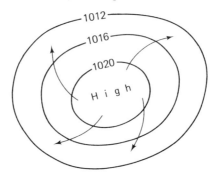

Fig. 9.19 The isobar pattern of an anticyclone

systems and causing them to move around it. In the British Isles, a prolonged spell of fine and sunny weather is usually due to the development of an anticyclone.

On the weather map an anticyclone appears as a number of usually well-spaced, roughly circular isobars, with the highest pressure at their centre. The air moves outwards and clockwise from the centre. Winds are usually gentle, since the barometric gradient is very slight. Even less is known about the formation of anticyclones than about depressions, but they appear to be extensions of the tropical air mass into temperate latitudes.

(c) Minor Pressure Systems
Depressions and anticyclones are the dominant pressure systems, but there are also four minor patterns of pressure which occur fairly frequently and usually in association with the major system.

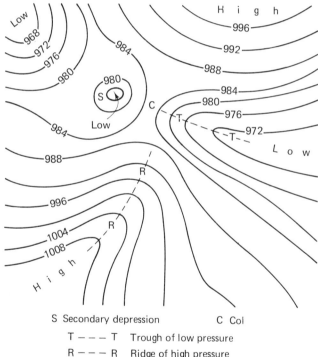

S Secondary depression   C Col

T − − − T   Trough of low pressure

R − − − R   Ridge of high pressure

Fig. 9.20 Minor pressure systems

A *trough of low pressure* is a frequent pressure system in north-western Europe, and consists of a narrow belt of low pressure, easily recognizable by its V-shaped isobars. A *ridge of high pressure* is its opposite, a long narrow belt of high pressure. The analogy between the barometric surface and the surface of the ground is maintained by the use of the term *col* for an area of pressure lying between two opposite anticyclones and two opposite depressions, as shown in Fig. 9.20. Lastly, a *secondary depression*—the source of so much unpleasant weather—is a small, less intense depression, found near the edge of a larger depression.

The spacing of the isobars in any system of atmospheric pressure is of vital importance, because it indicates the steepness of the pressure change, which is called the *barometric* or pressure gradient. If isobars are bunched close together, this means that there is a large pressure difference over a short distance which, in turn, means rapidly moving air or strong winds. Conversely, well-spaced isobars imply a gentle barometric gradient and light winds.

(d) Weather in a Depression

An almost continuous succession of depressions, interrupted by an occasional anticyclone, moves in from the Atlantic Ocean to give the weather of north-western Europe its day-to-day variations. No two depressions are the same. The pressure at the centre, the shape and spacing of the isobars, the speed of movement and the path followed all differ from one depression to the next, and they result in different patterns of weather. But it is possible to describe a 'typical depression', which has all the essential features and moves at an average speed along the path most commonly followed.

A typical depression covers an immense area. Its leading or eastern edge may be over Sweden, while its trailing, western edge may be well to the west of Ireland, an overall distance of more than 1 600 km. As such a depression moves eastwards a sequence of weather conditions such as those shown in Fig. 9.21 will be experienced. At **1** along the line S–T the cloud thickens and lowers and pressure is falling. There are showers and then more continuous drizzle which turns to steady rain. The wind is southerly. At **2** the temperature rises and pressure falls. The wind veers to the south-west and the rain eases and then stops. At **3** it is cloudy with occasional showers and some sunny periods. At **4** there is heavy rain and gusty winds. Pressure falls and there is sometimes hail, thunder and lightning. At **5** the cloud breaks up, temperature falls and pressure rises. Wind veers to the west and north-west, the rain may cease or showers may continue for a time.

(e) Weather in an Anticyclone

The weather in an anticyclone is apt to vary with the seasons. In summer the development of a 'high' may bring with it up to two weeks of fine daytime weather, with clear skies and abundant sunshine. At night the rapid radiation of heat may lead to the formation of mist or fog and dew. In early and late summer, night temperatures during an anticyclone may fall sufficiently to give frost, and it is conditions such as these which do most damage to fruit crops.

In winter, an anticyclone may also yield fine, sunny daytime weather, with sharp frosts at night and some fog in low-lying areas in the mornings. It may also give rise to much less pleasant weather, especially in December and January, when the sun is low in the sky and its heating capacity slight. A

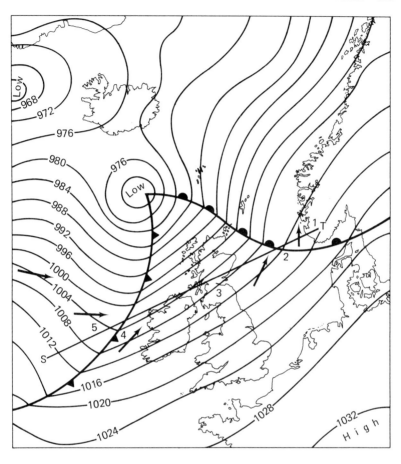

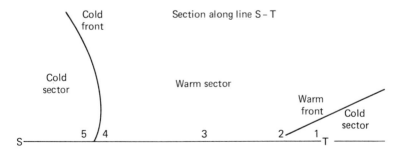

Fig. 9.21 A typical depression and its weather. (Notice the isobars change direction when crossing a front. The straight isobars in the warm sector suggest the direction in which the depression is moving)

persistent *temperature inversion* may develop (Section 9.6): cooler air lies in contact with the ground surface and is separated by an *inversion layer* from the warmer air which lies above it. Air rises to the inversion layer but cannot escape from it. Cloud spreads out below this level to form a layer of *stratus* cloud which produces a dullness sometimes called anticyclonic gloom. Such conditions are made worse over towns and industrial areas by the smoke, dust and fumes which are trapped below the inversion, unable to escape into the higher atmosphere. If this state of affairs persists for several days, there is not only chaos on the transport systems of large cities but the dense fog or *smog*, once known in London as pea-soup fog, may result in the death of many people suffering from lung ailments. The last such disaster in Britain was in December 1952, when London and the industrial conurbations experienced these exact conditions. Several thousand people died and visibility was down to a few metres for several days. Since then, the great improvements brought about by the clean air legislation of successive governments have made it unlikely that these conditions will recur.

9.12   Tropical Depressions

The pressure systems which we have discussed are, by and large, those which occur in the middle or temperate latitudes. They are the result of the meeting of two air masses with contrasting physical characteristics. But in tropical latitudes low-pressure systems develop which behave quite differently from those which we have already discussed.

Tropical storms usually develop over the sea, although they often move on to the land. They have different names in different parts of the world— *hurricane* in the Caribbean and on the east coast of the United States, *typhoon* in the China seas and the Pacific, *cyclone* in the Indian Ocean, and *willy-willy* off the northern coast of Australia. But all these pressure systems have several features in common. They are very much smaller than the depressions of higher latitudes, rarely exceeding 600 km in diameter. The pattern of isobars is almost circular, and the pressure gradient which they show is very steep, so winds are extremely strong. The storm is characterized by massive cumulo-nimbus clouds which tower up to greater altitudes than those in mid-latitude depressions, and the rainfall is usually torrential. Lastly, these tropical depressions usually have a distinct *eye*, a central area perhaps 50 km across, in which winds are lighter and rainfall is slight.

9.13   Tornadoes

A tornado usually occurs over land, and almost always in the central United States. It is a revolving cyclonic storm with a very small diameter—sometimes as little as 100 m—but it has enormous intensity. Pressure at the centre is very low, the barometric gradient so steep that it can be called precipitous, and the resulting winds are the fiercest known on earth. Tornadoes can uproot trees and destroy all except the most solidly constructed buildings. They appear as black columns reaching from the cloudbase down to the earth. Little whirling storms called *dust devils* are tornadoes in miniature, while a tornado over the sea draws up a column of water and is known as a *waterspout*.

Further Reading

Bucknell, J.: *Climatology*. Macmillan (London, 1964).
Chandler, T. J.: *Modern Meteorology and Climatology*. Nelson (London, 1972).
Gresswell, R. K.: *Weather and Climate of the British Isles*. Hulton Educational Publications (Amersham, 1961).
Hood, P.: *The Atmosphere*. Oxford University Press (London, 1952).
Lane, F. W.: *The Elements Rage*. David and Charles (Newton Abbot, 1966).
Strahler, A. N.: *Physical Geography*. John Wiley (Chichester, 1969), Chapters 7–11.
Sutton, P. G.: *Understanding Weather*. Penguin (Harmondsworth, 1964).

Questions

1. Explain why the atmosphere is heated from below. What examples can you give to prove this?
2. What is atmospheric pressure? With the aid of annotated diagrams, describe the instruments used to measure it.
3. What is meant by *mean monthly average temperature*? Describe the instrument used to make the necessary measurements, and explain the method used to calculate it.
4. What is humidity and how is it measured?
5. With the aid of diagrams, explain the ways in which rain may be formed.
6. Write an essay on *Clouds*.
7. Explain the ways in which wind speed may be measured and expressed.
8. How are depressions formed? Using diagrams, give an account of the stages in the life of an average depression.
9. Explain the following: (*a*) anticyclone, (*b*) pressure (barometric) gradient, (*c*) secondary depressions, (*d*) trough of low pressure.
10. With the aid of diagrams, say what you understand by the following terms: (*a*) isobar, (*b*) relative humidity, (*c*) dew point, (*d*) radiation fog, (*e*) wind rose, (*f*) Beaufort Scale, (*g*) tornado.
11. What is the weather represented by the following station plots?

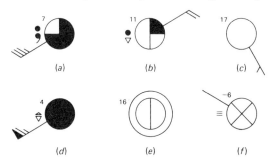

12. Draw the station plots for the following sets of weather conditions:

(a) 5 oktas cloud; wind: south, 11 knots; temperature: 8 °C; present weather: drizzle.

(b) 8 oktas cloud; wind: north-west, 39 knots; temperature: −5 °C; present weather: rain and snow showers.

(c) 2 oktas cloud; wind: north-east, 10 knots; temperature: 15 °C; present weather: fine and sunny.

(d) 7 oktas cloud; wind: west, 24 knots; temperature: 11 °C; present weather: thunderstorm.

(e) No cloud; wind: south, 2 knots; temperature: 23 °C; present weather: fine and sunny.

(f) 3 oktas cloud; wind: north-west, 16 knots; temperature: 14 °C; present weather: rain showers.

13. Answer the following questions, based on Weather Map A.

(a) What name can be given to the pressure system to the west of Britain?

(b) Draw and name the types of front which can be seen on the map.

(c) Describe the weather shown at the following stations: (i) Ocean Weather Ship M, (ii) Gibraltar N, (iii) Southern Sardinia P, (iv) Northern Norway Q.

(d) State the differences in weather conditions between southern England and Iceland in terms of cloud, wind, temperature and weather.

(e) Explain, as far as you can, the differences which you have described in (d).

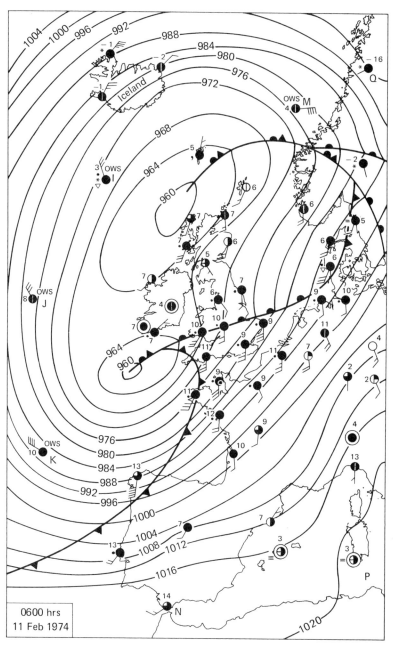

Weather Map *A*

158   The Weather

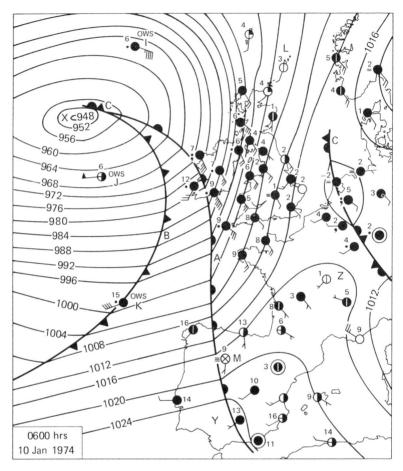

Weather Map *B*

14. Answer the following questions, based on Weather Map *B*.
   (*a*) What are (i) the lowest, (ii) the highest pressures marked on the map?
   (*b*) What names can be given to the pressure systems at *X*, *Y* and *Z*?
   (*c*) What type of fronts are *A*, *B* and *C*?
   (*d*) What weather conditions are represented by the station plots at (i) Ocean Weather Ship *K*, (ii) the Shetlands *L*, (iii) north-western Spain *M*?
   (*e*) State the differences in weather conditions between southern Ireland and central and southern France.
   (*f*) Account for the differences you have described in (*e*).
15. Answer the following questions based on Weather Map *C*.
   (*a*) What are (i) the lowest, (ii) the highest pressures shown on the map?

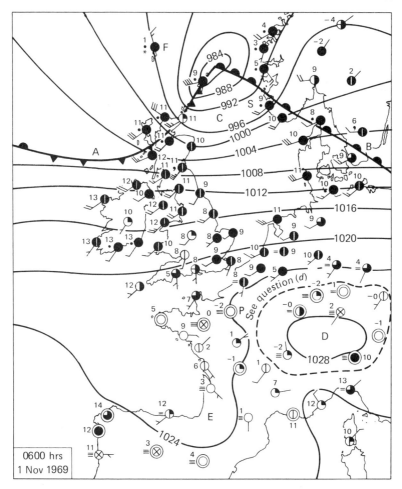

Weather Map C

(b) What names can be given to the fronts labelled A and B and the pressure features labelled C, D and E on the map?

(c) Describe and account for the weather being experienced at (i) Stavanger S, (ii) the Faroes F, (iii) Paris P.

(d) Describe and account for the weather differences between that part of central Europe denoted on the map by the broken line and western Scotland and the Hebrides.

(e) Can you suggest: (i) why temperatures in most of southern and south-eastern England are several degrees colder than those in southern Ireland? (ii) why winds in western Denmark are stronger than those in western France?

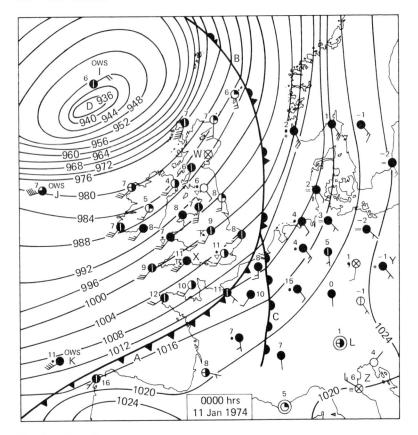

Weather Map *D*

16. Answer the following questions based on Weather Map *D*.
   (*a*) What are (i) the lowest, (ii) the highest pressures shown on the map?
   (*b*) Name the fronts *A*, *B* and *C* and the pressure system *D*.
   (*c*) Describe the weather at Ocean Weather Ship *J*, and Stations *X*, *Y* and *Z*. What is the significance of the Station plot at *W*?
   (*d*) Explain the difference in wind speed between Ocean Weather Ship *K* and Station *L*.
   (*e*) Describe and explain the differences in weather between southern Britain and Germany.

Unit Ten
Climatic Control Factors

Many features of the natural environment, such as the soil, natural vegetation and animal life, are a direct result of local climatic conditions. The climate which we experience also affects our way of life, particularly our agriculture, the type of clothing we wear and the design of the buildings in which we live and work. All these factors mean that the study of world climates is an important one for geographers.

10.1 What Is Climate?

As we discovered in Unit 9, climate is average weather: it is what we can reasonably expect to happen. We cannot possibly know in advance what the weather will be when we plan to visit New York, the French Riviera, Bombay or Hong Kong at a particular date in the future, but we can, and usually do, find out about the climate. This will determine the kind of clothes we take and the excursions and entertainments we plan.

Climate clearly varies from one place to another. The weather may be slightly different in Reading from what is experienced in Watford, Luton or Croydon, but in climatic terms they are the same. However, if we compare any place near London with, say, Nice or Marseilles in the south of France, the differences are no longer minor or unimportant. On average Nice is warmer than, say, Kew Gardens by about 4 °C throughout the year. While Kew Gardens has rainfall evenly spread through the year, with a slight summer maximum, Nice has a distinct winter maximum of rainfall. After studying the variations in climate over the surface of the earth, we can classify them into a number of climatic types. In Unit 11 we distinguish and describe twelve such climates.

Differences in climate can be explained in terms of a small number of *climatic control factors*. These are planetary factors, pressure and winds, ocean currents, altitude, aspect, mountain barriers and distance from the sea (continentality). We shall discuss these factors in Sections 10.2–10.8.

10.2 Planetary Factors

Planetary factors include the sequence of the seasons, the varying length of the periods of daylight and darkness, the altitude of the sun and the amount of insolation. They result from the movements of the earth and its relationship to the sun. We examined these factors in Unit 1, when we explained that the axis on which the earth rotates is inclined at an angle of $23\frac{1}{2}°$ to the vertical and the earth itself moves around the sun. These movements of the earth and its changing position in relation to the sun are mainly responsible for the seasons (Fig. 1.4).

At the equator, the length of day and night remain much the same throughout the year so there are no distinct seasons, since variations in insolation are an important factor in seasonal temperature changes (Section 1.3(c)). As we move away from the equator we find that there is a steady change in the relative lengths of daylight and darkness. In June there is no period of darkness at the North Pole and at the same time there is no period of daylight at the South Pole. Six months later the situation at the poles is reversed, although at the equator daylight and darkness are still of equal duration. This seasonal variation in insolation is a most important influence on the kind of climate that is experienced. The *intensity* of insolation is determined by the angle at which the sun rises above the horizon. An overhead sun always gives more solar energy per square metre to the earth's surface than when it is low in the sky (Fig. 1.10).

A combination of the altitude of the sun and the length of day (Figs. 1.5–1.9) accounts for a number of climatic features. Thus the highest temperatures in the world are not experienced at the equator, where the period of daylight never exceeds twelve hours, but in the hot deserts, where an overhead summer sun is combined with cloudless skies and a daylight period of about fourteen hours (conversely, this is why winter nights in the desert regions can be quite cool with even a possibility of frost).

10.3   Planetary Winds

Wind is the means by which air is moved from one part of the earth's surface to another, and winds may influence climate in two significant ways. First, air contains moisture in the form of water vapour. The likelihood of there being any form of precipitation depends on the relative humidity of the air (Section 9.5), and whether or not the air is cooled by any of the three methods we mentioned in Section 9.6 and illustrated in Fig. 9.10. Second, the wind affects temperature. In Britain wind from the south is warm, bringing some of the warmth of France or even the Mediterranean with it, while wind from a northerly quarter is likely to be much cooler, especially in winter.

(a) Pressure Belts

As we saw in Section 9.7, the movement of air which we call wind is due to differences in atmospheric pressure, with the winds always tending to blow from high-pressure to low-pressure areas. The British Isles experience frequent variations in pressure.

In some other parts of the world there are pressure systems which persist for most of the year, with only short-lived interruptions. There is, for example, a low-pressure system which forms a belt around the earth, close to the equator. Just outside the tropics, in each hemisphere, is a belt of high pressure and both polar regions are also characterized by high pressure. There is a belt of low pressure between these areas of high pressure, in the mid-latitudes of both northern and southern hemispheres. The British Isles lie in this belt. These pressure systems are shown in Fig. 10.1, but there are two qualifications. First, the apparent movement of the sun, from its overhead position at the Tropic of Capricorn in December to its position in June over the Tropic of Cancer, carries the pressure systems with it. The movement of the pressure belts is smaller (by 8–10° north and south of the equator) than that of the overhead sun, but the shift in the pressure, and hence in the wind systems, is enough to add appreciably to the seasonal contrasts. Second, these pressure systems are most clearly defined in the southern hemisphere, because the land masses are smaller here than in the northern hemisphere and thus have a less disturbing influence on the continuity of the pressure systems (Section 10.8).

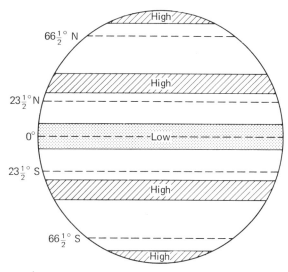

Fig. 10.1 Pressure belts. These belts move 8–10° north and south as the overhead sun moves

(b) Planetary Winds System

Winds blow from the high-pressure belts towards those of low-pressure—from the sub-tropical high towards both the equatorial low and the mid-latitude lows, and from the arctic high towards the mid-latitudes. These are the planetary winds, represented in Fig. 10.2, but the reality is less simple. The winds are deflected by the earth's rotation, to the right in the northern hemisphere and to the left in the southern. The whole planetary wind system moves towards the north during the northern summer, and to the south during the southern. But the most important source of disturbance to the planetary wind system is the existence of large land masses, especially north of the equator. Land masses become greatly heated in summer and are cooled in winter more than their latitude might suggest. This introduces a disturbing factor into the

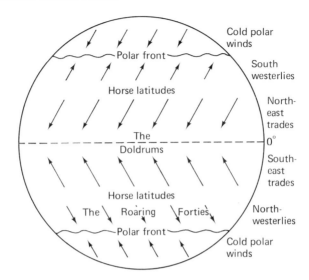

Fig. 10.2 The planetary wind system. These belts move north and south as the pressure belts move. The Doldrums is sometimes called the Inter-Tropical Convergence Zone (ITCZ)

wind systems, especially outside the tropics. In fact, the great land masses tend to become overspread by a mass of cold, heavy, sinking air in winter—a high-pressure system from which the winds blow outwards. In summer the land masses develop low-pressure systems into which winds blow from all quarters. It is only over the sea areas that the planetary wind system blows throughout the year in the pattern shown on Fig. 10.2.

(c) Local Winds
There are local winds in all parts of the world. As their name suggests, they only influence small areas.

Every continent has its own particular local winds. For example, when a depression moves eastwards through the Mediterranean basin, air is attracted towards it from both north and south (Fig. 10.3). Cold, heavy air from the north, some of it crossing the Alpine snowfields, is drawn down the valleys leading to the coast. It often does great damage because of its speed and its low temperature. Such a wind is known as the *mistral* in southern France, the *tramontana* in northern Italy and the *bora* on the Adriatic coast of Yugoslavia. On the southern side of the depression, hot dry air is drawn in from the Sahara region of North Africa. The result is the dusty and unpleasant winds known as the *sirocco* in Sicily, the *khamsin* in Egypt and the *leveche* in Algeria.

Another example is the *harmattan*, which blows from the Sahara across West Africa during the northern hemisphere's winter. It is a dust-laden wind, and may obscure the sun and deposit a veneer of fine particles on ships far out at sea off the west African coast. Nevertheless, its dryness is a welcome change

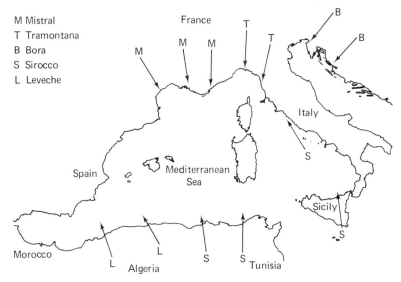

Fig. 10.3 Local winds in the western Mediterranean

from the high humidity of the winds which blow in this region during its 'high sun' or summer season. Another kind of local wind, the *chinook* of North America and the *föhn* of central Europe, will be described in Section 10.7.

(d) Land and Sea Breezes
The daytime sea breeze of coastal regions, sometimes alternating with a land breeze at night, results from the differential heating of land and sea. During the day the land is hotter than the sea. The air in contact with the heated land expands and rises, drawing in cooler air from the sea to take its place. The result is an *onshore* breeze. At night the situation may be reversed if the sky is clear. The land cools down, by radiating away the heat it has acquired during the day. The sea is now warmer than the land, and the movement of air is from land to sea. The daytime sea breeze is normally very much stronger than the night-time land breeze.

10.4   Ocean Currents

We saw in Unit 2 that the earth's ocean currents broadly correspond to the planetary winds, which are their primary cause. The winds in the northern hemisphere, particularly the north-east trade winds and the west winds, set up a rotary movement of the surface layers of the water, in a clockwise direction. In the southern hemisphere, the corresponding winds set up a similar movement in an anti-clockwise direction.

The trade winds drive the surface waters along the equator in a westerly direction. (It was this current which Thor Heyerdahl used when he crossed the

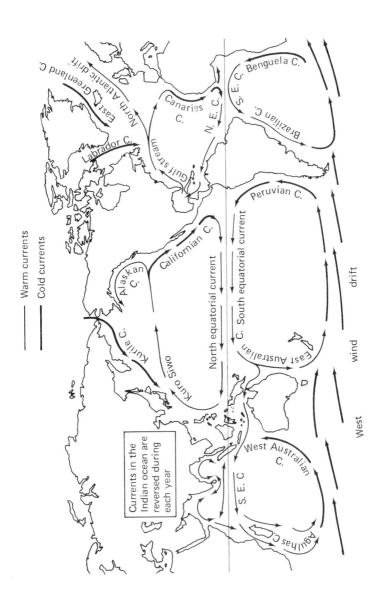

Warm currents
Cold currents

Fig. 10.4 Ocean currents

Pacific Ocean on his raft *Kon Tiki*. Indeed, prehistoric navigators had used it before him.) When the water reaches the western side of the ocean it is deflected either to the north or the south, until it reaches the latitude of the *westerlies*, between 35° and 50° of latitude. These winds then propel the waters eastwards to complete this rotation. Cold water from inside the polar circles is fed towards these rotary systems by the winds blowing outwards from the polar high-pressure centres. (The only exception to this generalization is in the Indian Ocean north of the equator, where the seasonal reversal of the monsoon winds causes the rotary current itself to change direction (Section 11.3(*d*)).)

Ocean currents have an important influence on the climate of neighbouring coastlands. Winds are warmed as they pass over a current of warm sea water from the tropical regions; they are chilled by passage over a cold water body. The most conspicuous and important example of an ocean current's influence on climate is found in the North Atlantic (Fig. 10.5). The North Atlantic Drift is propelled by the south-westerly winds from the region of the West Indies towards the shores of north-western Europe. The water, of course, becomes cooler as it moves into higher latitudes, but it does not completely lose its tropical warmth, and it flows to the west of the British Isles as a warm body of water. Relatively warm water even reaches the coast of Norway, as far north as the Arctic Circle, creating what has been called a *Gulf of Winter Warmth*. The North Atlantic Drift is the reason why the seas of north-western Europe do not, as a general rule, freeze in winter. Cold currents on the opposite side of the Atlantic—the southward-moving Labrador and East Greenland currents—carry cold water far to the south, even in summer. In winter the Gulf of

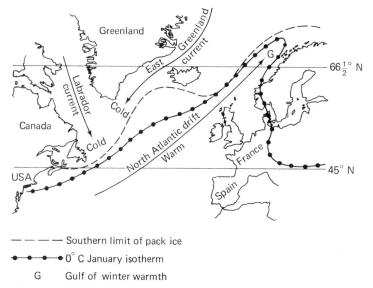

— — — — Southern limit of pack ice

●—●—●—● 0° C January isotherm

G   Gulf of winter warmth

Fig. 10.5 Winter difference between east and west sides of the Atlantic

St Lawrence and the coastal seas off Labrador and Newfoundland become covered by thick sea ice.

Ocean currents can, however, only influence the air temperature over adjacent land masses if the wind is blowing onshore regularly (Section 10.3 (*d*)). For example, the Gulf Stream exerts no influence along the eastern coast of the USA in winter, when the wind is offshore.

10.5   Altitude

Altitude influences temperature directly because the temperature falls on average by 1 °C for every 100 m of vertical ascent. Snow lies permanently at about 5 000 m on Mount Kilimanjaro, on the equator. Away from the equator, the

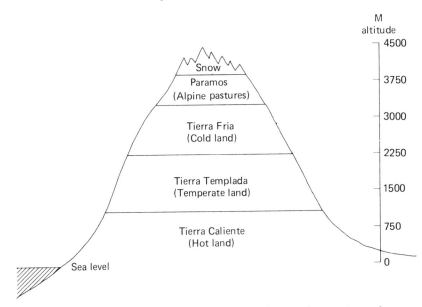

Fig. 10.6 Altitudinal zones in the north Andes. Both natural vegetation and crops change as the temperature decreases with altitude

snow line (that is, the lowest limit of permanent snow) sinks lower and lower. It is at about 2 700 m in the Swiss Alps, between 1 200 and 1 500 m in Norway and it reaches sea-level in the polar regions.

Mountains always interrupt the normal pattern of climate: they reduce the temperature and this reduces the maximum humidity of the air. As one ascends a high mountain, one passes through a series of altitudinal zones comparable with, although not quite the same as, those to be found on a journey from the region of the mountain to the poles. The northern Andes, in Venezuela, are probably the best example of this phenomenon (Fig. 10.6).

10.6   Aspect

The direction in which a slope faces is known as its aspect. The alignment of mountains can influence the amount of insolation, precipitation and exposure to wind of their slopes. Thus, in the northern hemisphere, slopes with a southerly aspect are warmer than those facing north, which may experience the direct rays of the sun for a much shorter period of the day, if at all in winter. In glaciated mountain areas—the Alps, for example—villages, hotels

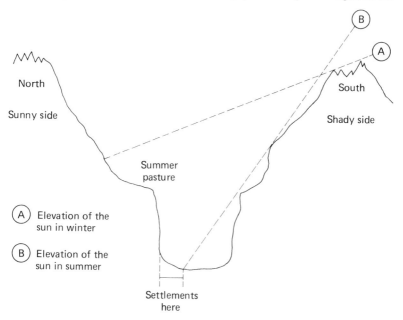

Fig. 10.7 The effect of aspect on a mountain valley

and cultivated land are usually located with reference to their aspect, so as to enjoy the maximum sunshine, while shady hillsides are likely to be forested with conifers. Indeed, valley slopes with different aspects are sometimes known by local names which have the general connotation of 'sunny side' and 'shady side'.

10.7   Mountain Barriers

Mountains also influence climate by acting as a barrier to the movement of air. A range of hills or mountains may cause *relief rain* on the windward side and a dry *rainshadow* on the lee or sheltered side. As an air stream rises to cross a mountain range it is cooled (**1** on Fig. 10.8) and loses moisture by condensation, giving cloud, rain and snow at high altitudes (**2**). Once over the crest of the range (on the lee side), gravity makes the air begin to sink, and it becomes warmer as it sinks lower (3). Such warming is not conducive to condensation, so conditions are much drier on the lee or *rainshadow* side of the range, compared with the heavy precipitation on the windward side (4).

This warm descending air may have a strong climatic influence, and it can even melt a winter's accumulation of snow in a day or two. Such a wind sometimes blows down the eastern slopes of the Rocky Mountains of Canada and the USA and its beneficial influence may be felt as far as 500 km out into

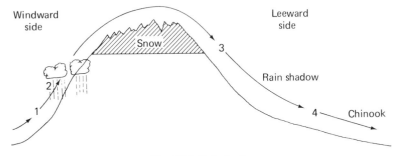

Fig. 10.8 Rainshadow

the plains. The Indians of the Canadian prairies called this wind the *chinook*, the 'eater of snow': it melts the snow on the wheat fields and so lengthens the growing season. A similar wind, blowing from the Mediterranean basin to a depression centred over central Europe, is known as the *föhn* in Switzerland. Although it may be beneficial in clearing the snow from the upland pastures, the föhn wind may be responsible for the sudden melting of snow which causes avalanches.

High ground parallel and close to the coast restricts the influence of the sea and often forms a climatic divide, such as the Kiolen Axis which separates Norway from Sweden. If the high ground is broken by gaps, the winds from the sea can penetrate further inland, so the climatic change is very much more gradual. The vast ranges of the Himalayas ensure that the cold winter conditions in the heart of the Asiatic continent do not greatly influence temperatures over the plains of northern India. But there is no such barrier between the interior of Asia and the plains of China, which experience to the full the cold winds which blow outwards in winter.

10.8   Distance from the Sea (Continentality)

Insolation and latitude are major factors affecting temperature, but distance from the sea is no less important. When solar energy falls upon large water bodies, such as seas, some of it is reflected back into the atmosphere. But the energy which is absorbed by the water penetrates to a depth of many metres, causing the sea to be warmed to a considerable depth. Land retains a higher

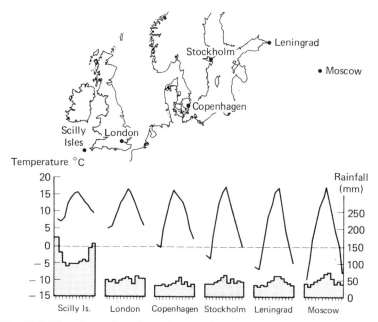

Fig. 10.9 The effect of continentality on the climate of Europe. Notice three trends towards the east: (a) annual temperature range increases, with winters becoming colder, (b) rainfall total decreases (c) rainfall distribution changes from winter maximum (typical of maritime climates) to summer maximum (typical of continental climates)

proportion of the solar energy which reaches it (unless the land is snow-covered), but the heat does not penetrate as deeply. It is mainly for these reasons that the land surface heats more rapidly under the sun's rays than the surface of the sea. But the land surface also cools more quickly, when it is no longer exposed to sunlight, because the heat has not penetrated deeply. The result is that, in temperate regions in summer, the land masses are warmer than the sea in the same latitude, but in winter the reverse is true. In coastal areas the presence of the sea and the breezes which blow from it tempers the summer heat but moderates the winter cold. This moderating influence diminishes, however, with increasing distance from the coast: winters become cooler and summers a little warmer. This factor is known as *continentality*, and it also influences rainfall. Air near the coast is more humid and more rain is likely to fall than in a continental interior, where the air is much drier.

A climate in which the influence of the sea is dominant is known as a *maritime climate*. A *continental climate* occurs in the heart of a land mass, where the influence of the sea is slight or non-existent. The bigger the land mass, the greater the effects of continentality. Table 10.1 summarizes the differences between maritime and continental climates, and Fig. 10.10 shows how these differences are represented on climatic graphs.

Table 10.1   A comparison between maritime and continental climates

	Maritime	Continental
Temperature range	*Small range.* Influence of the sea moderates temperature, keeping winter temperatures up and summer ones down	*Large range.* No maritime influence so winter temperatures drop very low, summer ones higher than on coast
Rainfall total	*Frequent depressions.* Open to sea air with abundant water vapour (high relative humidity) so high annual rainfall	*Fewer depressions.* Further inland so less water vapour in air (lower relative humidity) and lower annual rainfall
Rainfall distribution	*Winter maximum.* More frequent depressions in winter bring frontal rain. Summer has fewer depressions. Onshore westerly winds bring in humid maritime air	*Summer maximum.* Unaffected by maritime air and high pressure in winter keeps out depressions. Rain is of convectional type because of high summer temperatures

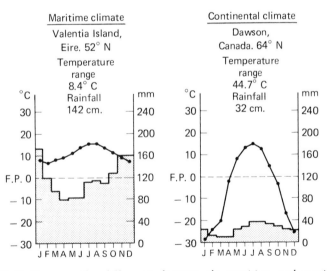

Fig. 10.10 Compare the differences between the maritime and continental climates shown on these graphs with the descriptions given in Table 10.1

Further Reading
Strahler, A. N.: *Physical Geography*. John Wiley (Chichester, 1969), Chapters 8, 9.

Questions
1. Explain the following: (*a*) temperature inversion, (*b*) insolation, (*c*) mistral, (*d*) aspect, (*e*) rainshadow, (*f*) continentality.
2. In what ways do planetary factors influence climate on earth?
3. Describe and explain the planetary winds system. How may these winds influence climate?
4. Explain how ocean currents influence climate, using diagrammatic examples.
5. In what ways do mountains influence climate? Give examples.
6. Describe and explain the differences between maritime and continental climates.

Unit Eleven
World Climate and Vegetation

In Unit 10 we discussed the factors which influence climate—the intensity of insolation and its seasonal variations, differences in the length of the daylight period, the planetary wind system and ocean currents, the size of the continents and the relief of the land. The world pattern of climates is so complex that we can only generalize very broadly. In this Unit we divide the land surface of the earth into a number of climatic regions, and within each one the climate has certain features in common. Of course it is not exactly the same over the whole area, but it would be difficult to mistake the climate in, say, a Mediterranean region for that found in a tropical desert or an equatorial forest.

11.1   Climatic Regions

We shall describe twelve climatic regions in this Unit. None of them occurs in a single compact area. Each type is found in at least two of the major land masses, but it is not difficult to understand and remember their distribution, because they form a regular pattern, as we shall see in Sections 11.3–11.6.

We have drawn the boundaries between these regions as firm lines on the maps, but in reality, of course, there is rarely a sharp divide between one region and another. Each passes gradually into the next, and no two geographers might fix the position of the boundary line in precisely the same way. They would agree, however, that it is necessary to establish climatic regions in order to understand the range and variety of climate in the world.

There are two sets of statistics which are essential for the study of climatic types: (a) the total rainfall and its distribution between the twelve months of the year, and (b) the mean monthly average temperature for each month (Section 9.4) and the annual range of temperature. Other factors are also important, such as cloudiness and sunshine, and liability to frost or thunderstorms, but we shall define the essentials of each region by using rainfall and temperature graphs.

(a) Rainfall
The rainfall *total* enables us to give a description to every climate. Less than 250 mm in a year means an *arid* climate, between 250 mm and 500 mm it is *semi-arid*, *moderate* rainfall is a total between 500 mm and 1 140 mm and over 1 140 mm is *heavy* rainfall. Rainfall distribution may be deduced by a study of the monthly totals, and we should differentiate between climates with rain all the year round and those with seasonal rainfall, where there are several

months with little or no rainfall. In the latter case, it is particularly important to recognize which parts of the year are wet and which are dry.

(b) Temperature

If the mean monthly average temperatures for each month are plotted on a graph (see, for example, Fig. 11.1) and we join each of the twelve points together, the shape of the resulting line can give us valuable information. Summer occurs in the warmest months. If these are in July and August the location is in the northern hemisphere, if they are in December and January the location is in the southern hemisphere (compare the graphs on Fig. 11.7). The position of the temperature graph in relation to the freezing point line (marked on many graphs) gives us an indication of the location of this particular climatic type. For instance, if the whole temperature line is well above freezing point and some temperatures are above 25 °C, the climate is tropical. However, when the line is nearer to, but still wholly above freezing point, with maximum temperatures about 15 °C, this suggests that the climate is temperate maritime, especially if the annual range of temperature is small, shown by a 'flat' line. When the temperature graph resembles a mountain peak, with several months below freezing point, the location is certainly temperate continental, with a large annual range of temperature (Table 10.1 and Fig. 10.10).

(c) Climatic Regions

You must remember that there is no general agreement on the extent of the twelve climatic regions we shall discuss in Sections 11.3–11.6. Even the names of the regions may vary from one book to another, but we shall use the following names:

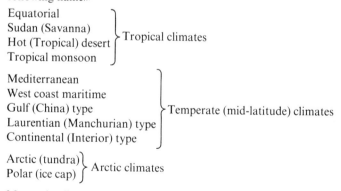

Equatorial
Sudan (Savanna)
Hot (Tropical) desert   } Tropical climates
Tropical monsoon

Mediterranean
West coast maritime
Gulf (China) type   } Temperate (mid-latitude) climates
Laurentian (Manchurian) type
Continental (Interior) type

Arctic (tundra)
Polar (ice cap)   } Arctic climates

Mountain climates

11.2   Natural Vegetation

The natural vegetation of any part of the earth's surface is directly related to the local climate, as well as to its soil (Unit 12). We shall describe each climatic type with its resulting vegetation in Sections 11.3–11.6.

The amount and distribution of rainfall are major climatic influences on the type of vegetation which can flourish. Rainfall well distributed throughout the year normally gives rise to forest—dense tropical forests where it is hot all year round, deciduous trees where there are distinct warm and cool seasons, and evergreen coniferous forest where it is cool or cold throughout the year. Where rainfall is distinctly seasonal, with a marked dry season, trees find it difficult to survive, unless they are adapted to withstand drought in some way. Under such seasonal rainfall conditions the vegetation is most likely to be some form of grass. If rainfall is very low—less than 250 mm per year—conditions are normally described as desert and no plant life can survive unless, again, its structure is especially adapted for life in such dry conditions.

Temperature also has an important influence on vegetation growth, for the effectiveness of rainfall largely depends on the temperature prevailing when it falls. At the high temperatures of the tropics, much of the rain which does fall evaporates back into the atmosphere and is effectively lost to the plants. Precipitation in the form of snow may also have little value, because plants cannot absorb water in solid form. Predominantly low temperatures lead to rather slow growth, providing that the rainfall is sufficient and effective; continuously high temperatures with heavy rainfall, such as that in the equatorial regions, produce rapid growth and a luxuriant vegetation. In general, plants grow very little at temperatures below 6·5 °C, and a great many are killed by freezing.

We must emphasize, however, that *natural* vegetation is that which would be found growing if man had not destroyed it or modified the physical conditions in which it grows. (He can do the latter by lowering the water-table and depriving trees of water, or by causing soil erosion which destroys vegetation.) Natural vegetation no longer exists over much of the earth. It has been replaced either by a vegetation which has been planted by man or by a type of *secondary* vegetation which has grown after man has destroyed the natural vegetation. In some parts of the world, the original vegetation was destroyed by man so long ago that we tend to accept the secondary growth as the natural vegetation of the area. This is best seen around parts of the Mediterranean Sea (Section 11.4(a)).

Over much of Europe, the natural vegetation was originally deciduous forest. A great deal of it remained two thousand years ago, and even a thousand years ago there were vast areas on which man's impact had been slight. Today, apart from some remote areas of Scandinavia, Europe's vegetation is almost entirely the result of man's activities. The same thing has happened throughout the eastern United States and over much of China. Much of the tropical grassland or savanna has been ruined by destructive agricultural practices, and desert scrub has grown in its place. Large areas of the soil in mid-latitude grasslands have been eroded, and their grass cover has been destroyed for ever. Only in the tropical and coniferous forest can extensive areas of natural vegetation still be found, but these too are being slowly modified or destroyed by man. In the future, natural vegetation may be found only in special parks and nature reserves.

11.3   Tropical Climates

In this Section we shall discuss the four types of climate which are found between or just outside the Tropics of Cancer and Capricorn. These are the Equatorial, Sudan (Savanna), Hot (Tropical) desert and Tropical monsoon climates.

(a) Equatorial Climate
Those parts of South America, Africa, west Malaysia and Indonesia which lie close to the equator experience equatorial climates (Fig. 11.1).

(i) **Climatic conditions.** The mid-day sun is high in the sky at all times, and it is directly overhead twice during the year. Temperatures are always high, with mean monthly averages between 21 and 27 °C, the annual range is small, and there are no distinct seasons. It has been said that 'Night is the winter of the tropics', meaning that the lowest temperatures in equatorial zones are experienced during the night.

Rainfall is heavy throughout the year, with an annual total which generally exceeds 1 500 mm. It usually shows distinct maxima during certain months, depending on a place's location in relation to the equator: as a general rule, rainfall is heaviest when the sun is overhead or soon afterwards. But the only real difference is between wet months and very wet months.

Most rainfall comes as heavy thunderstorms, normally during the afternoon. This is convectional rainfall, resulting from the vigorous convectional rise of the air, stimulated by the strong mid-day and early afternoon sunshine. Rain is also brought by the prevailing winds of the equatorial region, the trade winds. These converge on or near the equator in the Inter-tropical Convergence Zone (Fig. 10.2). Rainfall here is particularly heavy because the meeting place of the moist trade winds coincides with the rising air of the equatorial low-pressure belt. (The seasonal north-to-south movement of this belt of low pressure means that the months with maximum rainfall vary in different parts of the equatorial region.

A climate such as this, without distinct seasons and with the same length of daylight for every day of the year, is extremely monotonous. The combination of high temperatures with high humidity makes it unbearably sultry and oppressive to those who have not been acclimatized to it.

(ii) **A typical daily weather sequence.** Fig. 11.2 shows a typical weather sequence for a single day. The diurnal range of temperature may be 20 °C, which is far greater than the annual range of temperature (that is, between the averages of the hottest and coolest months). It is coolest just before sunrise in the very early morning (in this case 23 °C) and the relative humidity is highest at this time (98 per cent). The temperature rises steadily during the morning, which is usually sunny, and the lowest humidity (46 per cent) in this very humid climate occurs in the early afternoon when the temperature is highest (34 °C here). By this time, however, dense cumulonimbus clouds are beginning

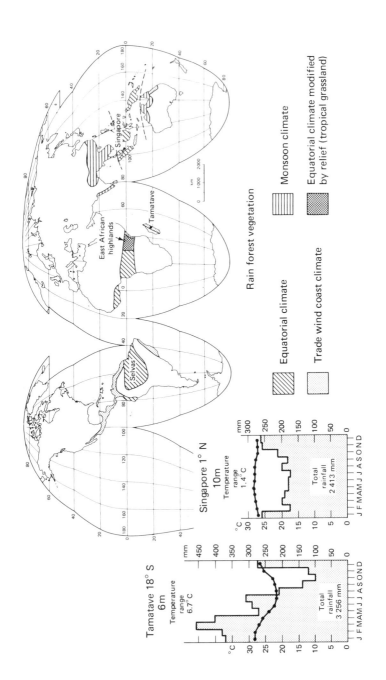

Fig. 11.1 Equatorial climate and vegetation

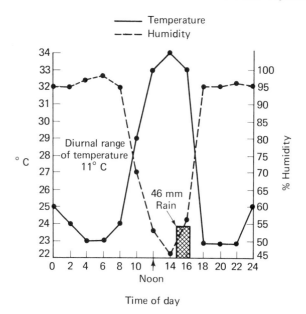

Fig. 11.2 Temperature, humidity and rainfall during a typical equatorial day

to form, as a result of the vigorous convectional rise of the air. Heavy rain is likely to fall during the mid-afternoon. By early evening the convectional rise diminishes, the clouds disperse and the day ends with a clear sky, bright sunshine and cooler temperatures.

(iii) **Trade wind coasts.** A similar climate is experienced along east-facing coasts as far north and south as the tropics, where the trade winds blow onshore for all or much of the year (Fig. 11.1). The islands of Indonesia, in particular, benefit from these winds.

Although the temperature range is slightly greater here, average temperatures are still consistently high (about 25 °C). Rainfall is as heavy as that along the equator, especially if the coast is backed by high ground as in eastern Brazil and eastern Malagasy (Tamatave graph, Fig. 11.1), because trade winds carry warm moist air onshore. The climate is usually called a trade wind coast climate for this reason, although the name *tropical marine* is often used as well.

(iv) **Altitude** also exerts a modifying influence on equatorial climates. The highlands of east Africa and the Andes in Ecuador both have a more congenial climate than the nearby lowlands (Fig. 11.1). They have the typically small equatorial temperature range but, at Quito in Ecuador, for example, monthly averages are about 14 °C below those in the plains (Section 11.6 and Fig. 11.20).

(v) **Equatorial rain forest (selvas).** The prevailing high temperatures, heavy rainfall and high humidity all contribute to the distinctive vegetation of this region—the equatorial rain forest or selvas. The plants are hygrophytic (that is, requiring abundant moisture), and they occupy vast regions in the basin of the Amazon in South America and in that of the Congo in Africa. These regions contain some of the largest areas of purely natural vegetation left in the world today. This vegetation type is not only found in regions of equatorial climate: both trade wind coasts and the wetter parts of monsoon areas are sufficiently wet for forests of this type to flourish although the species of tree in the monsoon forest may be different (Fig. 11.1).

The trees are deciduous, but do not all shed their leaves at the same time. The lack of distinct seasons induces a peculiar regime of flowering, fruiting and the budding and shedding of leaves, because all are going on at the same time on adjacent trees. Each tree has its own growth cycle.

There are many different kinds of tree in every square kilometre of equatorial rain forest. Stands of any single species do not occur naturally, as they do in temperate forests. Equatorial forests are dense and the trees tall, often rising to more than 60 m. Their topmost branches merge into a continuous canopy, shutting out the light from the ground below which is in continuous twilight. There is little undergrowth, except in clearings and along the banks of rivers. Parasitic plants, such as orchids, grow on the trees as do creepers like the long, rope-like lianas, which may reach down to the ground. The root system of the trees is usually shallow, but many of the tallest have buttress roots to give them additional support. Most of the trees are hardwood, such as mahogany, ebony and the rubber tree, though the well-known softwood, balsam, also comes from the equatorial forest. There may be mangrove swamps along the coast and over deltaic areas, where trees rise on stilt-like roots from the tidal mud flats. When the roots are under water, the trees obtain air via conical breathing roots which project from the mud.

The dense equatorial forests are among the world's most sparsely populated areas: the native inhabitants consist mainly of small groups of primitive people. Large settlements have only grown up along rivers and coasts, where communications are easier. Agriculture is generally backward and based on the method of shifting cultivation, known in different parts of the world's equatorial forests as ladang, milpa and swidden cultivation (*H & R*, Unit 3). The soil is kept fertile by the organic matter supplied by leaf-fall from the trees, but once the forest is cleared, the soil quickly loses this supply of nutrients. Crops can only be grown for two or three years on this cleared land before soil exhaustion and soil erosion set in, aided by the heavy rainfall (Unit 12). Forestry is restricted by disease, insect pests and difficulty of communications, and also by a shortage of labour, because it is almost impossible to work in such an enervating climate.

(*b*) **Sudan Climate**
The Sudan, sometimes called the Savanna climate, is to be found on the *outer* margins of the equatorial regions in South America and Africa, and in northern Australia, just inland of the coast.

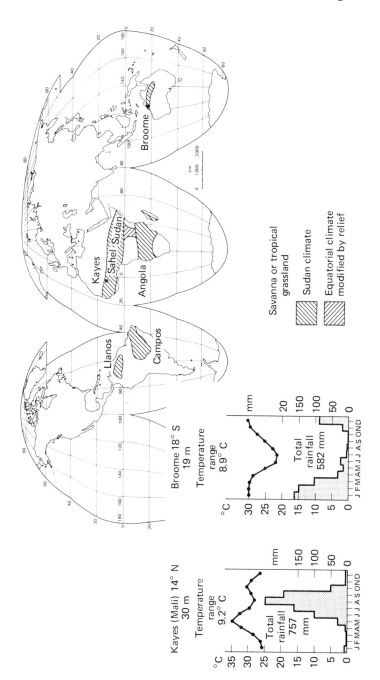

Fig. 11.3 Sudan climate and vegetation

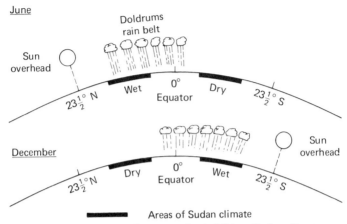

Fig. 11.4 *Reason for the seasonal rainfall in a Sudan climate*

(i) **Climatic conditions.** Average temperatures are high throughout the year, generally exceeding 25 °C. There is a slightly greater range than along the equator, because the sun is overhead in the hot season but lower in the sky in the cool season.

Distinct seasons begin to appear as one moves away from the equator but they are *rainfall seasons*. There is not yet sufficient variation between highest and lowest average temperatures to use the terms 'summer' and 'winter', so 'wet' and 'dry' are the most appropriate seasonal descriptions. Rainfall is

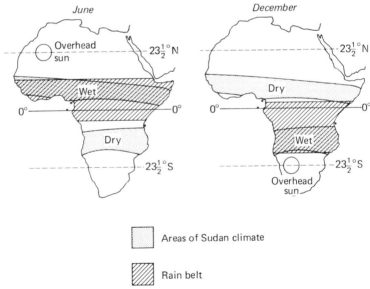

Fig. 11.5 *Seasonal movement of the doldrums rain belt in Africa*

heavy when the sun is high in the sky, because the equatorial low-pressure belt, with its rainfall, has moved to dominate the Sudan climate. At low-sun season, the sub-tropical high-pressure belt is dominant and rainfall is slight.

(ii) **Savanna vegetation.** The vegetation changes gradually from the selvas of the equatorial region to become thinner and more open as a dry season becomes apparent. Trees only grow along the banks of water courses and on the windward slopes of hills. Elsewhere, there is coarse grassland which merges into scrub and, eventually, desert. The vegetation is known as *tree savanna* where trees are dotted evenly over a grassland area.

Typically, the savanna is made up of coarse, tropical grass with scattered trees in damp areas. At the end of the dry season the vegetation is brown and the soil is parched. With the first rains of the wet season, new grass grows rapidly, sometimes to a height of over 2 m. Trees come into leaf and flowers bloom. At the end of the wet season, the trees begin to lose their leaves and the land again dries out. The only trees able to survive in this climate are those which are, in varying degrees, *xerophytic* (that is, biologically suited to withstand dry conditions). Such trees have deep roots and they lose their leaves or have leaves which are adapted to conserve moisture in the dry season. The baobab, acacia and Australian gum trees are typical examples of such vegetation.

Away from the equator, where the wet season becomes shorter and the annual rainfall total small, trees disappear and even grass becomes short and

Fig. 11.6 A baobab tree in northern Australia. This unusual xerophitic tree is more common in the tropical grassland (savanna) of Africa and Malagasy

patchy. Bunch grass appears, with areas of bare rock or dry soil between the tufts of vegetation.

Big game, including the elephant, giraffe, zebra and a great variety of antelope and deer, was once abundant on the savanna. All these animals are herbivorous, feeding on the natural vegetation while carnivores such as the lion, leopard and hyena prey on them. Man has, however, greatly changed the fauna over large areas of the savanna, and this range of wild life can now be encountered only in parks and game reservations.

Cattle rearing is an important activity in many areas of savanna. Commercial cattle herding is found in parts of South America—the Llanos of Venezuela and the Campos of Brazil, for example—and also in northern Australia. Subsistence cattle farming is important in parts of Africa—in Mali, Niger, Chad, Sudan, Kenya, Tanzania and Zambia—but large areas are infested with tsetse fly and cannot therefore support cattle which, like their human owners, are susceptible to disease carried by the fly. Some areas of savanna are highly suitable for coffee growing or for the cultivation of sugarcane and groundnuts.

(c) Hot or Tropical Deserts

(i) **Climatic conditions.** The highest temperatures ever recorded under natural conditions are experienced in the hot or tropical deserts. At Azizia in Libya, for instance, a temperature of nearly 58 °C has been registered. The reason is that the length of the daylight period in summer is greater than in the savanna and equatorial regions, while at the same time the skies are virtually cloudless and the sun is overhead. Winter temperatures are considerably lower since the sun is very much lower in the sky and days are shorter. The daytime heat is quickly radiated back into the atmosphere, and after sunset temperatures drop suddenly. Daytime temperatures may have been 40 °C but this does not prevent a touch of frost on a still night. This *diurnal* range of temperature is greater than in any other region of the world. This sudden and extreme variation in temperature accounts for the break-up of rocks by exfoliation and the formation of sand, which we noted in Section 3.1.

Hot deserts have an average rainfall of less than 250 mm a year and even this is very unreliable. When the average rainfall is between 250 mm and 500 mm a year, the region is called a *semi-desert*. The highly irregular rainfall comes mainly in the form of heavy but short-lived thunderstorms. This is because the hot deserts are regions of permanently high atmospheric pressure, with slowly sinking air. The convectional rise of air which is a major source of regular rainfall in the tropics is prevented by the predominantly sinking air of the high-pressure system. Thus any local convection which does occur does not ascend high enough into the atmosphere or cool sufficiently for clouds to form and rain to fall. Only very rarely does hot air burst upwards to form the towering cumulonimbus clouds which are associated with thunder and heavy rain.

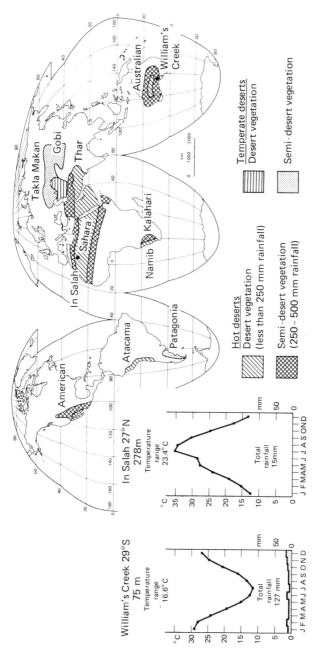

Fig. 11.7 Tropical (hot) deserts and temperate deserts: climate and vegetation

(ii) **Desert vegetation** is sparse or non-existent, except along water courses and in oases. Only xerophytic plants, such as the cactus, thorn scrub and spinifex grass, can grow and survive in these arid conditions. Desert plants reduce their loss of moisture through transpiration to a minimum. Their leaves are small to reduce the area exposed to the sun and in some species are waxy or hairy, while stems are often fleshy: all these factors help to conserve moisture. Most plants have long roots which can reach underground sources of water, and some roots are bulbous in order to store moisture. Seeds may lie dormant for years in the sand and gravel, waiting for one of the rare short-lived storms

Fig. 11.8 Vegetation in the Arizona Desert, south-western USA

which enable them to germinate, grow rapidly, flower and set seed before they die in the arid heat.

Settlement and agriculture are possible only where water is available and, since rainfall is too unreliable for any regular use, this supply must come from exotic streams or from the rocks. Oases are supplied by underground water flowing as springs or tapped by wells. Even here, where all agriculture is dependent on irrigation, only those crops which are sparing in their needs for water are grown.

(d) Tropical Monsoon Climate
This type of climate is associated primarily with south-east Asia and India, but it also occurs as a narrow coastal strip in northern Australia.

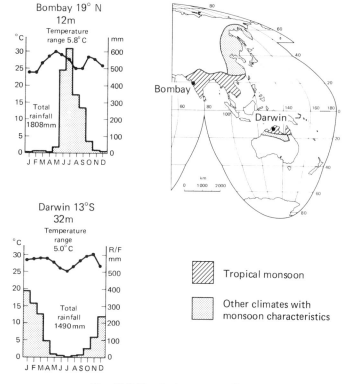

Fig. 11.9 Tropical monsoon climate

(i) **The monsoon climate** is characterized by high temperatures when the sun is overhead, the average being over 21 °C, but lower temperatures when the sun shines from a lower angle. The cool season is dry and cloudless and, for this reason, heat is radiated into the air after sunset so that night temperatures may even dip to freezing in hilly areas. Rainfall is strongly seasonal.

In a typical monsoon area, such as the west coast of India, the cooler season (November to January) is dry, sunny and warm, with temperatures averaging 20–25 °C. Spring (from February to May) becomes gradually hotter as the sun's angle in the sky increases and daytime temperatures of up to 40 °C may be recorded. The heat is almost suffocating towards the end of the hot season, and everyone waits and longs for rain. The monsoon 'breaks' some time in June, when warm, humid air comes in from the Indian Ocean. Banks of heavy cloud form over the coast and become lower and thicker; the rain pours down continuously for days, even weeks. During the rainy season (June to October), the temperature drops noticeably to an average of about 20 °C as the dense cloud cover excludes the direct rays of the sun.

In most parts of these regions there is actually a date when the monsoon is expected to arrive. Occasionally it is late, and this is serious, not only because water supplies are exhausted, but also because the farmer is waiting to sow his crops, especially rice. Late sowing means a late and perhaps less plentiful harvest. Hundreds of millions of peasant-farmers in India and south-east Asia await the arrival of the monsoon, knowing that famine may follow if it is late. At times the monsoon fails completely, and this causes great distress and widespread famine in the subsistence farming communities throughout south-east Asia.

Fig. 11.10 shows that, while the effect of the monsoon is felt most strongly near the coast, its cause lies in the seasonal changes in atmospheric pressure over the continental interiors of Asia and Australia. In June, with the sun overhead at the northern tropic, there are large low-pressure systems over central Asia and the Sind Desert in north-west India. These pressure systems attract warm, very humid air from adjacent sea areas. At the same time, a high-pressure centre develops over central Australia giving rise to outblowing winds and dry conditions along the north coast. Six months later, in December, the positions are reversed because the sun is overhead at the southern tropic: high pressure over central Asia and the Sind Desert now gives rise to outblowing winds but, with low pressure over the heart of Australia, onshore winds bring monsoon rain to the northern coastlands there.

The onshore winds in the rainy season blow from the warm waters of the Indian Ocean and the west Pacific near the equator, so the air has a high relative humidity when it reaches the coast. The result is torrential rain as the air surges over the coasts of India, Burma, Sri Lanka, south-east Asia and, somewhat less vigorously, southern China. The rain brought to northern Australia is not as heavy as that brought by the northern hemisphere monsoon. This is chiefly because the Australian low-pressure system is less intense than the one over Asia, but it is also a result of the flatness of the northern Australian coastlands. Rainfall is particularly heavy when high hills or mountains lie athwart the onshore winds, as in the Western Ghats of southern India, the mountains of Burma and, above all, the foothills of the Himalayas and the mountains of Assam, where they lie behind the Bay of Bengal. The highest rainfall ever recorded occurred here, at Cherrapunji (Fig. 11.20). In one year it received 22 400 mm of rainfall, and its average annual fall is 10 800 mm. Apart from these areas of high ground, rainfall normally decreases further inland: Calcutta has 1 600 mm, Allahabad 1 062 mm, Cawnpore 823 mm and New Delhi 635 mm.

(ii) **Monsoon vegetation.** The natural vegetation in the areas of heaviest rainfall is not unlike that of the equatorial region. But the forest is less dense than the selvas and the trees are of different types, because plants have to be able to survive a dry season in the monsoon forest. The most important trees are teak, sal and sandalwood. The more open nature of the forest permits sunlight to reach ground level and there is usually a dense undergrowth (unlike the equatorial forest), consisting mainly of bamboo, a giant variety of grass. Areas with lower rainfall have a sparser vegetation, such as drought-resistant thorn forest. There may be mangrove swamp along the coasts and along river estuaries.

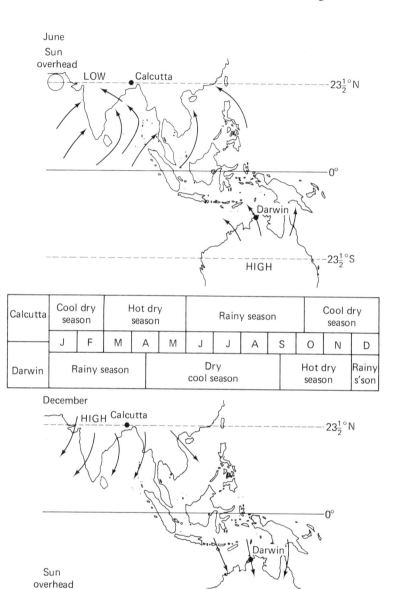

Calcutta	Cool dry season		Hot dry season		Rainy season				Cool dry season		
	J	F	M	A	M	J	J	A	S	O	N	D
Darwin	Rainy season			Dry cool season					Hot dry season		Rainy s'son

Fig. 11.10 The pressure changes which cause monsoons

Much of the monsoon forest has been cleared and the land brought under cultivation, especially in India, Pakistan and Bangladesh. Rice is grown wherever the land can be flooded during the monsoon rains; millet, wheat and barley are grown in drier areas. Sometimes two crops can be taken in a year, and occasionally three (*H & R*, Section 4.1). The natural monsoon forest is, however, still found in the mountains of Burma, Thailand, Laos and Vietnam, as well as along parts of the north Australian coast.

(*e*) Tropical Climates: a Summary

The four climatic types we have discussed so far have certain features in common. Temperatures are high and frost is virtually unknown, except at night in some desert areas and on higher land in the monsoon region. The annual temperature range is slight in the equatorial region, but increases as one moves away from the equator. There are greater contrasts in the amount and distribution of rainfall. There is rain in every month, even every day, in equatorial regions while the deserts have a very small average rainfall—200 mm a year or less—occurring at rare and irregular intervals. Rainfall is markedly seasonal in both Sudan and monsoon climates, but there are sharp contrasts between them in the volume and the violence of their storms. A monsoon climate may have several times as much rainfall, concentrated into three or four months, as the Sudan climate.

11.4   Temperate Climates

The sun is never directly overhead outside the tropics. It may be high in the sky in summer but it is low in winter (Fig. 1.5). Furthermore, the seasonal

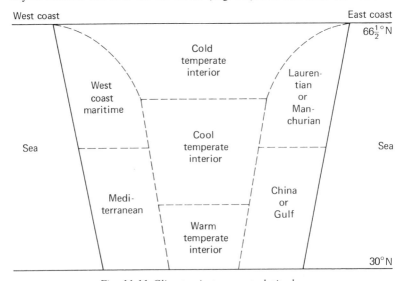

Fig. 11.11 Climates in temperate latitudes

variation in the length of daylight is very much greater than in the tropics. Thus, in temperate regions, contrasts between summer and winter temperatures are far more strongly marked.

The influence of continentality upon seasonal temperatures is another feature of these latitudes. As we saw in Section 10.8, winter in areas close to the sea is generally mild while in regions far from the coast it tends to be more severe. Conversely, summers are generally hotter in the interior of continental land masses than they are in maritime locations. These factors are most noticeable in temperate latitudes because the continents happen to have their greatest east-to-west extent here, especially in the northern hemisphere.

There is also a marked contrast between the climates of the western and eastern sides of land masses in these latitudes, as a result of the different winds which influence each coast (Fig. 10.2). West coasts are exposed to the prevailing westerly winds, which blow from the oceans, and both the winds and the ocean currents moderate the severity of winter and temper the summer heat. Rainfall is heavier in winter than summer because depressions are more active and more frequent. On east coasts dry offshore winds blow from the high-pressure centres over the continental interiors in winter, and they carry the severe cold of the inland areas with them. In summer the dominant winds are onshore because of low pressure in the continental interiors, especially over the large land masses of the northern hemisphere. This 'monsoonal' tendency (Section 11.3) gives a summer rainfall maximum, and it is particularly marked on the eastern Asiatic coast. We can see the extent of this contrast if we compare the climates of the east and west coasts of North America or Australia, or that of western Europe with eastern China and the Soviet Union. Compare the Vancouver graph on Fig. 11.12 with that of Boston, or Gibraltar with Nagasaki, and you will see these seasonal differences very clearly.

The frequency of depressions is another feature of these temperate climates and their wind systems. Depressions move from west to east at intervals, bringing with them the sequence of weather changes which we discussed in Section 9.11. They cause weather conditions in the mid-latitudes, particularly on the western coasts of land masses, to be far less predictable than those in the tropics, where there are fewer sharp day-to-day changes.

We can speak of four mid-latitude climates along the coasts, separated by a large area of continental interior climate, as in Fig. 11.11. We shall discuss each of these in turn.

The natural vegetation in temperate latitudes is not as straightforward as that in the tropics, where we have seen that each climatic type has its own distinctive vegetation. Local circumstances in different areas of the same climatic type result in a bewildering variety of vegetation. For example, the Andes create a temperate semi-desert in Patagonia where we might expect temperate forest, and the giant redwood forests are only found on the hill ranges of the west coast of the USA because the rainfall is heavier there than in any similar climatic region.

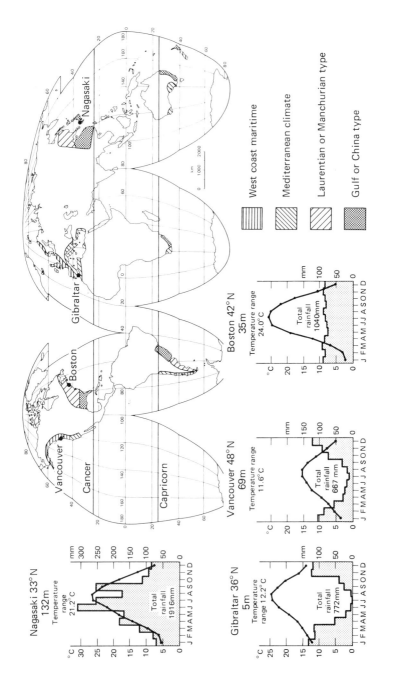

West coast maritime

Mediterranean climate

Laurentian or Manchurian type

Gulf or China type

Nagasaki 33° N
132m
Temperature
range
21.2° C
Total rainfall 1916mm

Vancouver 48° N
69m
Temperature range
11.6° C
Total rainfall 667 mm

Boston 42° N
35m
Temperature range
24.0° C
Total rainfall 1040mm

Gibraltar 36° N
5m
Temperature
range 12.2° C
Total rainfall 772mm

Fig. 11.12 Coastal climates in temperate latitudes

(a) Mediterranean Climate

The Mediterranean climate is one of the most distinctive climates in the world. It is named after that part of the world where it is most extensive, but it is also found on the west coasts of North and South America, in South Africa and in south-westerly parts of Australia. Thus there are regions with a Mediterranean climate on the western sides of land masses between 30° and 40° north and south of the equator.

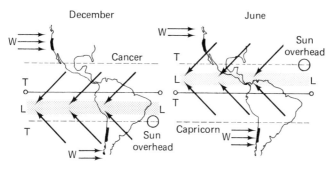

W = Westerly winds
T = Trade winds
L = Doldrums low pressure

Fig. 11.13 The movement of pressure and wind belts is responsible for seasonal differences in Mediterranean climates

(i) **Climatic conditions.** Variations in the sun's elevation in regions with a Mediterranean climate make summers hot (20–24 °C on average) and winters warm (12–16 °C). Frost is extremely rare. The seasonal movement of the wind belts (Section 10.3) brings the westerlies to these latitudes in winter, while in summer the westerlies have moved towards the pole and are replaced by the dominant influence of the sub-tropical high-pressure belt and offshore trade winds. The result is that summer conditions are akin to those of the deserts— hot, sunny and dry—but frequent depressions and the westerlies, blowing onshore, bring rain in winter.

The Mediterranean climate is unique in being the only climate with seasonal rainfall to have a summer drought. All other climates with seasonal rainfall have their wet period in the high sun or summer season. This has a major influence on the vegetation. The season when growth would normally take place is dry, and winter—when plants might be expected to lie dormant— receives the rainfall which encourages growth.

(ii) **Mediterranean vegetation.** Winters are mild as well as wet, and frost is rare except on high land. Thus 'Mediterranean' plants grow through the winter, flower in spring, fruit in early summer, and remain dormant during the period of intense drought which they are especially adapted to withstand. They may have thick bark, like the cork oak, to conserve water. Some plants have small waxy leaves, like the olive tree, which present a small surface to the sun and transpire little moisture. Others, like the grapevine, put down long tap roots.

The typical Mediterranean vegetation is an evergreen scrub known as *maquis* in Europe and *chaparral* in California. The beautiful flowering olean-der is common along valley bottoms. Conifers are found on higher ground, where there is often heavier and more prolonged rainfall. There were once extensive forests of Aleppo pine in the hills of the Mediterranean region itself, cedar forests in the mountains of Lebanon, and redwoods in California, but vast areas of forest have been destroyed as man has settled in these areas. It is likely that much of the maquis developed as secondary vegetation because the coniferous forest failed to re-establish itself as the dominant vegetation when the original forests were cleared.

The natural vegetation has been cleared to make way for agriculture over large areas, especially in countries such as Italy and Greece where there is a long history of human settlement. The climate is well-suited to crop-growing, even in winter, because temperatures rarely fall below the critical point of 6·5 °C, at which plant growth generally ceases. On the other hand, irrigation is usually necessary if plants are to be cultivated through the summer. Fruit trees, the roots of which can penetrate deeply into the soil, are an important cash crop, particularly the grape vine, orange, lemon and the typical plant of the Mediterranean region, the olive. Cereals, mainly wheat and maize, are grown only as a subsistence crop by the peasant-farmers. They are sown in late autumn, grow in the wet winter, ripen in spring and are harvested in early summer.

(b) West Coast Maritime Climate

The Mediterranean regions merge into the west coast maritime at about latitude 40°, in Europe and North and South America. This climate is sometimes called the north-west European type, and this tells us that it is found only along the coasts of north-west Europe and in corresponding west coast locations in North and South America, Tasmania and New Zealand (Fig. 11.12).

(i) **Climatic conditions.** The west coast maritime climate is found outside the trade wind belt. It lies in the track of the prevailing westerlies, in the zone of convergence between the warm sub-tropical winds and the cold outblowing arctic air. Consequently, it has frequent depressions with their associated rapid changes in weather (Section 9.11).

Summers are warm, with average temperatures between 12·8 °C and 16·7 °C, and winters are mild (1·7 °C–1·5 °C), although the mildness of winter gives way to severe conditions a few hundred kilometres inland. There is a strong contrast between the amount of insolation in summer, with its long period of daylight, and that during the short days of winter, on account of variations in the sun's elevation. We would expect to find a corresponding difference in temperature conditions also, but this is not the case because of the moderating influence of the sea, the warm ocean currents and the mild winds which blow from sea to land most of the time.

Rainfall may occur at any time of the year in this climate, since it is related to the flow of moist air from the ocean and the passage of fronts. There does, however, tend to be more rain in the winter months since the depressions, which are its chief cause, are usually deeper and more frequent then. But the rainfall is also due to relief and occurs where humid air blowing onshore rises to cross ranges of hills which lie in its path, such as the Pennines and the mountains of Scotland and Wales. There may even be convection rain on hot summer afternoons.

(ii) **West coast maritime vegetation** was originally deciduous forest, except on the high ground and on coasts exposed to westerly gales. The typical trees were the oak, ash, beech, chestnut and sycamore, with willow and alder on lower and damper ground. They lose their leaves in winter, and growth stops as temperatures fall below 6·5 °C. Little of this natural vegetation cover has survived in Europe, and there is not much more in the other regions of west coast maritime climate. The trees have been used for building and charcoal burning, or just destroyed to make way for crops. Deciduous forest, with its regular leaf-fall, produces a good soil which has always attracted man. (If you study Fig. 11.14 you will notice that, in Europe, cool temperate deciduous forests grow well outside this climatic area. This is because the transitional zone between it and the cool temperate interior has sufficient rainfall to support deciduous trees.)

There are also areas of coniferous forest to be found in west coast maritime regions, especially on higher ground (for example, the west coasts of North and South America) and on poorer soils. Large areas of coniferous trees are the result of recent afforestation projects, especially in the Breckland of East Anglia and over the North German plain. There are a few areas in which tree growth has never been abundant, including the Canterbury Plains of New Zealand, which lie in the rainshadow of the Southern Alps, and the loess belt of northern Europe, which is well-drained and dry.

Settlement is dense in much of the European west coast maritime climate. This results from historical as well as geographical factors, but the most important ones include the fertility of the soil, abundant mineral resources, a climate capable of producing a variety of crops and permanently ice-free coastal waters abounding with fish. Agriculture is intensive, heavily mechanized and geared almost exclusively to supplying food to a dense urban population.

(c) Gulf or China Type Climate

The westerly air stream only blows off the land in winter, on the eastern side of the land masses (Fig. 11.12). It brings the cool temperate conditions of the continental interiors to the coast, and it propels the surface waters of the oceans eastwards, bringing cooler water up in their place. Winters are cooler than in corresponding latitudes on the west coasts, and also considerably

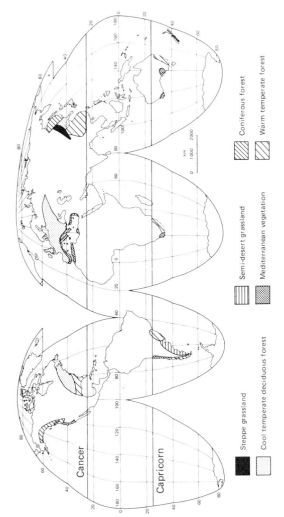

Fig. 11.14 Vegetation of the temperate coasts

Steppe grassland

Cool temperate deciduous forest

Semi-desert grassland

Mediterranean vegetation

Coniferous forest

Warm temperate forest

Cancer

Capricorn

km

0   1000   2000

drier. The monsoon effect, slight in North America but strongly developed in China, means that the climate here is marked by a summer maximum of rainfall on the larger land masses, unlike the Mediterranean areas in the same latitude on the west coasts.

The China or Gulf type is the more tropical of the two east coast climates (the other is the Laurentian or Manchurian, as shown in Fig. 11.12), but they merge into one another and it is difficult to draw a line between them. The China type occurs in China, Japan, the south-eastern United States, southern Brazil, neighbouring Uruguay and Argentina and south-eastern Australia.

(i) **Climatic conditions.** Summers are hot with average temperatures between 21 and 25 °C, and winters cool or cold. This results from the variations in the sun's elevation as well as the difference in wind direction between the seasons. There is, in fact, a great variation in winter conditions and, usually, the largest continents have the coldest winters. Southern China and the south-eastern United States sometimes experience spells of bitterly cold weather, when the orange groves of Florida are destroyed as temperatures drop to several degrees of frost. These regions enjoy a rainfall of about 1 000 mm a year which is fully adequate for agriculture. There is usually a summer maximum—owing to the monsoonal influence, and it is very strongly marked in southern China.

Fig. 11.15 A stand of loblolly pine in South Carolina, USA. These conifers grow in a Gulf type climate on poor sandy soils. Growth is rapid because of the warm climate, and these trees are ideal for lumbering

(ii) **The China type vegetation** is naturally forest. Temperature is generally high enough for growth to continue during much if not all the year. There are extensive areas of swamp along the coast of the south-eastern United States, with cypress the predominant tree. The natural vegetation has been cleared from much of the sub-tropical region of China to make way for cultivation, and large areas in the United States and South America are now used for agriculture as well.

(*d*) **Laurentian or Manchurian Climate**
The contrast between east and west coasts is nowhere better illustrated than on the opposite shores of the Atlantic (Fig. 10.5). New York City lies almost in the latitude of Lisbon. The latter experiences hot, dry summers and mild, sunny winters when the Mediterranean shrubs do not cease blooming. New York has very hot and often humid summers, but the winters are marked by heavy snow and periods of such severe cold that ice may form on the waters of New York harbour. New York is a typical example of the Laurentian or Manchurian climate, which is a poleward extension of the Gulf type climate.

(i) **Climatic conditions.** Summers are warm, but winters are much longer and more severe than Gulf regions experience. Part of the reason for this is the greater seasonal variation in the altitude of the sun and the length of daylight period, but conditions in the continental interiors of the land masses are also a major influence.

Rainfall is generally well distributed, sometimes with a maximum in the summer months, a tendency which we noticed in the Gulf type of climate where crops grow through the winter. But there is no growth in winter in the Laurentian climatic regions and, indeed, most crops would not survive the cold. This is a region for summer crops, including maize, tobacco, millet in the moister areas, wheat in the drier, and rice when irrigation is possible.

In eastern Canada the land is snow-covered and the coasts ice-bound for the whole of the winter. Similar conditions prevail in Manchuria, Korea and eastern Siberia. Conditions are less severe in northern Japan because the surrounding sea moderates the winter climate. Patagonia in South America also experiences this climate in a drier form, because it lies in the rainshadow of the Andes. Winter conditions are also less extreme here, because the continent is not more than 1 000 km wide and oceanic influences can reach the region.

(ii) **Laurentian vegetation.** Deciduous forest, with maple, oak and hickory predominating on the lower ground, passes gradually into coniferous forest as climatic conditions become more severe, especially in winter. The deciduous forest has largely been destroyed and the land brought under cultivation. But the soil which underlies the coniferous forest is not valuable agriculturally, so forestry is important in these regions, for example in the south-eastern United States. In South America the corresponding region is relatively dry, with less than 250 mm of rain a year, and the natural vegetation is semi-desert. In

Manchuria, where rainfall is slightly more plentiful, the natural vegetation is steppe grassland with deciduous woodland on the coast and in the valleys.

(e) Continental Climates

Continental climates are those found in the interior of the mid-latitude land masses. Climate here is determined by distance from the ocean and the absence of marine influences. It is characterized by low rainfall—in general below 500 mm, with a summer maximum—and by a large annual range of temperature. All these features, including the tendency to have heavy convection rainfall in summer, derive from this distance from the sea (continentality).

Continental climates extend over such vast areas that we cannot expect much uniformity (Fig. 11.16). Rainfall diminishes with increasing distance from the ocean and, as the latitude increases, winters become colder and the annual range of temperature greater. For convenience we can divide continental interior climates into warm temperate, cool temperate and cold temperate varieties but, as with all climatic types, these merge into each other.

(i) **Warm temperate interior climates** occur primarily in the southern hemisphere in the interior of South Africa, in the Murray–Darling basin of Australia, and in Paraguay and northern Argentina in South America. Summers are hot, with average temperatures between 18 and 23 °C, and winters warm, 5–10 °C (Kimberley graph, Fig. 11.16). The rainfall maximum generally comes in summer. The vegetation is normally grassland, often with trees along the water courses, but this passes into short grass and scrub. The veld of South Africa, the Murray–Darling Downs and the pampas of Argentina are good examples of these features.

The only significant occurrence of this climatic type in the northern hemisphere is in North America, where the Gulf type climate merges westwards into an area of warm continental climate.

(ii) **Cool temperate interior climates** only occur in the northern hemisphere, since the land masses of the southern hemisphere do not extend far enough to the south. This type of climate extends over much of the interior of North America, and is typical of eastern Europe, the Soviet Union and the interior of China (Fig. 11.16). In general it lies remote from the seas, between the latitudes of 40° and 60° N.

The climate is marked by hot summers and very long, cold winters with, in extreme cases, up to five months of temperatures below freezing. Some of the greatest seasonal temperature ranges are experienced in this climatic region. The lowest temperatures occur in Asia, where the effects of continentality are greatest (see the graph for Semipalatinsk, Fig. 11.16). Rainfall is unreliable and low. It is rarely more than 500 mm with a maximum in the summer months, when convection rain is most likely. Low-pressure systems give rise to thunderstorms and tornadoes, sometimes of great violence.

This climatic region is so dry in central Asia that it gives rise to the Gobi

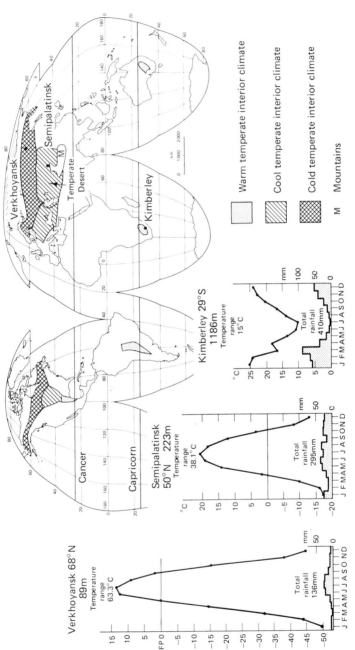

Fig. 11.16 Continental interior climates

and Takla Makan Deserts. Winter temperatures are very low here, so these are called *temperate deserts* to distinguish them from the tropical deserts (Fig. 11.7).

The natural vegetation of this region is grassland—tall grass where the rainfall is highest (about 500 mm), short grass where it is lower, about 400 mm, and scrub and spinifex grass where it is lowest, furthest from the sea. The tall grass prairie of North America and the corresponding regions of the Soviet Union, Europe and northern and north-western China have been ploughed and brought under cultivation. The short grass prairie in North America is traditionally ranching country, given over to the rearing of cattle, which are shipped into the cultivated regions furthest east for fattening. There are virtually no sheep on the North American prairie. Cattle, sheep and goats are reared in central Asia.

The American short grass prairie was opened up for cultivation in the 1920s. In this land of severe winters, low rainfall and strong winds, the surface soil was dried out by the wind during a sequence of drought years and stripped, creating the *Dust Bowl*. Much of this area has now been restored to grass. Cultivation is restricted to selected areas, and carried on under carefully controlled conditions (*H & R*, Unit 25). The Soviet experience in ploughing up the *Virgin Lands* of central Asia has been broadly similar. But greater care has been taken to restrict the blowing of the topsoil, by planting trees as shelter belts.

(iii) **Cold temperate interior climates.** This type of continental climate, sometimes described as *boreal*, only occurs in Alaska, Canada and the northern parts of Scandinavia and the Soviet Union. Summers are short and warm, winters long and very cold, with six or even more months below freezing. Annual temperature ranges are the largest in the world. The seasonal contrast is intensified by the great length of the sunny summer days (between 20 and 24 hours) and the corresponding short period of daylight in winter. The lowest temperature ever recorded under natural conditions outside the Antarctic ($-68\,^\circ$C) was experienced in this climatic region, at Verkhoyansk in Siberia (see graph on Fig. 11.16).

Rainfall is low, usually less than 500 mm, with a maximum in summer. The precipitation comes as fine, dry snow for half of the year or even more. It is light and powdery and so is easily blown by the wind, giving rise to blizzards: the snow is driven along, close to the ground, and it can overwhelm and bury people, vehicles and even houses.

The prevailing vegetation in these regions is coniferous forest or *taiga*. There are vast areas of forest—the most extensive on the face of the earth—made up of relatively few species, chiefly pine, spruce, fir and larch, with some deciduous birch. Conifers are well adapted to the physical conditions of the region, which can be described as biological drought; water is present most of the time but, since it is frozen, it is not in a form which trees can absorb. Accordingly the trees have a shallow root system which enables them to grow in a shallow soil and take full advantage of any melt water. Their needle-like

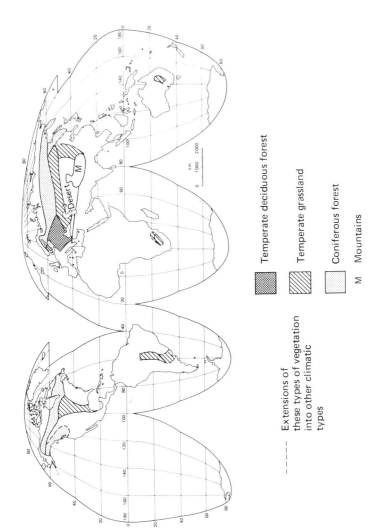

Fig. 11.17 Vegetation of the continental interiors

leavès transpire very little moisture and their thick bark protects the wood against the cold. They are tolerant of acid soils (Unit 12). The conical shape of most of these trees prevents branches being broken off.

These forests supply most the world's softwood, and lumbering is an important activity in the more accessible parts of the region. The industry is greatly assisted by the fact that large areas or *stands* occur of particular species (*H & R*, Unit 4). On their northern margins the coniferous forest thins out. The trees become stunted in growth and twisted by the wind, until they disappear on the borders of the Arctic.

11.5 Arctic and Polar Climates

(a) Arctic Climate

This climatic type is restricted to the extreme northern parts of the land masses in the northern hemisphere, where it occupies a vast area in North America, Asia and the whole of Greenland. Apart from the extreme coldness of the winters in these regions, they are remarkable mainly for the relative lengths of their daylight and darkness periods. In fact, inside the Arctic Circle, the length of the period of continuous daylight in summer and continuous darkness in winter increases towards the pole so that, at the northernmost extremities of the land, the sun remains above the horizon for anything up to four months in summer and below the horizon for the same length of time in winter (Section 1.3). In such climatic conditions it is hardly surprising that both settlement and vegetation are sparse, agriculture impossible and communications very difficult.

Summers are warm, with average temperatures between 5 and 10 °C, but they are very short. The length of daylight approaches 24 hours around midsummer, although the sun shines from a low elevation; plants can grow quickly under these conditions. But winters are long and severe, and there may be no daylight at all at midwinter. Average temperatures drop to −28 °C, and the frost penetrates the soil to such a depth that it does not entirely thaw out in the short summer. The result is the formation of *permafrost*, a permanently frozen sub-soil. The melted ice and snow produce a quagmire of varying depth above it in summer known as *muskeg*.

Precipitation is very low, generally no more than 250 mm a year. There may be a little light rain in summer but, as in the coniferous forest regions, most precipitation comes as a light and powdery snow. Blizzards are even more severe here than in the forest, because there are no trees to give protection from the wind.

North of the coniferous forest lies the tundra vegetation. The shortness of the growing season inhibits trees, and the vegetation consists mainly of mosses, lichens, low-growing bushes, dwarf alder and birch trees, and plants which flower brightly during the short, cool summer. In some areas the ground is carpeted with a mass of vividly coloured flowers, known as *bloom mats*. Their seeds lie inactive during the winter, germinate in spring and rapidly flower and seed in the short summer.

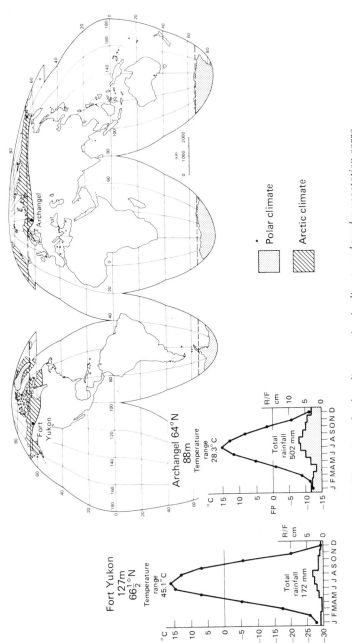

Fig. 11.18 Arctic and polar climates. Arctic climate and tundra vegetation correspond exactly, except for the extensions marked in Alaska and Scandinavia

(*b*) **Polar Climate**
In polar regions the temperature is below freezing for most if not all of the
year. There is thus a permanent snow cover which gives rise to ice caps over
the larger areas of land, such as Greenland and the Antarctic continent, where
the lowest temperatures on earth have been recorded. Several weather stations
were established during the International Geophysical Year (1957–8) in various parts of the Antarctic Continent. At Sovietskaya Base, about 1 100 km
from the South Pole, a temperature of $-86 \cdot 7\ °C$ was recorded.

In these regions there can be no plant growth and even in summer there is
very little melting.

11.6   Mountain Climates

All over the world mountains make their own climates. They always have
lower temperatures than nearby lowland and, on average, the temperature
drops at the rate of 1 °C for every 100 m of ascent. This can be clearly seen in
the climatic graph for the equatorial city of Quito, which lies at an altitude of
2 851 m (Fig. 11.20).

Up to a limit which varies with latitude—in the Swiss Alps it is about
2 000 m above sea-level—mountains are usually wetter than nearby lowlands,
although much depends on the relationship of the mountains to the prevailing
winds. Furthermore, there is less moisture and atmospheric dust in the air at
higher altitudes. The sun's rays are stronger, but mountains cast long
shadows. In many mountain valleys, especially those lying roughly from west
to east, one side receives abundant sunshine while the other lies in the shade,
except perhaps for à short time in summer. The result is a sharp climatic
contrast over a short distance, often reflected in the pattern of land use and
human settlement (Section 10.5).

Local winds are common in mountainous areas; we have already discussed
the föhn and chinook (Section 10.7). Some winds are localized to individual
valleys: heating during the day causes air to move up the valley but night-time
cooling causes the heavier air to move down the valley, and a temperature
inversion may occur.

Further Reading
Chandler, T. J.: *Modern Meteorology and Climatology.* Nelson (London,
1972).
Eyre, S. R.: *Vegetation and Soils.* Arnold (London, 1968).
Manley, G.: *Climate and the British Scene.* Fontana (London, 1970).
Riley, D. and Young, A.: *World Vegetation.* Cambridge University Press
(London, 1968).
Sparks, B. W.: *Geomorphology.* Longman (Harlow, 1970), Chapter 10.
Strahler, A. N.: *Physical Geography.* John Wiley (Chichester, 1969), Chapters
12–15.

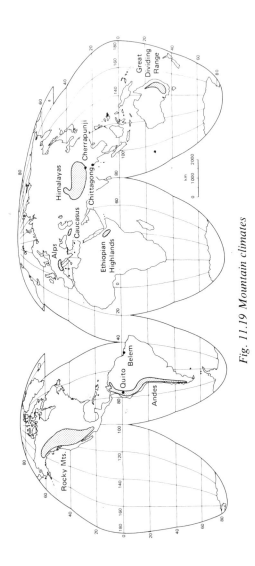

Fig. 11.19 Mountain climates

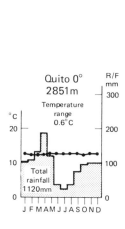

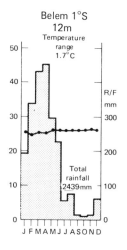

(a)

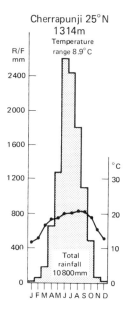

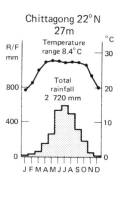

(b)

Fig. 11.20 (a) Compare the graphs of Quito and Belem (Fig. 11.19) for
evidence of the influence of relief on temperature
(b) Compare the graphs of Cherrapunji and Chittagong (Fig. 11.19) for
evidence of the influence of relief on rainfall

Questions

1. Explain the ways in which climate influences vegetation.
2. Explain the following:
   (*a*) the annual temperature range is small in equatorial climates;
   (*b*) 'night is the winter of the tropics';
   (*c*) the seasonal rainfall of the Sudan climate;
   (*d*) there is a winter maximum of rainfall in a Mediterranean climate;
   (*e*) why continental climates have a large annual range of temperature.
3. Describe the principal features of equatorial forest vegetation, and name *two* areas where it may be found.
4. Describe and explain the differences between tropical and temperate grassland. Name an area where each may be found.
5. Write an essay on *Monsoon Climates*.
6. Explain the differences between the climates of land masses in temperate latitudes on west coasts and those on east coasts.
7. What is xerophytic vegetation? Give examples found in three different climates.
8. Describe and explain the distribution and characteristics of coniferous forest vegetation.
9. Describe and explain the distinctive features of tundra vegetation.
10. What do you understand by the following: (*a*) baobab, (*b*) hygrophytic vegetation, (*c*) cork oak, (*d*) mangrove, (*e*) redwood, (*f*) chaparral?
11. Explain why the terms *winter* and *summer* may be used in temperate climates, whereas other expressions must be used to describe seasonal differences in tropical climates.
12. Compare (*a*) the temperature and (*b*) the rainfall of the graphs *A* and *B*. What climate does each represent? Name an area where each may be found.

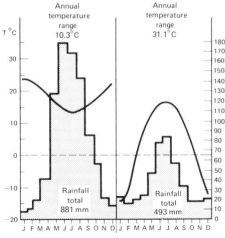

Unit Twelve

Soil and Its Conservation

Most of the land masses of the earth are covered by a thin surface of soil, which is about 450 mm deep, on average. Soil forms slowly over a period of thousands of years and, like minerals and fuels, it is one of man's most valuable natural resources. All food is derived from the soil, with the exception of sea-food, and it also provides many other necessities, such as timber and textile fibres. Yet man may destroy the soil cover in a few years by stripping the protective cover of vegetation, leaving the soil bare to be washed away by rainfall or blown away by the wind (Section 12.4).

12.1 The Soil and Its Constituents

The soil or *regolith* is made up of five essential constituents: rock and mineral particles, organic matter or humus derived from decomposing plant and animal materials, water, air and living organisms, including bacteria. The soil is likely to lack certain of the properties necessary for it to yield crops if any of these constituents are missing.

(a) Rock and Mineral Particles

Normally, rock and mineral particles result from the break-up of the parent rock which underlies the soil. Rock disintegrates when soil water and acids percolate into it; sometimes it is shattered by frost, and it may even be broken up by burrowing animals (Section 12.1(e)). Occasionally, however, the rock and mineral component may have been transported from a distance. For example, some soils develop on gravel beds or on alluvium which are themselves deposits, usually laid down by rivers in flood. Glaciation also spreads rock fragments over large areas in the form of boulder clay, outwash deposits and moraines (Section 6.4).

The mineral constituents of the soil are important in two respects: they determine the soil's texture, and also its chemical composition.

(i) **Soil texture** depends on the size of the grains which make it up. Coarse-grained or sandy soils, derived mainly from rocks such as sandstone or granite, contain a high proportion of quartz fragments which give the soil a gritty feel. There are usually large spaces between the grains of such a soil and these allow water to pass through easily. This soil, therefore, is well-drained—too well-drained in many instances, because often it does not hold enough water to grow crops. Fine-grained or clay soils, by contrast, are made up of very small particles which adhere to one another so closely and tightly that there are only minute spaces between them. Water quickly fills these spaces, and is held there by surface tension: this soil does not readily allow water to pass through it, and it is heavy and difficult to plough. But it is potentially fertile and can usually be made to yield good crops if it is artificially drained and well cared for. A medium-grained soil is usually a sandy clay or loam: it is intermediate between a light and a heavy soil. Loam is highly fertile, because it has the richness of mineral composition characteristic of clays, together with the lightness and the ease of ploughing which are features of sandy soils.

(ii) **Chemical composition.** The minerals which derive from the parent rock are also the principal determinants of the soil's chemical composition and quality. Quartz (sand) imparts an acid quality to soil, while calcium carbonate (lime) gives it an alkaline character. One of the most important measurements of soil quality is that of its acid–alkali ratio, expressed in terms of the *pH value*.

Table 12.1   The pH value of soil

pH value	4	5	6	7	8
Soil type	acid	ideal for agriculture		neutral	alkaline

It is relatively easy to determine the pH value of soil by chemical analysis, and it is used regularly to choose the most suitable fertilizer to add to a soil.

(*b*) **Humus**

Humus is a dark substance formed in the soil from the decay of animal and vegetable matter. It provides growing plants with most of the essential minerals they need—nitrogen, phosphorus, calcium, potassium—in a form which allows them to be readily absorbed by the roots of plants. Humus also contributes to the water-holding quality of light or sandy soils, and it assists percolation and drainage in a heavy soil. It is so vital to the fertility of the soil—and so readily removed, both by growing vegetation and by solution—that man adds it to the soil in a variety of forms. Animal manure, green manure (a crop grown in order to be ploughed in), compost, seaweed, even human excrement and the 'shoddy' waste from woollen mills are all added to the soil to make it more fertile.

The most fertile soils, such as chernozem (Section 12.2(*c*)), contain about 16 per cent humus, most of it derived from the decay of leaves and the roots of grasses. The contribution of humus to the soil is smaller on heathland and in pine woods, partly because such vegetation yields only a small amount of leaf material, and partly because these grow mainly in cool and moist areas, where the decay of organic matter is slower and there are fewer earthworms to rework the soil. The soil which results from bracken and pine needles is therefore acid and infertile, and usually belongs to a type known as podsol (Section 12.2(*a*)).

(c) Water

The amount of water that a soil can hold largely depends on its texture. As we have seen, a coarse-grained soil usually drains rapidly and retains little water for plant growth; a desert soil, for example, usually holds none at all, because of percolation and evaporation. A fine-grained soil holds a great deal of water, but it is relatively impermeable (that is, water lies on the ground after rain). The soil may become waterlogged, so that air is excluded, and this makes most plant growth impossible. There is also a scarcity of living organisms in very wet soils, as well as in very dry ones.

Water in the soil is responsible for two related processes, leaching and the formation of hardpans. Leaching occurs when percolating water removes the soluble elements and the humus from the surface layers of the soil and carries them downwards, beyond the reach of all plants except those with the deepest root systems. Minerals leached from the upper layers of the soil may be precipitated lower down to form a hardpan, an impervious layer, rich in iron compounds, which impedes drainage and may lead eventually to the waterlogging of the soil above it. A soil which has been extensively leached is known as a *pedalfer*, while one which has undergone only a small degree of leaching is a *pedocal*.

(d) Air

The balance between air and water within the soil is of the utmost importance. Air occupies the spaces between mineral particles not already filled with water. Without air certain chemical processes essential in maintaining soil fertility could not take place.

(e) Living Organisms

Organisms perform a valuable role. They burrow in the soil, opening up cavities by which air can enter. When they die their remains contribute to the humus content of the soil.

12.2 Soil Profiles

The scientific study of the soil, known as pedology, began in Russia early this century. It concentrated on the *profile of the soil*, which is the sequence of layers occurring in every soil, from the surface down to bedrock. The soil profile can be readily seen and examined at the edge of a quarry, a cliff top, a railway cutting or even a trench cut for laying pipes. The several layers in a profile are known as horizons and they are distinguished as follows:

A-horizon, close to the surface, from a few millimetres to a metre in thickness, and usually rich in humus.

B-horizon, a zone of leaching, at the base of which there may be a layer of hardpan.

C-horizon, the parent or bedrock.

Soil profiles differ greatly between different soils, because of variations in parent rock, natural vegetation and climate. The parent rock is normally the source of the rock and mineral particles, while the natural vegetation is responsible for most of the humus. But climate is the most important influence on soil formation and it largely determines the soil profile; its influence is so important, in fact, that there is a high measure of agreement between the distribution of the major soil types and that of the climatic regions we discussed in Unit 11. Soils which are closely associated with particular types of climate and natural vegetation are known as *zonal* soils. The most important of the zonal soils are podsol, brown earths, chernozem, latosol, gley soils and desert soils, and each occupies a large part of the earth's surface.

Table 12.2   An approximate correlation between the principal zonal soils and climate and vegetation types

Zonal soil type	Principal climatic types	Principal natural vegetation types
Podsol	Cold temperate interiors and some mountain climates	Coniferous forests (taiga), and temperate heathlands
Brown earth (brown forest soil)	Laurentian type, west coast maritime and damper parts of cool temperate interior	Temperate deciduous forests
Chernozem (black earth)	Drier parts of cool temperate interior	Temperate grasslands
Latosol (tropical red earth)	Tropical climates with heavy rainfall	Rain forests and wetter savannas
Gley soil	Arctic	Tundra
Desert soil	Arid climate or desert and semi-desert	Desert

(a) **Podsol**
Podsol is a Russian word meaning ash-coloured, and the name refers to the grey colour of the soil's surface layers. Podsols are highly leached, with strongly developed B-horizons. They are typical of a cool or cold moist climate in middle and high latitudes, and are found almost entirely in the northern hemisphere. Podsol has a pH value of 4, and is an acid soil. The needles and roots of coniferous trees and heathland vegetation decompose very slowly in these cool climates, so there is a scarcity of humus. There is also a scarcity of soil organisms to assist the decomposing process. Soluble materials near the surface are carried downwards and, as a general rule, redeposited near the base of the B-horizon to form a hardpan which restricts drainage.

(b) **Brown Earth or Brown Forest Soil**
Deciduous trees formerly covered most of the moister mid-latitude regions, especially in Europe, eastern North America and the Far East. The regular autumn leaf-fall contributes to the abundant supply of humus. The climate is warmer here than in the podsol regions, and soil organisms are more abun-

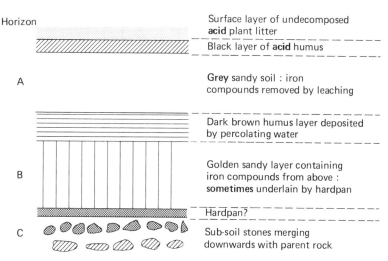

Horizon

Surface layer of undecomposed **acid** plant litter

Black layer of **acid** humus

A   Grey sandy soil : iron compounds removed by leaching

Dark brown humus layer deposited by percolating water

B   Golden sandy layer containing iron compounds from above : **sometimes** underlain by hardpan

Hardpan?

C   Sub-soil stones merging downwards with parent rock

Fig. 12.1 Podsol soil profile

dant and active. The degree of leaching varies with rainfall, but these soils are generally fertile.

In many areas, particularly in Europe, brown earths have been cultivated for so long that they have become almost man-made. They have been limed, manured, ploughed, fertilized and drained so frequently that their original character has been almost entirely destroyed. These soils are recognizable chiefly by their brown colour and the absence of clearly defined horizons.

(c) Chernozem or Black Earth

Chernozem is one of the most distinctive soils and again it is closely related to the climate. It is typical of the dry grasslands found in the interior of continental land masses, and it is best developed in the steppes of the Soviet Union, particularly the Ukraine, and in the North American prairies, where an abundance of humus is derived from the decaying leaves and roots of grass. The low rainfall and high rate of evaporation mean that there is little leaching, so the humus is concentrated near the surface, in the A-horizon.

The chernozem soils are dark in colour—hence their other name, black earth—and they cover vast areas of flat or gently rolling land. As we saw in Section 11.4, continental climates typically have hot summers, when maximum rainfall occurs, and cold winters. All these factors make the areas of chernozem soil ideal for wheat cultivation.

(d) Latosol or Tropical Red Earth

This is a very deeply coloured red, orange or yellow soil, typical of the hot, wet tropical lands. Heavy rainfall and high temperatures throughout the year contribute to the vigorous chemical weathering, even deep within the soil.

Horizon

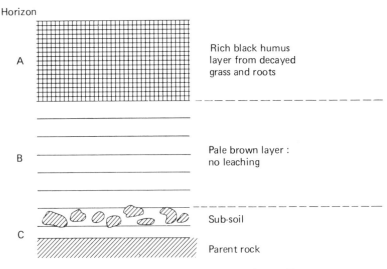

Fig. 12.2 Chernozem (black earth) profile

Rock disintegration and leaching sometimes extend to a depth of more than 15 m. All soluble materials are dissolved and removed until, in extreme cases, only insoluble iron and aluminium compounds are left in the surface layers, which gives them their bright and distinctive coloration.

Latosols are heavy, acid, porous and, because of the absence of humus, highly infertile. They are deep and relatively uniform with no distinctive horizons, although there may be a layer of hardpan, known as the laterite layer, at a depth which varies with the intensity of the rainfall and the amount of percolation and leaching. If the laterite layer occurs near the surface, the soil is liable to become waterlogged, thus restricting the growth of vegetation and making agriculture impossible. Latosols are some of the least fertile soils and, as a general rule, can only be cropped for a year or two before they have to be abandoned.

It is paradoxical that such poor soils should be found beneath vegetation as lush and rich as that of the equatorial rain forests (Section 11.3). The trees yield a continuous supply of plant litter which quickly decomposes and is absorbed by the shallow root system of the trees; they can thus go on growing throughout the year. If this cycle is broken by destroying the forest to plant crops, the supply of plant food left in the soil is rapidly used up after a year or two. Soil erosion sets in, because the heavy tropical rain can now beat directly on to the bare soil. This accelerates the process of leaching and, after a few years, the soil is useless.

(e) **Gley Soil**
About 4 per cent of the land surface of the earth—lying mainly in a belt across

the northern hemisphere—has tundra vegetation and an Arctic climate. There may be only four months in the year with an average temperature above freezing. This is usually too short a time for the sub-soil to thaw out, so it may remain permanently frozen (*permafrost*). The surface layers will thaw out but, on slopes, they may slide downhill under the influence of gravity (solifluction). In this badly drained, waterlogged horizon, oxidation is prevented because of the absence of air, and this gives the sticky, clay-like compounds a blue or blue-grey colour typical of gley soil. If solifluction takes place, the soil becomes a churned-up mess of blue mud and stones.

Vegetation growth is severely restricted by the long cold winter and by the permafrost. Humus only accumulates very slowly, because of the slow rate of decomposition of organic matter. Precipitation is generally so slight that there is little leaching and a series of horizons does not develop. Recent discoveries by soil scientists have revealed that gley soils also exist in the tropics, under conditions of bad drainage and waterlogging.

(f) Desert Soil
Low rainfall and sparse vegetation are the typical features of deserts. Leaching is absent because of the sparse rainfall and there is little or no humus. The soil consists mainly of variable depths of loose sand, and in these arid conditions it may also be highly saline, as a result of the evaporation of salty water being drawn to the surface by *capillary action* (the force that causes liquids to move upwards in permeable rocks, like water spreading through blotting paper). This leaves a thin white crust of salt, in which only restricted types of vegetation can grow. Such a soil is known as a *solonchak*.

12.3 Soil Fertility

Man began to cultivate the soil some 8–10 000 years ago, but it was a long time before he learned that plants remove certain of the soil's constituents in order to grow. If these compounds of calcium, nitrogen, phosphorus and potassium are not returned to the soil, the crop yield will slowly decrease as the soil becomes exhausted, until a point is reached when it is no longer worth the trouble of cultivation.

(a) Fallowing
In the Middle Ages, farmers tried to counter this loss by allowing the soil a period of rest. A shifting agriculture was used, in which a patch was ploughed and cultivated for a year or two and then left uncultivated for a period of several years to replenish its humus supplies. This is, in fact, still the practice in the primitive agricultural system known as ladang which is in use in parts of the tropics (*H & R*, Unit 3). In Europe, the system developed into one of two or three years of cultivation followed by a fallow year.

(b) Crop Rotations
In the eighteenth century, it was discovered that different crops take different

substances from the soil. It is possible to grow a succession of crops without detriment to the soil, whereas it would be impossible to repeat the same crop for an equivalent period. Crop rotations were devised to suit the properties of different soils. Most rotations included one or more grain crops, a root crop (such as potatoes, turnips or sugar-beet) and a leguminous crop (such as peas, beans or clover), which has the property of returning nitrogen to the soil through nodules developed in its root system. One of the most widely adopted of such systems is the Norfolk rotation, a four-year cycle consisting of wheat, a root crop, barley and a leguminous crop.

(c) Fertilizers

Fallowing was only abandoned completely when it became possible to add materials to the soil which compensated for those which had been removed by growing crops. Farmers learned to modify both the texture and the chemical quality of their soils, by adding sand to heavy soil to lighten it, and marl, a clay with a small lime content, to sandy soils to improve their water-holding properties. Manure, compost and seaweed can be added to poor and worn-out soils to improve their fertility. In China a system has evolved over a period of thousands of years by which everything which comes from the soil is ultimately returned to it in the form of vegetable and animal waste and even human excrement. Fertility has been maintained in some areas in this way for 4 000 years.

In the more 'advanced' societies today, chemical fertilizers are used in large quantities in order to maintain soil fertility and to increase crop-yields. It is usual to make a chemical analysis of the soil and to prepare a fertilizer that will make good its deficiencies. This is the only means by which a truly intensive agriculture can be maintained.

(d) 'Man-made' Soils

Soils which have been cultivated for a long time have ceased to be purely a product of Nature, and have become something of a human creation. As a result of manuring, marling, ploughing, cropping, draining and irrigating, they have become a product of man's careful and deliberate management. Parts of Flanders and East Anglia, where there were extensive areas of infertile sand, have been treated and tended for so many years that they now have man-made soils of high fertility.

12.4   Soil Erosion

Man has done much to keep soils fertile and to make poor soils productive, but there are large areas where thoughtless agriculture and poor soil management have combined to destroy in a few years soil which had taken thousands of years to form. This process is known as *soil erosion*, and it consists of the destruction of the soil—often right down to the C-horizon—by the normal agents of erosion.

Soil erosion can only take place when the soil has been laid bare for some reason. This usually happens when the natural vegetation is disturbed or removed in climatically marginal areas: vegetation binds and holds the soil together by means of its root system, and prevents rain falling on to bare soils. Thus if the grassland in semi-arid areas is ploughed up, the wind can get to the soil and blow it away in clouds of dust. If the grass or woodland cover is removed from steep slopes, heavy rainfall can form gullies which widen and spread until the soil has been washed away. Overgrazing, when animals crop the vegetation so closely that plants are destroyed, can have the same result. Excessive cultivation, or overcropping, leaves the soil depleted of humus and ready to be destroyed by wind or run-off.

(a) Wind Erosion

Wind erosion is severest in the flat grassland regions where rainfall is low, winters cold and winds frequently very strong. In the 1920s a growing demand for bread grains took wheat farming into the drier parts of Kansas, Oklahoma and Texas. The land had previously been short grass prairie, grazed by buffalo and hunted over by the Indians, and it should have been left under grass. But it was ploughed up and cultivated. Only a few crops could be taken before the

Fig. 12.3 Soil accumulation on a deserted homestead in Dallam County, Texas in 1937, after a dust storm. Drifts are over 1 m deep where soil has collected around the cart and in the weeds of the fence

wind stripped away the topsoil. This was how the *Dust Bowl* was formed (*H & R*, Unit 25).

The average rainfall in such areas may be adequate for agriculture, but the chief characteristic of this cool temperate interior type of climate is the highly unreliable nature of its rainfall, which in some years is far heavier than is necessary for cultivation, while in other years it is quite inadequate. The prospect of the fat years drew settlers into this area of North America, mostly 'homesteaders' who cultivated their farms on a family basis, and the epic story of the settlement and abandonment of parts of the High Plains in Oklahoma has been told by John Steinbeck in his book *The Grapes of Wrath*.

The area of the Dust Bowl should never have been cultivated, of course—at least by the methods employed in the 1930s. Parts of the area are now being used for crops again, but only after extensive precautions have been taken against wind erosion. Shelter belts—lines of trees planted across the direction of the predominant winds—greatly reduce the hazards. In certain areas subject to wind erosion, farmers plough the land in strips and leave belts of grassland between each.

Similar conditions may also be found on the dry south-eastern margin of the steppes in the Soviet Union. In the 1950s and 1960s these *Virgin Lands* were ploughed up to increase the supply of bread grains but soil erosion has been extensive, despite precautions to prevent it. Wind erosion has also become a serious problem in parts of Great Britain, notably in East Anglia, in the Fenland and on Salisbury Plain. All these areas have a fine soil and a flat or gently rolling topography across which strong winds can blow unobstructed.

(b) Water Erosion

Rainfall can also remove the soil, in areas which have been stripped of their natural cover of protective vegetation, either by sheet erosion or by gullying. In the former, rainwater washes the soil away from gentle slopes in a uniform layer. In the latter, the run-off becomes concentrated, and the resulting stream cuts a V-shaped gully which deepens until bedrock is reached.

Gullying is a typical development of the hills and mountains of Appalachia, in the USA (*H & R*, Unit 22). Before the coming of Europeans, this region was covered with hardwood forest. The tree roots held the soil together, while the heavy foliage protected the soil from the fierce and torrential summer rains. But the trees were uprooted by the early settlers, to be used for building and firing, and the exposed soil was quickly gullied by the rain. The soil which was lost from the mountain sides was washed into the valleys, where it not only choked the rivers, impeded navigation and led to flooding but also buried the soil and hindered agriculture in the valleys.

Anything that can focus or concentrate the run-off on a steep slope can give rise to a gully. Ruts made by the wheels of farm carts, tracks made by animals, furrows ploughed up and down a slope, even the drip of water from a barn gutter, can all initiate the process, which accelerates and is most difficult to stop. Gorge-like gullies, tens of metres deep, can form and merge into one another so that a system of gullies may cover many square kilometres.

Fig. 12.4 Land badly eroded by water in the Tennessee valley in the 1930s. (Notice the similarity between the gully which runs away from the bottom left-hand corner of the picture and the upper course of a river)

(c) Soil Erosion in the United States

The United States has become the scene of the most violent and destructive soil erosion of all time. This is largely because the North American continent, with almost untouched resources, was suddenly opened up by people used to the wetter conditions of Europe and utterly unaware of the fiercely destructive nature of the American climate. The result of their ignorance and their reck-lessness was that, by the 1930s, nearly 60 per cent of the total land capable of cultivation had been affected by soil erosion to a greater or lesser degree. Of this, 15 per cent had been rendered useless for agriculture because it had lost all its topsoil, and the agricultural value had been gravely impaired in the rest.

The gravity of the situation went unrecognized until the early 1930s, when dust from the fields of Kansas and Oklahoma had to be scraped from the dome of the Capitol Building in Washington over 2 000 km away. There was a series of very dry and windy years on the prairies in the 1930s, and dust clouds blanketed the eastern cities to an extent that even the legislators could not ignore. At the same time, the seriousness of gullying began to be understood, together with the danger which it presented to the health and livelihood of those who lived in the hilly regions of the south-east.

The Soil Conservation Service was formed in 1935 by the United States

Fig. 12.5 A gigantic gully in California, eroded along cow trails down a steep slope. Continued erosion on visible cow trails is apparent in the form of small gullies in the centre of the picture

Government. It was charged with the task of stopping these inroads on the country's soil resources and restoring the ravaged lands, as far as this was possible. The problems were tackled in a variety of ways. Gullying was reduced by building dams, made of whatever rough material was available, in order to check the flow of water. Steep hillsides were terraced and forest was re-established wherever possible to hold the soil. Farmers were persuaded to plough along the contours where land had to be cultivated, so that their furrows could not contribute to the formation of gullies.

Wind-breaks were planted in more open country which was subject to blowing. Fast-growing forms of vegetation, particularly the *kudzu* and *lespedeza*, introduced from Korea (ground-cover plants which spread quickly across a large area), were established on land which was particularly prone to erosion. Unploughed strips were left between strips of ploughed land, aligned across the direction of the wind. Crop rotation replaced the earlier practice of taking a crop every other year. Irrigation was adopted in areas close to the rivers which cross the prairies, and attempts were also made to change the texture of the soil by increasing its humus content.

One of the earliest areas to benefit from these new techniques was the

Fig. 12.6 Lush farmland in Wisconsin, patterned by contour ploughing. Farmers plough along *the hillside and not up and down the slope to prevent water flowing down the furrows*

drainage basin of the Tennessee river. This had long been a depressed area, the quality of farming was poor, farm incomes were low, and the reclamation of the whole region by the Tennessee Valley Authority (TVA) was part of President Roosevelt's New Deal in 1933. Soil erosion was checked, trees planted and hydro-electricity stations built along the rivers, which were cleared of silt and made navigable and free of flooding, as far as this was possible.

(*d*) Soil Erosion in the Rest of the World

The United States by no means has a monopoly of acute soil erosion, but it was that country's bold and successful policies that drew the attention of other parts of the world to the seriousness of the problem. Soil erosion is, in fact, a world problem. Overgrazing on the hills of some Mediterranean lands has slowly destroyed the vegetation cover, and the soil has been washed down the slopes. The shifting cultivation of many tropical regions also tends to leave the soil bare of vegetation and exposed to erosion by the torrential tropical rains. In recent years this has become more serious, as increasing population and a growing demand for agricultural products has led to a shorter fallow period and more frequent cultivation. In the savanna regions grass is commonly burned at the end of the dry season in order to encourage the growth of new grass. What happens all too often is that the soil is eroded before the new grass has had a chance to grow, and the neighbouring desert takes over.

Many other careless or thoughtless agricultural practices result in a poor, easily eroded soil. In the highlands of Ethiopia, nomadic pastoralists are destroying the natural plant cover by overgrazing and trampling the soil. In India the relentless felling of trees and the use of dung as fuel instead of fertilizer is having the same disastrous effect on the soil, and the clean weeding of soil between the rows of coffee trees in Brazil is causing its erosion by the torrential tropical rains. In the Soviet Union the rash experiment of cultivating the dry margin of the steppe continues, despite the American experience in the 1930s, and it is reaping its predictable reward of poor harvests and a wasted land.

Further Reading
Briggs, E. M.: *World Soils.* Cambridge University Press (London, 1970).
Bunting, B. T.: *The Geography of Soil.* Hutchinson (London, 1967).

Fig. 12.7 Successful reclamation in North Carolina. A few years before this picture was taken both fields were equally badly gullied. The owner of the field on the left co-operated with the TVA, and by the use of the correct seed and fertilizer the land was improved and livestock production made possible

Jacks, G. V. and Whyte, R. O.: *The Rape of the Earth*. Faber (London, 1939).
Strahler, A. N.: *Physical Geography*. John Wiley (Chichester, 1969), Chapters 16, 17.
Vogt, W.: *Road to Survival*. Gollancz (London, 1949).
Wayte, M. E.: *Mining Soil*. Chatto & Windus (London, 1963).
The Precious Soil. Marshall Cavendish Learning System (London, 1969).

Questions

1. To what extent is parent rock important in the composition of a soil?
2. Describe and explain podsol, with the aid of a soil profile.
3. Describe the conditions under which chernozem forms. Explain why it is fertile, with the aid of a soil profile.
4. What do you understand by these terms: (*a*) humus, (*b*) pH value, (*c*) loam, (*d*) leaching, (*e*) soil horizon?
5. Describe the methods which man has devised to improve soil
6. Write an essay on *Soil Erosion*.
7. Describe the methods used to counteract soil erosion.

Unit Thirteen
Map Reading and Interpretation

.

Maps can be a source of great pleasure and satisfaction. A train journey is more interesting if you can study the view from the window in conjunction with a map. You will appreciate the countryside much more if you are prepared to explore it on foot, using a map so that you do not lose your way. A knowledge of map reading is also vital in several sports and hobbies such as orienteering, rally driving, cycling, hiking and camping. Your ability to understand maps will be increased greatly if you have a map of your local area and several maps of other areas, and use them regularly. The local map is for *map reading*, which is using the map in relation to the land surface it represents. The other maps may be used for *map interpretation*: you can work out what you think the countryside will look like by studying them. In fact, if you ever visit any other part of Britain, it is interesting to study a map of the area beforehand to work out what you expect to see and, when you get there, compare your deductions with the actual landscape.

A map is the aerial representation of a piece of countryside. It will not, however, be exactly identical to the ground it depicts because houses, roads and factories may have been built in the time between the survey of the area and publication of the map. No map is ever completely up to date for this reason. By far the best maps of Britain are those published by the Ordnance Survey (OS), covering the whole of the country. They give great detail of both natural landscape and man's activities. The OS maps most frequently used by geographers are

(*a*) 1 : 50 000, at a scale of 2 cm to 1 km, and

(*b*) 1 : 25 000, at a scale of 4 cm to 1 km

and we shall be chiefly concerned with these maps in this Unit.

In the following Sections we shall be looking at map reading and map interpretation with two objects in mind. First, we shall cover the necessary mapwork required by the O-level syllabus. Second, we hope that those readers who study maps for interest and pleasure will discover ways of increasing their appreciation of them.

13.1 Setting the Map

It is excellent map reading practice to take an OS map into the countryside and study the map and landscape together. When you do this it is advisable to start by setting the map, a process sometimes known as *orientation*. This means setting out the map so that north on the map corresponds to north on the ground. North is at the top on all OS maps, and if you have any difficulty working out the direction of north on the ground, there are three ways which will help you to find it.

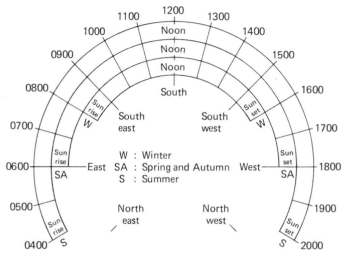

Fig. 13.1 The direction of the sun at different times and seasons

In the first place you can work out north from the position of the sun. The sun rises in the east and moves through south—where it is at midday in the northern hemisphere—to set in the west. Fig. 13.1 shows the relationship between the direction of the sun and the time of day. Secondly, you can use

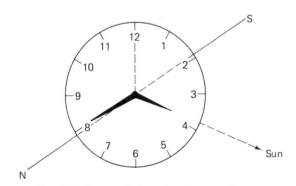

Fig. 13.2 How to find north with a watch

your watch to discover north. If you point the hour hand at the sun and bisect the angle between the hour hand and the figure 12, as shown in Fig. 13.2, the bisector is a north-to-south line. Third, you can, of course, use a compass to find out the direction of north on the ground, by studying the direction in which the compass needle points.

There is a diagram showing three different north directions in the margin of every OS map. Fig. 13.3 shows these. True north is the direction from the map area to the North Pole; magnetic north is the direction shown by a compass needle; grid north is a direction which is shown by north–south grid lines on the map (Section 13.3).

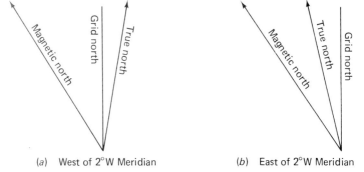

(a)   West of 2°W Meridian   (b)   East of 2°W Meridian

Fig. 13.3 The three north directions. True north and grid north coincide along the 2°W meridian. (Longitude is marked along the north and south margins of OS maps)

13.2   The Scale of a Map

The scale of a map is the proportion between a distance measured on the map and the corresponding distance on the ground. Thus, if the scale of a map is 2 cm to 1 km, and the distance between two points on the map is 2 cm, the actual distance between them will be 1 km. All maps must bear some indication of scale so that distances can be calculated easily.

(a) Scale on OS Maps
Scales are shown in the margin of OS maps in three ways.

(i) **Statement.** The scale is *stated*, relating a map distance to its equivalent ground distance, for example, '2 cm to 1 km'.

(ii) **Representative fraction (RF).** This is a mathematical way of expressing scale as a direct proportion between map and ground. 1 : 50 000 means that 1 cm on the map is equivalent to 50 000 cm on the ground. (By simple conversion we can convert this ground distance to 500 m, which is 0·5 km.) Thus if 1 cm is equivalent to 0·5 km, 2 cm is equivalent to 1 km. An RF of 1 : 25 000 means a scale of 4 cm to 1 km.

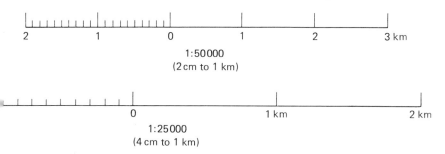

Fig. 13.4 Examples of line scales. These should be used for the measurements of distance required in the map-reading exercises, pages 260–77.

(iii) **Line (linear) scale.** This is a line divided up into map units, such as centimetres, but labelled in ground units, such as kilometres. As we shall see in Section 13.5, the main use of this scale is to measure distances on the map.

(*b*) Conventional Signs

A map's scale determines how much detail can be shown on it. An atlas map with a scale of 1 : 25 000 000 (1 cm to 250 km) will show a large town as a mere dot, but an OS map of 1 : 2 500 (1 cm to 25 m) can show details of streets and even individual houses and gardens. A large scale map, such as 1 : 2 500, on which all the features may be shown exactly to scale, is called a *plan*. Such detail is not possible on the smaller scale maps with which we are mainly concerned in this Unit. Much information has to be omitted and those features which are shown, such as roads, railways and buildings, are exaggerated and are indicated by symbols or *conventional signs*. The full range of signs for 1 : 50 000 maps, and those for 1 : 25 000 maps appear on pages 258–9 and 268.

13.3   The National Grid

A simple, precise method of locating points is used on OS maps, known as the *National Grid*. There are two sets of numbered parallel lines at right angles to each other on every OS map, and these are part of the National Grid which covers the whole of Britain. The main purpose of the Grid is to enable any point on the map to be given a *Grid Reference* (GR), which is accurate to 100 m on the ground. Fig. 13.5 shows the network of 100 km squares for the whole of Great Britain, each with its reference letters. On larger scale OS maps, further grid lines are drawn within each of these 100 km squares at 1 km intervals, and they are numbered from 00, 01, 02 . . . to 97, 98, 99, along all four margins of the map.

The part of the National Grid which is shown on any OS map sheet consists of two sets of these parallel lines at 1 km intervals. The lines running from north to south and labelled with numbers on the north and south margins of the map are called *eastings*, and those drawn from east to west, labelled with numbers along the east and west margins of the map are called *northings*.

These may be used in three ways. In the first place, they enable you to work out a six-figure reference for any point on the map. Second, and conversely,

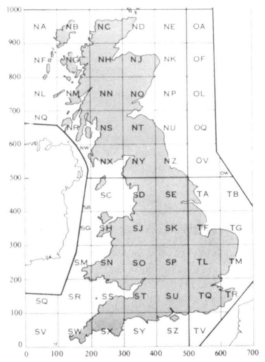

Fig. 13.5 100 kilometre squares of the National Grid

given a six-figure reference, you can work out the place's position on a map. Third, by using a four-figure reference, you can indicate a whole grid square.

(a) Working Out a Six-figure GR

As an example we shall work out the GR of point A on the set of grid lines in Fig. 13.6.

(i) Select the two lines which make up the south-western corner of the square containing point A and write down the eastings and then the northings numbers of these lines, that is, 33 65.

(ii) Within this square, estimate how many tenths of a km point A lies eastward of the 33 line. This is x on Fig. 13.6, and it is $\frac{8}{10}$, so write 8 after the 33.

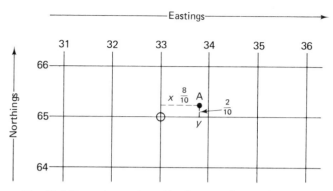

Fig. 13.6 To work out the grid reference of point A: 338652

(iii) Repeat this procedure northward from the 65 line; this is y on Fig. 13.6, and it is $\frac{2}{10}$ so write 2 after the 65. This completes the six-figure reference, which is thus 338652.

Any six-figure GR may be worked out in any 100 km square in this way, because every 100 km square has an identical set of eastings and northings lines, labelled from 00 to 99. It is possible to make a GR unique (that is, the only one of its kind) by writing the letters of the appropriate 100 km square before the six-figure reference (Fig. 13.5). The Youth Hostel in Bridport is at 464927 in square SY, so its unique GR is SY 464927. Details of the appropriate 100 km squares are given in the map margin on every OS map.

(b) Locating a Point from its Six-figure GR

We now know that any six-figure GR really consists of two sets of figures—762038 means that 762 is an eastings figure and 038 a northings figure—and that each of these figures means something on the map. Locating a point from its six-figure GR is really the reverse of working out a GR.

If we want to locate point 762038 on Fig. 13.7, we merely find the intersection of easting 76 and northing 03, which together form the south-west corner

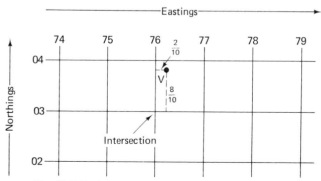

Fig. 13.7 To locate grid reference 762038 at point V

of the required square. Then, inside this square, go $\frac{2}{10}$ east from 76 and $\frac{8}{10}$ north from 03, and this gives us point V.

(c) Indicating a Grid Square
When a large feature such as a wood, lake or hill slope has to be indicated on a map, it is easier to give just the four-figure or *square* reference. This is simply the numbers of the two lines which form the south-west corner of the square in which the feature lies.

13.4   Measurement of Bearing

The relative positions of any two points on the map may be indicated in one of two ways.

(a) Cardinal Point Method
The direction between any two points on the map may be shown by using the main or cardinal points of the compass in relation to grid north.

(b) Whole Circle Bearing
A more accurate measurement may be obtained by using a protractor to find the clockwise angle from grid north between any two points on the map. Such a bearing may be of any size between 0° and 360°, as shown on Fig. 13.9.

13.5   Measurement of Distance

You should always express a distance measured on an OS map in ground units, such as metres or kilometres, using a line scale to do the calculation (Section 13.2). The simplest, quickest and most accurate method of measuring distance on OS maps is to use the straight edge of a piece of paper and a sharp pencil, whether you are measuring distances between two points on a straight line or along a road, railway, stream or footpath which is not straight.

(a) Straight Line Distance
The best way to measure the distance between the two churches shown on Fig. 13.11 is described below.

(i) Place the straight edge of a piece of paper on the map so that it is lined up between the two churches.

(ii) Mark the location of the two churches on the paper as A and B.

(iii) Transfer the paper to the appropriate line scale and measure the distance by placing mark A at zero on the line scale. Mark B will lie somewhere between 4 and 5 km (Fig. 13.11).

(iv) To work out the exact distance, move B back to the 4 km mark so that A moves the same amount to the left, where it may be read directly from the divided unit at the left end of the line scale. In this case, the distance is 4·4 km.

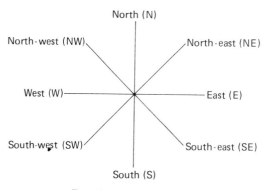

Fig. 13.8 Cardinal points

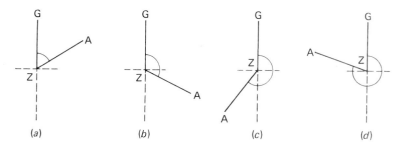

Fig. 13.9 Whole circle bearings. The grid bearing from Z to point A in each diagram is: (a) A = 60°, (b) A = 115°, (c) A = 220°, (d) A = 290°

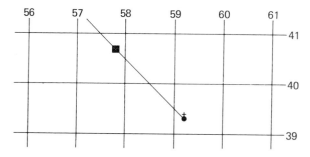

Fig. 13.10 Measure the bearing from the church at 592393 to the building at 578407 (314°)

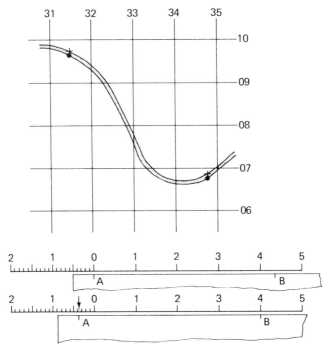

Fig. 13.11 Measurement of straight line distance and use of the line scale

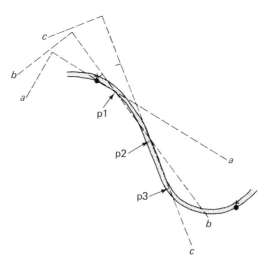

Fig. 13.12 Measurement of the distance along a road. a–a, b–b, c–c are successive positions of the paper. Points p1, p2, p3 are successive positions at which the paper is pivoted

(*b*) **Distance along a Road, Railway, Stream or Footpath**

The procedure is more complex if we measure the distance between the two churches in Fig. 13.11 along the road.

(i) Place the edge of the piece of paper against the church at A and mark its position. Arrange the paper so that its edge runs along the road, until the road bends away from the paper (Fig. 13.12).

(ii) Place the pencil point firmly at the point where the road and paper separate. Pivot the paper until its edge is once again along the road for a short distance.

(iii) Continue this procedure until you reach the church at B where you mark the paper again.

(iv) The distance along the road is now set out along the edge of the paper as a straight line distance between the two marks. You can now measure it along the line scale in the same way that you did with Fig. 13.11.

13.6 Relief on OS Maps

Relief means the shape of the land surface. Portrayal of this third dimension on a flat sheet of paper has given map makers great problems for centuries. If old or antique maps showed relief at all, it was drawn with the hills in profile, as if they were being viewed from the side.

(*a*) **Ways of Showing Relief**

(i) **Hachures.** Early OS maps used hachures, which are tadpole-like lines with the pointed end always indicating the downhill direction. These were used to give a visual impression of relief, but they were far from satisfactory. In the 1840s, *contours* were introduced on OS maps and they are still the best way of depicting relief. Hachures are still used for certain conventional signs, however, particularly when a feature is too small to be shown by contours but large enough to merit being shown on the map. Look at some of the features shown on the OS maps in the book, such as tumuli (Map 7, 964823) cuttings and embankments (Map 1, 1909, Map 3, 7956 and 8057) and cliffs (Map 2, 8680), and you will see that they still incorporate hachures.

(ii) **Contours.** A contour is a line drawn on a map joining all points which are the same height above mean or average sea-level (MSL). Contours are drawn at regular *vertical intervals* (VI) on each map scale (Table 13.1), and the vertical height above MSL is written on each contour. These height labels are always printed in a gap in the contour line so that there is no doubt as to which label refers to which contour. At certain intervals contours are drawn thicker than the rest, to enable you to work out heights more easily.

The two map scales with which we are mainly concerned in this Unit, 1 : 50 000 and 1 : 25 000, have their contours drawn as shown in Table 13.1.

On 1 : 50 000 maps you may be confused by the fact that the vertical interval does not seem to be regular. The *actual* vertical interval is 15·24 m, the

Table 13.1　Contour details

Scale	Vertical interval	Thicker every
1 : 50 000	15·24 m, but labelled to the nearest metre*	5th contour
1 : 25 000	25 feet	100 feet
1 : 63 360 (one inch to one mile)	50 feet	250 feet

* See Table 13.2.

metric equivalent of 50 feet, but contours are labelled to the nearest metre. Most intervals are 15 m, but some are 16 m. Table 13.2 gives all the contour heights you are likely to find on any map of Britain; the heights of the thicker contours are printed in italics. With this table you will also be able to work out contour heights more easily when you are dealing with gradients (Section 13.7) and section drawing (Section 13.8).

Table 13.2　Contour heights on 1 : 50 000 maps (in metres)*

15	411	808	1 204
30	427	823	*1 219*
46	442	*838*	1 234
61	*457*	853	1 250
76	472	869	1 265
91	488	884	1 280
107	503	899	*1 295*
122	518	*914*	1 311
137	*533*	930	1 326
152	549	945	
168	564	960	
183	579	975	
198	594	*991*	
213	*610*	1 006	
229	625	1 021	
244	640	1 036	
259	655	1 052	
274	671	*1 067*	
290	686	1 082	
305	701	1 097	
320	716	1 113	
335	732	1 128	
351	747	*1 143*	
366	*762*	1 158	
381	777	1 173	
396	792	1 189	

* Thicker contours are printed in italics.

Contours alone cannot give all the necessary information about the height of the land surface above sea-level. The contour pattern can tell you the general shape of the land surface, but the real height of any point which is not on a contour must be shown in some other way. Spot heights, triangulation stations and bench marks are the usual way of showing this, on OS maps.

(iii) **Spot heights** are marked on hills to indicate the exact height and location of the hill top. They are also marked along roads to show the rises and dips which contours are unable to show. In areas of very flat land, such as the English Fens or the Somerset Levels, the almost total absence of contours is compensated for by more frequent spot heights. The symbol for a spot height is shown on page 258.

(iv) **Triangulation stations** show the height and location of a summit. They differ from spot heights in that they actually exist on the ground in the form of a triangulation pillar, as on Map 4, Ingleborough Hill, 742746.

(v) **Bench marks** are either arrowhead-like marks, engraved in stone on buildings, walls or gate posts, or rectangular bronze plates set into walls. They may be found in towns and in the country. Their location is marked on 1 : 25 000 maps (see page 268) but their height is not given. The height of a bench mark above MSL is given on 1 : 10 560 or six inch to one mile maps.

(*b*) **Contour Patterns**
Contours are not, of course, marked on the ground, but there is a direct relationship between the contour pattern on a map and the land surface which that pattern represents. (If you look at a landscape and imagine how the contours would appear over it, your understanding of landforms on a map will be greatly increased.)

The contour pattern indicates the shape of the land surface, and there are certain landforms which are recognizable by their 'standard pattern' on a map. These are so vital to a thorough understanding of relief on maps that we show them in Fig. 13.13. Although they are shown separately here, each one forms only part of the overall contour pattern on an OS map.

The distance between the contours may vary in every one of the contour patterns. The spacing of the contours shows the steepness of the land surface so that, quite simply, the closer the contours are, the steeper the slope.

(*c*) **To Divide a Map into Relief Areas**
There may be a considerable variety of relief within a small area on any map. Once you can interpret contours, you will find it helpful to draw sketch maps at a smaller scale than that of the OS map, to show areas of different relief. (When you draw a sketch map at a reduced scale, remember that when the scale is reduced in a certain proportion, the map area is reduced by the *square* of that proportion. Thus, if the map scale is *halved* the map area is reduced to a *quarter* of its original size.) A map of relief areas should be drawn as simply

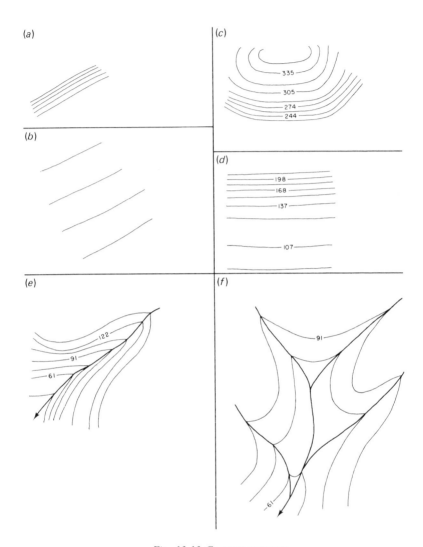

Fig. 13.13 Contour patterns
(a) *Steep slope (e.g. Map 1, 223110)*
(b) *Gentle slope (e.g. Map 4, 7274)*
(c) *Convex slope, steepest at the base (e.g. Map 4, 742745–738750)*
(d) *Concave slope, steepest at the top (e.g. Map 1, 2211)*
(e) *Valley—**V**-shaped contours pointing to higher ground, and the spacing of the contours determines the shape of the valley (e.g. Map 2 8282–8384)*
(f) *A set of connected valleys on a gentle slope*

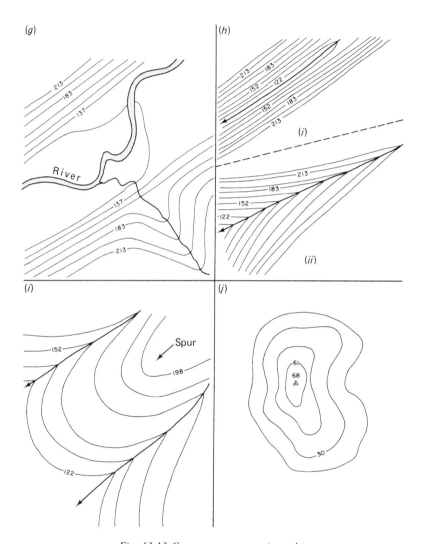

Fig. 13.13 Contour patterns—(contd.)
(g) U-*shaped glacial valley with hanging valley on south side*
(h) *Gorge (canyon) (i) with steep sides but gently sloping floor, (ii) with steep
sides and steeply sloping floor*
(i) *Spur—* V *shaped or rounded contours pointing to* lower ground *(e.g. Map 8,
4315, 4212)*
(j) *Isolated hill or knoll (e.g. Map 5, 630146)*

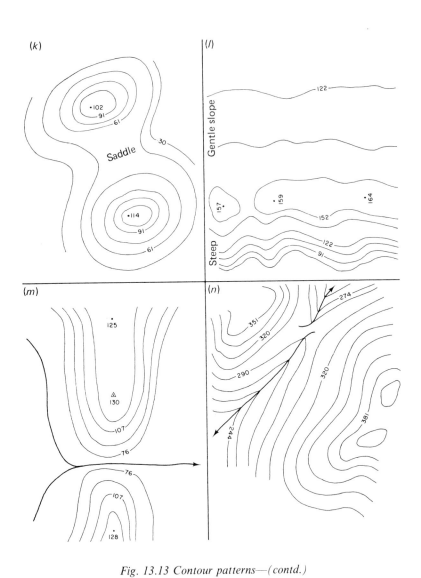

Fig. 13.13 Contour patterns—(contd.)
(k) *Saddle or col (e.g. Map 8, 4314)*
(l) *Escarpment or cuesta*
(m) *Ridge with a gap (e.g. Map 7, 950824–980820)*
(n) *Pass*

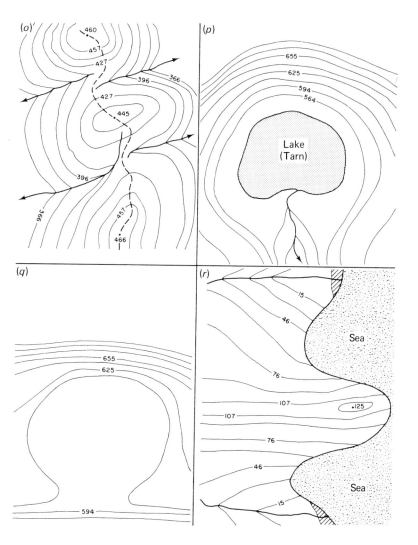

Fig. 13.13 Contour patterns—(contd.)
(o) *Watershed or water divide*
(p) *Corrie, cwm or cirque (e.g. Map 8, 4410)*
(q) *Corrie without a tarn (e.g. Map 8, 444122)*
(r) *A cliff coast (e.g. Map 2, 815801, 844801, 8680)*

and clearly as possible. You should not try to reproduce every contour line but, with bold, clear lines, draw and label only those contours which separate the areas of different relief from each other. Fig. 13.14 shows such a reduced scale sketch map for Map 1, page 262.

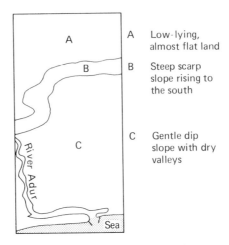

A   Low-lying, almost flat land

B   Steep scarp slope rising to the south

C   Gentle dip slope with dry valleys

Fig. 13.14 Reduced scale sketch map of Map 1 on page 262

13.7   Gradient

Gradient means steepness, and it is expressed as a mathematical ratio, such as 1 : 5. On 1 : 50 000 maps there are two conventional signs which express gradient. One shows those roads which slope at gradients of between 1 : 5 and 1 : 7 and the other shows those steeper than 1 : 5.

Calculating a gradient from information on a map is easier if you understand exactly what is meant by gradient. With a gradient of 1 : 5, there is a vertical rise of one unit for every five horizontal units; a gradient of 1 : 8 has eight horizontal units for every one vertical unit, so it is not as steep as 1 : 5.

We use the formula

$$\text{Gradient} = \frac{\text{Difference in height}}{\text{Horizontal distance}}$$

to calculate the gradient between two points on a map. *Difference in height* and *horizontal distance* may be calculated from information you will find on the map. Both measurements will be in metres on 1 : 50 000 maps, but on 1 : 25 000 maps and 1 : 63 360 maps you should remember to convert the horizontal distance from yards to feet so that it is in the same unit as the difference in height, which is calculated from the contours.

As an example, we shall calculate the gradient between points A and B in Fig. 13.15. It becomes easier if you set out all known facts on a triangle.

(i) Calculate the heights of A and B from the map and put these heights on the triangle in the correct positions. As AC represents the horizontal, the height of C is the same as that of A.

(ii) The difference in height between the two points (BC) may be worked out from this information, by subtraction.

(iii) The horizontal distance between A and B on the map is simply the straight line distance between them (Section 13.5). This is represented on the

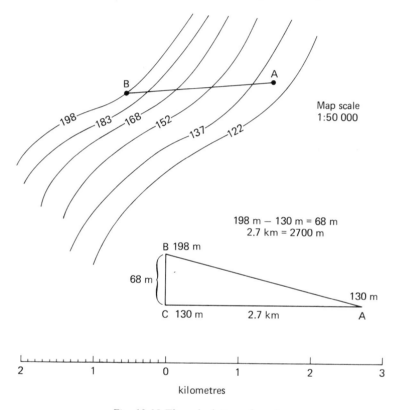

Fig. 13.15 The calculation of gradient:

$$G = \frac{68}{2700} = \frac{1}{39} = 1 : 39$$

triangle by AC, because all distances measured on a map are horizontal distances and do not take into account the slope of the surface. (If you wish to calculate a gradient between two points on a road or stream which is not straight, the distance should be measured as in Section 13.5.)

(iv) The gradient can now be calculated to the nearest whole number, using the formula given above, by dividing the numerator (the top of the formula) into the denominator (the bottom of the formula).

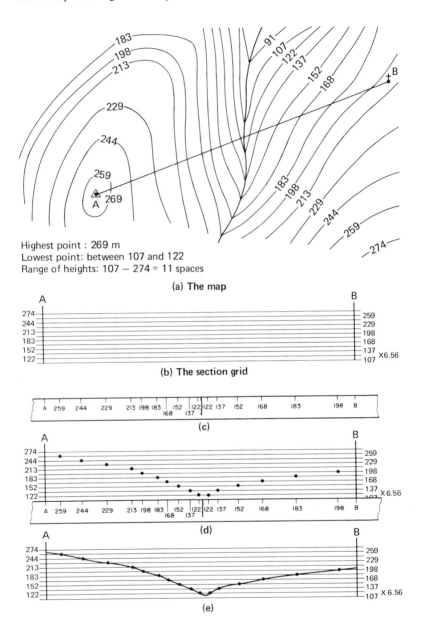

Highest point : 269 m
Lowest point: between 107 and 122
Range of heights: 107 − 274 = 11 spaces

(a) The map

(b) The section grid

(c)

(d)

(e)

Fig. 13.16 Section drawing

13.8   Drawing a Cross-section

The shape of the land surface between any two points on an OS map may be drawn to scale by means of a cross-section. A section must have its vertical (upwards) scale drawn much larger than its horizontal scale and a simple example will explain the reason for this. The horizontal scale of a section is normally the same as that of the map from which it is being drawn. This means that on 1 : 50 000 maps 10 mm on the section is equivalent to 500 m on the ground. If the difference between the highest and lowest points on the section is 250 m, the whole relief range, including sixteen different contour heights, has to be shown on the section in a band only 5 mm wide. This is so obviously impossible that the vertical scale must be exaggerated, but if the degree of exaggeration is too big, gently rolling hills will appear on the section as steep mountains. An ideal vertical scale is 2 mm to the vertical interval of the map. If you look at Table 13.1 you will see this means 2 mm to 15·24 m on 1 : 50 000 maps, and 2 mm to 25 feet on 1 : 25 000 maps.

As an example we shall draw a cross-section between A and B on the contour map shown on Fig. 13.16, following the step-by-step procedure outlined below.

(i) Mark out the distance AB horizontally on a piece of paper and draw a line at right angles at each end.

(ii) Study line AB closely on the map to find the heights of the highest and lowest points along it. The highest point on Fig. 13.16 is 269 m while the lowest point is between 107 m and 122 m.

(iii) Go to the contour *above* the highest point (274 m here) and the contour *below* the lowest point (107 m here). (It is not usually necessary to go down to sea-level on every section.) Table 13.2 shows that there are eleven contours between 107 m and 274 m. Mark eleven points, each 2 mm apart, along both of the perpendicular lines on Fig. 13.16, and draw pencil lines lightly between equivalent points. Label each horizontal line with its correct contour height to give a network known as the *section grid* (Fig. 13.16(*b*)).

(iv) Place the edge of another piece of paper along the line AB on the map. Mark A, B and the position and height of every contour which crosses the line AB carefully on it. If you try this on Fig. 13.16 the result should look like Fig. 13.16(*c*).

(v) Place this piece of paper along the base line of the section grid so that the As and Bs coincide. Put a small dot vertically above each contour mark on the appropriate horizontal line on the section grid (Fig. 13.16(*d*)).

(vi) Join up the dots carefully to produce a cross-section between A and B as shown in Fig. 13.16(*e*).

13.9   Rock Types on OS Maps

Geological maps are published for the whole of Britain by the OS, and these give great detail of the rock types which outcrop on the land surface. But it is possible to work out some rock types from normal OS maps by applying what you have learned in earlier Units. The rocks which can be identified most easily from OS maps are chalk, clay and limestone (Section 3.2).

(a) **Chalk** (see Map 1)

Chalk gives rise to rolling country, and hills composed of this rock frequently form an escarpment or cuesta (Map 1, page 262). There is a distinct absence of surface drainage, and dry valleys are plentiful. If there is surface water, it is likely to be an exotic stream, that is, one which rises outside the chalk area and flows across it on a layer of its own alluvium. Villages with names containing the word *winterbourne* usually lie on chalk.

(b) **Clay** (see Map 1)

Low-lying, open country is normally associated with clay. Surface drainage is abundant on this impervious rock, and much of it may be artificial, in the form of man-made drainage ditches. These can be distinguished from natural drainage by the straightness of their streams which, together, may form a rectangular pattern (Map 5, 6314). The contrasts between clay and chalk become even more apparent when, as often happens, these rocks are found next to each other to form scarp and vale country (Fig. 3.10).

(c) **Limestone** (see Map 4)

Carboniferous limestone is a hard rock, forming high ground with steep outcrops and rocky inland cliffs known as crags or scars. The unusual drainage features include disappearing streams: the OS map does not, of course, show underground drainage but swallow holes or pot-holes indicate where streams go or, at some time in the past have gone, underground. Caves are common and streams flow out of some of them. Any flat rock surfaces may consist of limestone pavement with clints and grykes (Fig. 3.7).

Many other landscape features which we covered in Units 3–8 may be found on OS maps, in addition to the various rock types we have just discussed. The map extracts in this book have been specially chosen to show the association of landscape and map features. Map interpretation will become a fascinating pastime if you can look at an OS map and try to recognize and name the landforms we have described in earlier Units.

13.10 Settlements on OS maps

Both 1 : 50 000 and 1 : 25 000 OS maps show details of man's activities, including his settlements, roads, railways, agriculture and industry. Much archaeological and historical information is also given on these maps.

(a) **Antiquities**

The features known collectively as antiquities on the conventional sign panel are printed in two styles (page 259). All Roman features are shown in an upright Roman script (Map 3, 8257) and these include Roman roads (Map 8, 4515), villas, camps and the names of settlements. Other antiquities are shown in Old English script. There are many of these but the most common are burial chambers, burial mounds such as tumuli (Map 8, 469130 and Map 2, 8382) and barrows (Map 2, 864817), field systems (Map 1, 2308 and 2409), cultivation terraces (Map 1, 2009), strip lynchets (a form of agricultural terrace), stone circles, hill forts (Map 4, 741746), Motte and Bailey (Map 1, 2311), moat (Map 3, 790632) and earthworks or dykes (Map 2, 824802 to 847802).

In addition, there are many antiquities with local names, such as Wool Bridge (Map 2, 844872), Lulworth Castle (Map 2, 855822), Civil War Fort (Map 3, 7856) and Morton's House (Map 7, 963820). All this information gives us a good idea of the areas where man has lived in the past. But OS maps give even greater detail of the size, layout, shape and distribution of present-day settlements.

(b) Settlement Size
You may find it difficult to deduce the size of a settlement from a map, and may not know whether to call it a hamlet, village or market town. There is a simple solution: look at the appearance of several settlements of different sizes that you know, for example in your home area, on the local map sheet, and then use this information for comparison with settlements on other map sheets. By this means you will soon be able to use such terms as hamlet, village, small market town, large town and city accurately.

(c) Layout
Any settlement may have at least two distinct parts. The older core is usually central, with at least one church and sometimes a cathedral, castle or antiquity of some kind, often with a local name, the town hall and a jumbled layout of narrow streets. There are more modern areas around the core; geometrical street layouts represent housing and industrial estates, built over the last 100 years. The majority of large towns can be divided into a number of *functional* areas, each dominated by a particular activity. The Cardiff map extract (Map 6, page 274) clearly shows such districts as the shopping and business centre, an administrative area, a factory area, the docks, railway stations and sidings, a residential area, and recreational and leisure areas. Fig. 13.17 is a simplified map of Cardiff's functional areas, and we list the map evidence for this division.

(i) **Shopping and business.** Central location, straight roads, large blocks of buildings, main railway station, bus station, cathedral, town hall.

(ii) **Industry.** 'Works' with railway sidings to main line, gas works, electricity generating stations, industrial estate.

(iii) **Commerce.** Docks (large rectangular tidal basins, locks, warehouses, railway sidings to dockside, dry docks), railways (network of railway lines, large areas of sidings, goods depot), canals.

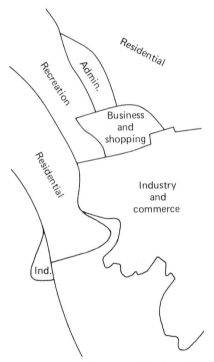

Fig. 13.17 Functional areas of Cardiff. See Map 6 on page 274

(iv) **Residential.** Close road network, lines of buildings, numerous schools, churches, railway halts, hospitals.

(v) **Administrative.** Town hall, assizes, barracks, county hall.

(vi) **Recreation and leisure.** Parks, gardens, sports stadium, swimming pool, recreation ground, named buildings of historical interest.

(*d*) **Settlement Plans**
The shape or plan of settlements varies so much that we cannot make a single classification of types, but two shapes do appear regularly on OS maps and may be easily recognized.

(i) Ribbon or linear developments are found where the houses in a village or those on the outskirts of a town straggle 'one-house deep' for a distance along the road, with open country away from the road (see Corfe Castle on Map 7 and North Collingham on Map 3, and also Fig. 13.18(*a*)).

(ii) Nucleated or nodal settlements are those which have grown up around a centre—usually at the meeting of roads or a bridge over a river—which may be the core of the settlement (see Map 2, 8486 and Fig. 13.18(*b*)).

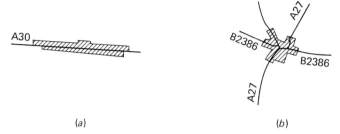

Fig. 13.18 Settlement types: (a) *ribbon (linear),* (b) *nucleated (nodal)*

(e) Settlement Distribution

Sometimes a number of small settlements on an OS map may conform to a recognizable pattern, usually as the result of physical factors. When high ground lies close to the sea, settlements can only grow up on the coast in sheltered locations. On high ground away from the coast, settlements are located only on the valley floors, as linear villages. The mining settlements in the valleys of the south Wales coalfield are excellent examples of this pattern (*H & R*, Unit 12).

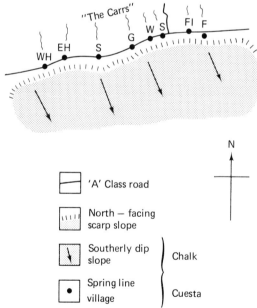

Fig. 13.19 Spring line settlements in Yorkshire. Settlement is very sparse on the chalk surface, but at the foot of the north facing scarp slope springs rise and streams flow northwards. Villages have grown up along the spring line at the foot of the scarp slope but above flood level in the low-lying marshy area known as The Carrs, which is now artificially drained

Villages are rare in chalk areas because of the difficulties of water supply, but a line of villages may grow up along the edge of the chalk, often at the foot of a cuesta (Section 3.2). Each village lies at a point where a stream emerges near the junction of the chalk and its underlying clay, so these are called spring line settlements. In undulating lowlands, villages may not conform to any recognizable pattern because there are no factors restricting the location of settlements.

13.11   The Location of Settlements

It is an interesting exercise in map interpretation to try to work out from an OS map the reasons why a settlement has grown up in its particular location. Many factors affecting the location of settlements show clearly on OS maps, but there are likely to be some which do not appear on the map, particularly those which have exerted an influence in the past but are no longer important.

(a) Historical Factors
Most settlements are hundreds of years old, whatever their size now, and many of today's large towns have grown up from humble origins.

Some settlements began their existence in vastly different conditions from those shown on modern OS maps. In its natural state much of the low-lying clay land in Britain was marshy and likely to flood, so settlements avoided it. Villages grew up on the edge of the clay where they still exist today, although the marsh has been drained and is now used for agriculture. Centuries ago many villages grew up at an easy crossing point on a river, usually at a ford. Since then, bridges have been built in most such places so the ford is omitted from the map. Many riverside settlements grew up as ports, at the inland limit of the tides, but a combination of silting and the increasing size of ships has destroyed the port activities of such settlements. These simple examples of 'lost' factors, which were once important influences on settlement but are no longer evident from OS maps, are part of the fascinating study of the interrelationship of geography and history. It is too large a topic for us to cover here, but if you are interested in pursuing this aspect of settlement study, W. G. Hoskins has written several interesting books on the subject (see *Suggested Further Reading*, p. 255).

There are, however, many factors influencing the location of settlements which do show up clearly on an OS Map, and we shall discuss each major one in turn.

(b) Prehistoric or Roman Settlements
The age of a settlement may be deduced from the presence of antiquities in it or nearby. A settlement of Roman origin has its name printed in Roman script near its modern name.

(c) Defence

In the past, considerations of defence were a most important locating factor, and the existence of a castle, a hilltop site often surrounded by earthworks (shown on the map by hachures, as on Map 1 at 229084) or any other form of natural protection, such as a marsh or river, may have been important in establishing the site of the settlement (Map 7, Corfe Castle).

(d) Water Supply

In the past settlements were often located near surface water. Many undoubtedly obtained their water from underground sources (wells) or springs, which may not be shown on present-day maps, but you should study carefully the settlements we referred to in Section 13.11(a) and (b) to see if there is an obvious source of water. The absence of surface water actively discouraged settlement so that a chalk surface is usually sparsely populated (Map 1, south of northing line 11). Villages which have grown up on chalk are usually situated in a valley bottom, so as to be nearer the water-table. We have already explained the significance of spring line settlements in Section 13.10(e), and the continued importance of water supply can be seen on many OS maps of highland areas, where reservoirs are named (Map 8).

(e) Shelter

Natural protection has always been a vital factor when locating settlements in certain environments. Floods are common on low-lying land and on flat land (Map 2, Wool and Map 3). At times, a small settlement may be located away from the river but not at the valley edge. This suggests that the hamlet may have grown up on a river terrace, high enough to be above flood level but not high enough to be shown by the contours on the map. The existence of a river terrace may, however, be indicated by the presence of a number of unfenced, unmetalled tracks leading towards the river but stopping abruptly before reaching it. Such tracks run across the flat surface of the terrace but stop at the steep terrace edge.

In mountainous or hilly areas settlements are normally located in valleys, so as to obtain the maximum protection from wind and storm. On Maps 4 and 8 the only settlements are in the valleys, where the comparative ease of communications is also an important factor. An exception to this general rule may occasionally be seen in narrow valleys which run east to west, such as the Yorkshire Dales. Farms and hamlets may be sited some distance above the valley floor on the north side, in order to take advantage of the extra sunshine which results from a southerly aspect (Section 10.6).

Settlements on exposed coasts are usually located on the sheltered side of a headland or a short distance up a river or inlet, to protect them from storm and gale damage. Even then, the inhabitants of such a settlement may have found it necessary to build a small, curved breakwater to protect their boats from the large storm waves which come from a direction from which they have no natural shelter. These breakwaters are marked on OS maps.

(*f*) **Bridge Point**

A settlement on or near a river may be sited to take advantage of a particularly good crossing point. The reasons for this will become evident if you study OS maps. Thus, the inland limit of tidal water may be chosen as a good bridge point, not only because bridge building was probably easier there but, possibly, so as not to obstruct navigation up to the tidal limit. Flat-bottomed, formerly marshy valley floors were often difficult to cross and the easiest crossing point may have been at a point where the valley sides come close together. The lower valley-side contours will show whether this factor is important: not only is a settlement likely to grow at this point but a road or even a railway may cross the valley at the same place.

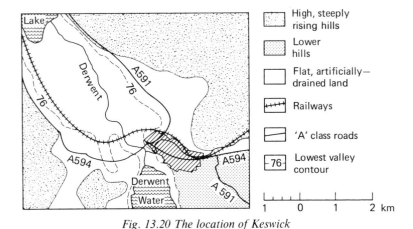

Fig. 13.20 The location of Keswick

Fig. 13.20 shows the location of Keswick, which grew up at this point for three main reasons. In the first place, it was near the easiest crossing point of the flat, formerly marshy floor of the river Derwent flood plain (see the 76 m contour on Fig. 13.20). Second, it was at the northern end of Derwent Water, where the hills bordering the lake are lower and less steep, making access from the south-east easier. Third, it was at the confluence of the rivers Greta and Derwent. The railway follows the Greta into Keswick and crosses the flat valley floor close to the road, so as to take advantage of the narrower valley floor.

(*g*) **Routes Centres (Nodal Settlements)**

Certain sites have developed as the natural meeting place of roads.

(i) **Bridge points** may attract roads from a wide area, on both sides of the river. The lowest crossing point on a river is particularly significant in this respect, because it is where many routes are likely to converge (Map 2, Wool and Fig. 13.20).

(ii) **Gaps in a hill ridge.** Routes from a wide area may converge on a gap from both sides of a ridge, to take advantage of this easy way through the ridge (Map 7, Corfe Castle).

(iii) **Confluences.** A settlement is likely to grow up at a point where several valleys and their streams meet, mainly because roads tend to follow valleys. OS 1 : 50 000 map, sheet 184 shows how Salisbury has grown up at a position where several river valleys meet.

Fig. 13.21 shows the location of Salisbury, and S is the site of Old Sarum, the earliest town in the area. It lies about 30 m above the river Avon and is defended by circular ditches and banks; it became a Roman town called Sorviodunum and, later, was the site of a Norman cathedral. Water supply was always a problem at this hilltop site and, in the thirteenth century, a cathedral (C) was built 3 km to the south on well-watered meadows where the flood plain narrows slightly. Modern Salisbury (New Sarum) still avoids the low-lying flood plains and has expanded on to the spurs between the river valleys. It is an excellent example of a route centre.

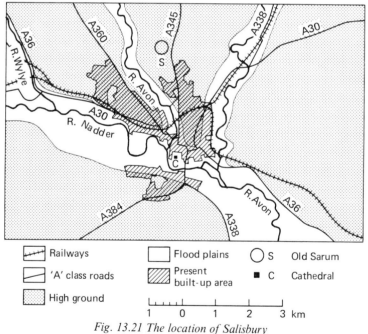

Fig. 13.21 The location of Salisbury

(iv) **Dry sites.** On very flat land, a slight rise in the surface may have been sufficient protection against floods in the past to give a dry site in marsh or fen-land. After the marsh has been drained such a site may become the dominant settlement in the area and roads may converge on it. Excellent examples of this may be seen in Ely (1 : 50 000 map sheet 143 at TL 5480) and Othery and Middlezoy in Somerset (1 : 50 000 map sheet 182, SS 3831 and SS 3732). All these settlements were formerly fen islands on slight rises above the surrounding marshy fenland. Now that the fen has been drained, the only evidence on the map of their site is the 15 m contour around them.

(*h*) Agricultural Land

Much indirect information about the extent of farming is given on OS maps, although there is little direct information about agriculture on them. Open land which is not covered by any form of natural vegetation (marked on OS maps by one of the conventional signs for woodland, marshland or rough grassland) is most likely to be farmland, either arable (crops) or pasture (grass) (Map 1, 2011 and 2107). If farms are named on the map it is likely that agriculture is an important activity (see the northern part of Map 1), and 1 : 25 000 maps show field boundaries which are also evidence of agriculture (Map 7, 9781).

In hilly areas of Britain, such as the Lake District (Map 8), North Wales (Map 5), the Scottish Highlands and the Pennines (Map 4), there are large areas of rough grassland which suggest some form of hill farming, usually sheep rearing. The presence of field boundaries in such an area (on 1 : 25 000 maps only) supports this deduction. Flat valley bottom land with drainage ditches or even patches of marsh is most likely to be used for cattle rearing (Map 2, 8387, Map 5, 6114). The presence of large orchards or areas of glass houses—each is shown by a conventional sign—is evidence of market gardening as an important type of agriculture in the area.

(*i*) Local Resources

People may live in an area in order to exploit its resources. Many of these resources are marked on or may be deduced from the map, and we shall discuss five of the major types.

(i) **Mines and quarries** are usually named (Map 5, 612164, Map 4, 730766, Map 8, 4010). Even if they are no longer operative they are likely to be marked and even named, such as 'old quarry' (Map 4, 728759) and 'quarries, disused' (Map 5, 626131).

(ii) **Industry** is shown as large groups of buildings, often with railway sidings built especially to serve them. 'Works' may be printed on the map, but there is usually little evidence of the type of factory. Examples may be seen on Map 1, 244078, 200087, Map 3, 827629 and Map 7, 956828. Paradoxically, the full name of some industrial sites is marked, such as the Nuclear Research Station (Map 2, 8186).

(iii) **Lumbering.** You must be cautious here as a large area of woodland does not necessarily mean that lumbering takes place. There are vast areas of private parkland in Britain retained largely for their natural beauty or for sporting purposes. Forestry Commission plantations are not marked as such on the map, but they may be detected fairly easily because they are entirely coniferous and have unfenced access tracks, known as rides, running through them (Map 7, 9784).

(iv) **Mills** are normally named on the map beside a stream, if they are water-mills, or indicated by a conventional sign if they are windmills (page 259) Their presence suggests that milling, usually of grain, has been important in the past, but it is unlikely that they are of any great local significance today. In places, although no trace of the mill itself is shown, a local place name suggests that one has existed in the past. Mill Hill (Map 1, 213067) is an example of this.

(v) **Tourism.** Certain areas of beautiful inland or coastal scenery may attract tourists, particularly the country's National Parks, the extent of which is shown on 1 : 50 000 maps. Special recreational facilities are sometimes shown on the map, such as motor racing tracks, water skiing centres or horse racing tracks. Mountaineering areas are dotted with mountain rescue posts (Map 8, 4312 and 483139).

(j) Coastal Settlements

There are a number of reasons which help to explain why settlements are located on or near the coast. We have already mentioned a number of them, but we shall now discuss them in more detail.

(i) **Sheltered water** may occur naturally because of the shelter of a headland, or artificially due to the protection given by a man-made breakwater (Map 1, 2304, Map 5, 613152).

(ii) **Deep navigable water** may be shown by the absence of any form of sea-floor exposure at low tide. Sometimes the word harbour is printed on the map (Map 1, 2304), and the navigable approaches to a port of any size are usually marked with buoys, beacons, lightships or lighthouses. Furthermore, the presence of such services as coastguard and lifeboat stations (Map 1, 2304, Map 2, 825797, Map 5, 618155) suggests that ships use that part of the coast.

(iii) **Port activities.** In large commercial ports you may find evidence of large scale trade and industry in the form of docks, jetties, locks, railways on the quayside, large buildings (usually warehouses or mills), a Customs House and the obviously rectangular (that is, man-made) shape of the coast (Map 6, 1974 and 1975).

(iv) **Tourism.** A popular holiday resort may possess such tourist facilities as a pier, boating lake, pleasure grounds and large, sheltered, sandy beaches, often with groynes (Map 1, 2004).

(*k*) **Site and Situation**
We have dealt in considerable detail with those factors influencing the location of settlements which are shown on OS maps. The location of a settlement comprises two elements, site and situation.

The *site* of a settlement is its exact position in a particular spot or, in the case of a large town, the exact position of the small settlement from which it has grown. The principal reasons which help to explain the site are defence, water supply, confluence, gap, bridge point and, sometimes, a particular local resource.

On the other hand, the *situation* of a settlement infers its position in relation to the surrounding area in which it has grown up. The reasons which help to determine situation include route centre, agriculture, valley bottom location and the factor which influences many others, the geology of the area.

13.12   Communications

In many respects, the settlement pattern is closely related to the network of communications—roads, railways and canals—all of which are clearly shown on OS maps. These lines of communication have been specifically built to carry people and goods, so it is not surprising that they generally run between settlements. The recently constructed by-passes and motorways are an exception to this rule because they deliberately avoid towns to reduce traffic congestion, thus enabling through-traffic to reach its destination more quickly.

(*a*) **Roads**
Roads of a sort—tracks, bridle-paths and footpaths—have connected settlements for centuries, following the easiest routes across country. The earliest roads were used by people on foot or horseback and by horse-drawn vehicles; they were generally made for agricultural purposes, linking farms to other farms, and farms to villages. In the seventeenth and eighteenth centuries, turnpike roads between the larger towns were surfaced—after a fashion—and sometimes straightened. But Britain's present road system has developed over the past 50 years, as a result of the increasing use of the internal-combustion (petrol) engine, although most of these roads tend to follow the course of an older routeway.

Many roads follow valley floors, especially in hilly and mountainous countryside (Map 8). To cross higher ground, roads may follow a *pass* by going up one valley, across the watershed and down another valley (Fig. 13.13(*n*)).

A gap is another easy way for a road to pass from one side of a hill ridge to the other (Map 7, Corfe Castle), but some roads actually follow the ridgeway (that is, a route which runs along the level crest of a range of hills for much of its length). The existence of such a road usually denotes that the route is an old one, chosen centuries ago to cross the bare, windswept hills and avoid the marshy wooded valleys (Map 8, 4515).

Roads generally avoid high, steep, rocky hillsides and low-lying flat land, especially the flood plains of rivers which were probably marshland at one time (Map 3, A 1(T) and A 1133 roads). When these types of terrain lie next to each other, the road follows a route between them: it runs slightly above the flat land but at the base of the steep slope (Map 5, from 633136 to 615122, and Map 1, 246113 to 200102).

(b) Railways

Railways are a comparatively recent form of transport and have seldom been responsible for the location of a settlement. Railway routes were often chosen specifically to go through towns so that they could be used for passengers and freight. Conventional railway locomotives cannot climb steep gradients, so the routes followed by railway lines are closely controlled by the relief of the land; they may be very roundabout in hilly country. Railway lines have frequent cuttings and embankments which have been built to keep the railway track as nearly level as possible: conventional signs are used to illustrate these features on OS maps (page 258). Tunnels are constructed when the land is so high or steep that building cuttings or embankments is not possible; these are also clearly marked on OS maps.

In the last few years many railway lines have been abandoned but their cuttings, embankments, bridges and disused stations may still be shown on the map, with the course of the former railway line usually marked as a footpath (see Map 1, north-west corner).

(c) Canals

Britain once had a dense canal network, especially in the Midlands and south-eastern England, but there are few working canals left in Britain today. Some of the disused canals may still be marked on the map. This means of communication must follow a level or 'contour' route more than any other, and a canal can only cross sloping land if locks are built. A lock must also be constructed at a point where a canal meets a river or the sea. A small port may grow up at such a site.

Further Reading

Balchin, W. G. V.: *The Making of the English Landscape*. Hodder & Stoughton (London). A series with a book for each county.

Birch, T. W.: *Maps*. Oxford University Press (London, 1964).

Hoskins, W. G.: *The Making of the English Landscape*. Penguin (Harmondsworth, 1970).

Hoskins, W. G.: *English Landscapes*. BBC Publications (London, 1973).

Tooley, R. V.: *Maps and Map Makers*. Batsford (London, 1970).

British Landscape through Maps. A set of booklets published by the Geographical Association, each one devoted to an individual map or set of maps.

Reprint of the First Edition of the One Inch Ordnance Survey Map of England and Wales (97 sheets). David & Charles (Newton Abbot).

Ordnance Survey Maps

As we said previously, the Ordnance Survey publishes a comprehensive range of maps of the British Isles, on a number of different scales. The two scales most widely used by geographers are 1 : 50 000 (2 cm to 1 km) and 1 : 25 000 (4 cm to 1 km).

In this Section we are reproducing eight extracts from Ordnance Survey maps, as well as the conventional signs for 1 : 50 000 maps (on pages 258 and 259), and for 1 : 25 000 maps (on page 268). Maps 1, 2 and 3 (on pages 262, 263 and 265) are on the 1 : 50 000 scale. Maps 4, 5, 6 and 7 (on pages 269, 272, 274 and 275) are on the 1 : 25 000 scale. Map 8 (on pages 278–9) is the old one inch to a mile scale, now being replaced by 1 : 50 000 maps, but as many people will still be using these maps for a number of years we include an extract for general interest and information.

With each map extract is a set of questions and exercises, similar to those set in GCE O level. Answers to these questions appear at the end of the book.

1 : 50 000 Scale Maps

The sheets in this series give a detailed topographical picture of the country, showing virtually all roads and using colours to indicate road classifications, types of surface and width. The 1 : 50 000 series incorporates all the information previously shown on the one-inch maps, but on a rather larger scale and with new colouring and clearer detail. It is compiled on new sheet lines— although it is based on updated one-inch material— so that conurbations and recreational areas can be shown, as far as possible, on a minimum number of sheets.

The 1 : 50 000 extracts we show are as follows:

Conventional Signs
Map 1:   Sheet 198 (Brighton and the Downs)
Map 2:   Sheet 194 (Dorchester and Weymouth)
Map 3:   Sheet 121 (Lincoln)

Conventional Signs (1 : 50 000)

ROADS AND PATHS

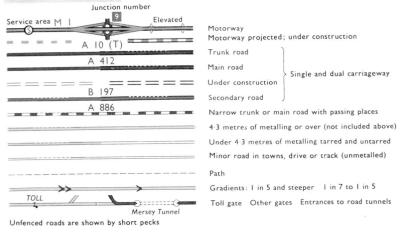

Motorway
Motorway projected; under construction

Trunk road

Main road

Under construction

Secondary road

Single and dual carriageway

Narrow trunk or main road with passing places

4·3 metres of metalling or over (not included above)

Under 4·3 metres of metalling tarred and untarred

Minor road in towns, drive or track (unmetalled)

Path

Gradients: 1 in 5 and steeper   1 in 7 to 1 in 5

Toll gate   Other gates   Entrances to road tunnels

Unfenced roads are shown by short pecks

PUBLIC RIGHTS OF WAY

Public paths { Footpath / Bridleway }

Road used as a public path or byway open to all traffic

Public rights of way indicated by these symbols have been derived from Definitive Maps as amended by later enactments or instruments held by Ordnance Survey on 1st December 1972, and are shown subject to the limitations imposed by the scale of mapping

The representation on this map of any other road, track or path is no evidence of the existence of a right of way

RAILWAYS

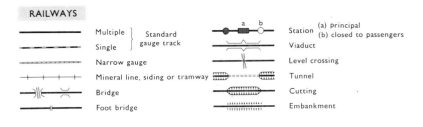

Multiple } Standard gauge track
Single

Narrow gauge

Mineral line, siding or tramway

Bridge

Foot bridge

Station (a) principal (b) closed to passengers

Viaduct

Level crossing

Tunnel

Cutting

Embankment

WATER FEATURES

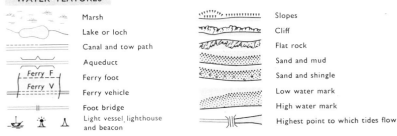

Marsh

Lake or loch

Canal and tow path

Aqueduct

Ferry foot

Ferry vehicle

Foot bridge

Light vessel, lighthouse and beacon

Slopes

Cliff

Flat rock

Sand and mud

Sand and shingle

Low water mark

High water mark

Highest point to which tides flow

GENERAL FEATURES

Electricity transmission line
(with pylons spaced conventionally)

Pipe line
(arrow indicates direction of flow)

Quarry

Open pit

Wood

Orchard

Park or ornamental grounds

Bracken, heath and rough grassland

Dunes

Broadcasting station (mast or tower)

Bus or coach station

Church { with tower

or { with spire

Chapel { without tower or spire

Glasshouse

Graticule intersection at 5' intervals

Triangulation pillar

Windmill (in use)

Windmill (disused)

Wind pump

Youth hostel

RELIEF

Contour values are given to the nearest metre. The vertical interval is, however, 50 feet

.144

Heights are to the nearest metre above mean sea level. Heights shown close to a triangulation pillar refer to the station height at ground level and not necessarily to the summit. Details of the summit height may be obtained from the Ordnance Survey
I metre = 3·2808 feet   15·24 metres = 50 feet

BOUNDARIES

— + — + — + National

—∘— ∘— ∘— ∘— London Borough

National Park

— · — · — · — County or Metropolitan County

··················· Civil Parish or equivalent

The county areas and names shown on this map are effective on 1st April 1974
Urban Civil Parishes cease to exist on 1st April 1974

NT

NT

} National Trust { always open

opening restricted

ABBREVIATIONS

P   Post office
PH   Public house
CH   Club house
.MP   Mile post
.MS   Mile stone

TH   Town hall, Guildhall or equivalent
PC   Public convenience (in rural areas)
.T
.A   } Telephone call box { PO / AA / RAC
.R

ANTIQUITIES

VILLA   Roman
Tumulus Non-Roman

+   Site of antiquity

⤬
1066   Battlefield (with date)

Map 1   (1 : 50 000, Sheet 198 (Brighton and the Downs))

Questions

1. Give the grid references of the A 27(T) road bridge over the river Adur and of the two railway stations in the south of the area.

2. Measure (a) the bearing, (b) the straight line distance and (c) the distance along the A class roads from the church with a tower at 208060 to the public house at 213129. (Distances should be measured to the nearest tenth of a km.)

3. List the conventional signs in square 2307.

4. Imagine yourself walking north to south along the 22 easting grid line. Describe the nature of the surface as you walk southwards. Does this description suggest any particular landform?

5. Calculate the gradient between the triangulation pillar 216 on Truleigh Hill (226108) and Truleigh Manor Farm (224115).

6. Compare the shape of the surface in square 2110 with that in square 1911.

7. Can you explain why the drainage pattern is so complex in the four grid squares of which 200120 is the centre?

8. Describe the course followed by the river Adur as it flows north to south across the area.

9. Between the road from Fulking (2411) to Upper Beeding (2010) and the A 27(T) road there is no evidence of surface water but there are several valleys. What does this suggest?

10. The mouth of the river Adur makes a sharp bend eastwards just before reaching the sea. Can you give any reasons for this? What are the short black lines projecting seawards along much of the coast?

11. What evidence is there that man has lived in this area for many centuries?

12. Present-day settlement is in two distinct strips, one along the coast and the other between Fulking and square 1910. Can you explain this pattern of settlement? Why do you think there is very little settlement between these two strips? (See Fig. 3.10.)

13. (*a*) What is the significance of the unusual pattern of roads in square 2006?

(*b*) In square 2308, what are the four parallel black lines which run approximately north to south? What does this suggest may lie just off the south-east corner of the map?

14. (*a*) Give reasons for the location of Shoreham Airport (2005).

(*b*) What are the advantages of the location of the works at 200086? Can you suggest what type of works this is? (The answer to Question 9 may give you a clue.)

Map 1   (1 : 50 000, Sheet 198 (Brighton and the Downs))

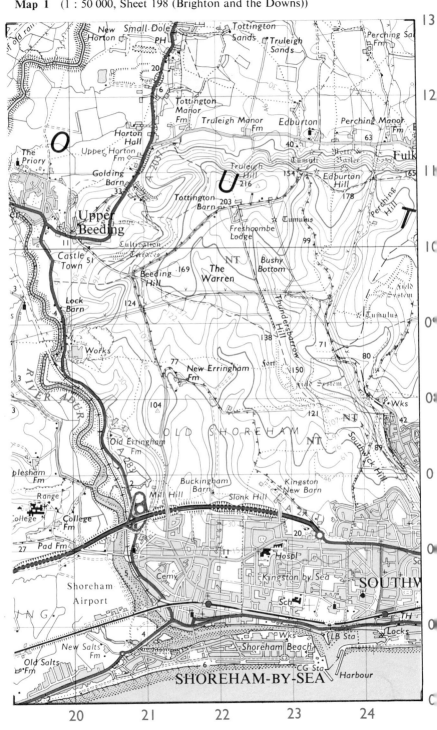

©Crown copyright 1976

Map 2   (1 : 50 000, Sheet 194 (Dorchester and Weymouth))

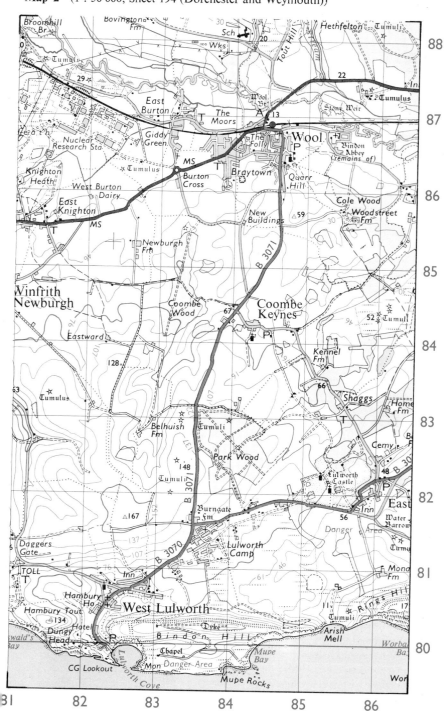

©Crown copyright 1976

Map 2   (1 : 50 000, Sheet 194 (Dorchester and Weymouth))

Questions

1. Give the grid references of the level crossing in Wool, the church with a tower in West Lulworth and the triangulation pillar 134 on Hambury Tout.
2. Measure (*a*) the bearing, (*b*) the straight line distance and (*c*) the shortest road distance from Wool railway station to the Inn at East Lulworth (858818). (Distance should be measured to the nearest tenth of a km.)
3. What is the length of the coastline in this area, to the nearest km?
4. List the conventional signs in square 8287.
5. This section is drawn along the 84 eastings line.

840882   840840

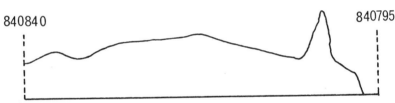

840840   840795

Trace it and on your trace mark clearly the following features: an electricity transmission line, an area of wood, a flood plain, a meandering river, a multiple track railway, an *A* class road, a *B* class road, a tumulus, an area of heath, bracken and rough grass, a steep-sided ridge.

6. Calculate the gradient between the triangulation pillar 167 at 826816 and the cross roads at 829809.
7. (*a*) Describe the relief in (i) the southern half of square 8380, (ii) square 8183, (iii) square 8287.
   (*b*) How high is the cliff at 826800?
8. How many forms of natural vegetation can you identify in this area? What suggests that much of the land here is farmland?
9. The river flowing across the northern part of the area is the river Frome. In which direction does it flow? Describe the nature of its course and its valley. (Use as many relevant geomorphological terms as you can.)
10. South of the river Frome there is little surface water. Can you give any explanation for this?
11. What evidence is there that this area has been inhabited for a long time?
12. What does man use this area for today?
13. What reasons can you give for the location of the settlements at (*a*) Wool, (*b*) West Lulworth?

Map 3 (1 : 50 000, Sheet 121 (Lincoln))

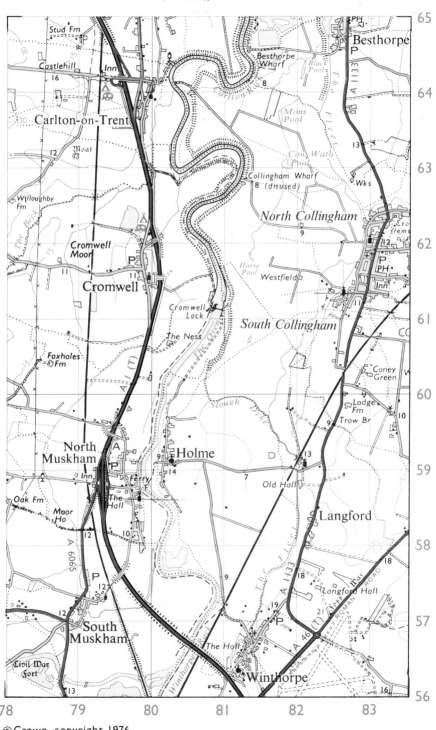

©Crown copyright 1976

Map 3   (1 : 50 000, Sheet 121 (Lincoln))

Questions

1. Give the grid references of the church in Cromwell, the civil war fort in the south-west corner of the area and the churches in Holme and Winthorpe.
2. (*a*) Measure the length, to the nearest tenth of a km, of the river (the Trent) north of the A 1(T) road bridge.
   (*b*) What is the bearing from the church at 798586 to the church at 826613?
3. List the conventional signs in squares 7856 and 7964.
4. (*a*) What is the significance of the pattern of broken lines in and around square 8256?
   (*b*) What does the letter *F* at 799588 tell you?
   (*c*) How can you tell that most of this area is farmland?
5. What is the highest point in this area? Give its height and grid reference. How many level crossings are there along the railways? What does this suggest about the nature of the surface? Can you verify this in any other way?
6. Which way does the Trent flow? What happens at 809611? Describe the course of the river and the shape of its valley. Why do you think there is only one bridge across the Trent?
7. Can you explain the unusual pattern of roads on the A 1(T) in square 7958?
8. Describe the location of settlements in this area. Can you explain this location? What name can be given to the type of settlement shown here?

1 : 25 000 Scale Maps

These maps show fuller detail over a smaller area than the 1 : 50 000 scale, so they are ideal for students and geographers studying the countryside, and also for walkers, cyclists, archaeologists and others.

First Series

Each sheet in this series covers an area 10 km square, showing buildings, footpaths, woods, parks and many other features in great detail. Motorable roads are coloured and road classifications are shown where applicable.

The 1 : 25 000 (First Series) extracts we show are as follows:

Conventional Signs
Map 4:   Sheet SD 77 (Ingleborough Hill)
Map 5:   Sheet SH 61 (Barmouth)
Map 6:   Sheet ST 17 (Cardiff (South West))

Second Series

This series is based on modern surveys begun in 1965, and all maps of this scale are now being published in this new and improved style. The main changes are in the conventional signs: (i) woodland is shown *green* with tree symbols, (ii) field boundaries are *black* lines, (iii) footpaths are shown in *green*, (iv) there are several new signs in country areas only, such as Pol Sta (Police Station), PC (Public Convenience) and PH (Public House).

We show one extract from a 1 : 25 000 (Second Series) map:

Map 7:   Sheet SY 87/97/SZ 07 (Purbeck)

Most Second Series sheets cover an area 20 km east to west by 10 km north to south, thus covering twice the area of First Series sheets.

Conventional Signs (1 : 25 000)

Roads

Motorway, Trunk and Main Road (Dual Carriageway) .... M4 or A6(M)   A123 or A123(T)

Trunk & Main Road .... A123 or A123(T)

Secondary Road .... Fenced   B2314   Unfenced

Road Under Construction ....

Other Roads .... Good, metalled   Poor, or unmetalled

Footpaths .... FP Fenced   FP Unfenced

Railways, Multiple Track .... Station   Road over   Cutting   Tunnel   (Footbridge) FB

,,   Single Track .... Sidings   Viaduct   Level Crossing   Embankment   Road under

,,   Narrow Gauge ....

London & Glasgow Transport Underground Stations .... Interchange Stations

Aerial Ropeway .... Aerial Ropeway

Boundaries { County or County Borough
              ,,   ,, County of City (in Scotland)

,,   ,,   ,,   ,,   with Parish

,,   Parish

Pipe Line (Oil, Water) .... Pipe Line

Electricity Transmission Lines (Pylons shown at bends and spaced conventionally)–

Post Offices (In Villages & Rural Areas only)   P   Town Hall....TH   Public House....PH

Church or Chapel with Tower   Church or Chapel with Spire   Church or Chapel without either   +

Triangulation Station   △   on Church with Tower   without Tower

Intersected Point on Chy   ○   on Church with Spire   without Spire   +   on Building

Guide Post....GP.   Mile Post....MP.   Mile Stone....MS.   Boundary Stone....BS ○   Boundary Post....BP ○

Youth Hostel....Y   Telephone Call Box (Public)....T   (AA)....A   (RAC)....R   Antiquity (site of)

Public Buildings   Glasshouses

Quarry & Gravel Pit   Orchard

National Trust Area   Sheen Common NT   Furze

,,   ,,   ,,   Scotland....NTS   Rough Pasture Heath & Moor

Osier Bed   Marsh

Reeds   Well....W ○

Park, Fenced   Spring....Spr ○

Wind Pump....Wd Pp .

Wood, Coniferous, Fenced

Wood, Non-Coniferous Unfenced   Contours are at 25 feet vertical interval.

Brushwood, Fenced & Unfenced   Spot Height....123·

Ferries   Sand Hills
Foot   Vehicle   Mud   Flat Rock
LWMMT
Slopes   Beacon   Lightship
HWMMT
Lake   Highest point to which Medium Tides flow   Sand   Lightship
Canal   Bridge   Lock   Weir   Sand & Shingle
Towing   Aqueduct   Ford   FB   Cliff
Path   (Footbridge)   Lighthouse
Dam

(High & Low Water Mark of Ordinary Spring Tides, in Scotland)

Map 4 (1 : 25 000, Sheet SD 77 (Ingleborough Hill))

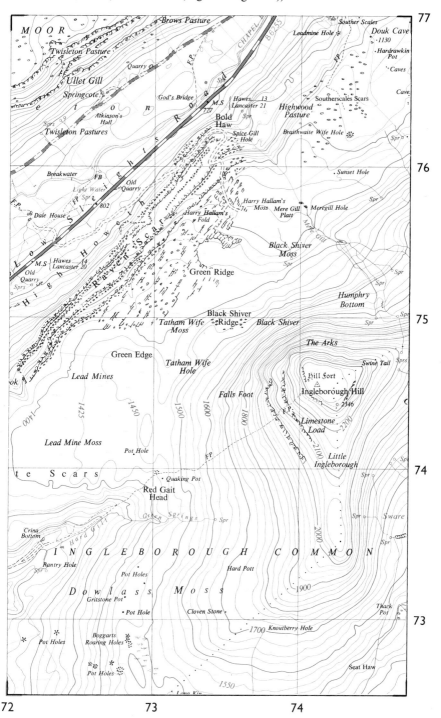

©Crown copyright 1976

Map 4   (1 : 25 000, Sheet SD 77 (Ingleborough Hill))

Questions

1. What are the grid references of the triangulation pillar on Ingleborough Hill and the milestone which is nearest to Lancaster on the B 6255 road?

2. (*a*) What is the length of metalled (surfaced) road in this area? What is the distance from the old quarry (728758) to Lancaster (5 miles = 8 km). Give both measurements to the nearest tenth of a km.

    (*b*) Measure the bearings from the summit of Ingleborough Hill to (i) Braithwaite Wife Hole (743762), (ii) the building at Crina Bottom (724735), (iii) the spot height 802 (726757).

3. List the conventional signs in square 7276.

4. Draw a section along the 74 northing line between its intersections with eastings lines 72 and 74. Use a vertical scale of one tenth of an inch to fifty feet. Calculate the vertical exaggeration of the section.

5. Calculate the gradient between Braithwaite Wife Hole (743762) and spot height 777 at 733764.

6. Compare the valleys of Hard Gill (square 7273) and Chapel Beck between 737770 and 720758. Which way does Chapel Beck flow?

7. Describe the nature and slope of the surface on a walk between the crest of Ingleborough Hill and the old quarry at 728758.

8. What is unusual about the streams in squares 7475 and 7476? Does this drainage pattern suggest anything which might enable you to deduce the type of rock found over much of this area? Is there any further evidence to support this deduction?

9. Why are there few roads and little settlement in this area? How would you describe the location of the settlements and roads?

Map 5   (1 : 25 000, Sheet SH 61 (Barmouth))

Questions

1. Give the grid reference of Barmouth Junction railway station, the milestone one mile east of Barmouth and the railway station in Fairbourne.

2. Measure (a) the bearing, (b) the straight line distance and (c) the distance along the railway from Barmouth Junction station to Barmouth railway station. (Measure distances to the nearest tenth of a km.)

3. List the conventional signs in square 6214.

4. Calculate the gradient between the spot heights 870 at 618165 and 14 at 623157.

5. What name can be given to the contour feature Fegla Fawr in squares 6214–6314?

6. To the south of the estuary there are two areas of greatly contrasting relief, separated by the road.

   (a) How can you tell that these two areas are very different from each other? Describe each one.

   (b) Can you suggest any way in which the northern of these two areas came into existence?

7. Describe the appearance of the estuary (a) at low tide, (b) at high tide.

8. What name can you give to the stretch of land in square 6114? Describe how it was formed.

9. What evidence is there that the land in square 6113 has been made suitable for agriculture?

10. Describe and give reasons for the location of the roads in the area.

11. What reasons can you give for the location of Barmouth?

Map 5   (1 : 25 000, Sheet SH 61 (Barmouth))

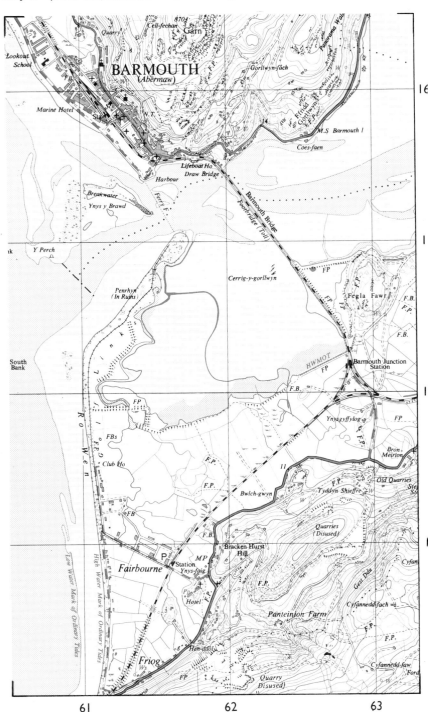

61   62   63

©Crown copyright 1976

Map 6   (1 : 25 000, Sheet ST 17 (Cardiff))

Questions

1. Give the grid reference of the Fort in Cathays Park, the railway station in Temperance Town and Cardiff Bridge.
2. Measure (*a*) the bearing, (*b*) the straight line distance and (*c*) the shortest road distance from the Chapel at road junction 177753 to the Infirmary (193769). Measure distances to the nearest tenth of a km.
3. If you walked across square 1773 and square 1977 what differences would you notice in the nature of their surface?
4. Describe the appearance of square 1873 (*a*) at low tide, (*b*) at high tide.
5. What is there at the entrance to every dock? Why is this necessary?
6. What are the black lines meeting the dockside, such as those between 198735 and 200739 and between 195750 and 192756? What are the large buildings close to the dockside as at 197740 and 198756? Do these answers tell you anything about the main activity in the docks? The small inlets of the sea at 190743 are for an entirely different purpose: what is it and what name can be given to inlets such as these?
7. Large blocks of building occupy much of the southern part of square 1876. What kind of buildings are these? In what ways are these buildings different from those in square 1977 (see Question 3)?
8. How would you describe the area alongside the river (Taff) from the north-west corner of the area to Cardiff Bridge? Cathays Park lies to the east of this area; what are the buildings here?
9. What other features typical of a large town may be seen in this area?
10. What is there between the two railway lines in square 1774?

Map 6   (1 : 25 000, Sheet ST 17 (Cardiff))

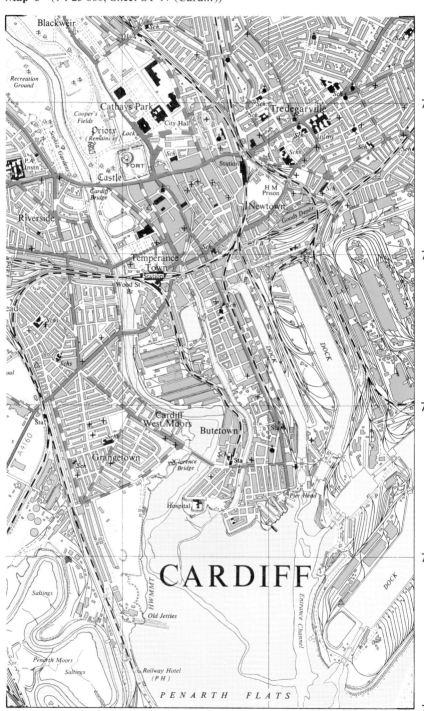

Map 7 (1 : 25 000 (Second Series), Sheet SY 87/97/SZ 07 (Purbeck))

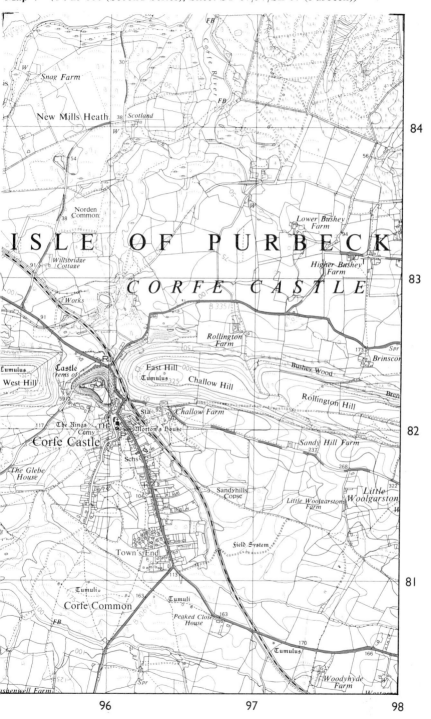

96   97   98

)Crown copyright 1976

Map 7   (1 : 25 000 (Second Series), Sheet SY 87/97/SZ 07 (Purbeck))

Questions

1. Give the grid references of the church with a tower in Corfe Castle, the tumulus on East Hill and the RAC telephone north of the Castle.

2. Measure (*a*) the bearing, (*b*) the straight line distance and (*c*) the main road distance from the railway bridge at 970806 to the road junction at 954828. (Distances should be measured to the nearest tenth of a km.)

3. What do the short black lines (hachures) signify on three sides of the Castle at 959823? How would you describe this feature?

4. List the conventional signs in square 9682.

5. Construct a section between Woodhyde Farm (975804) and Lower Bushey Farm (973833), using a vertical scale of 2 mm to 25 feet. Calculate the vertical exaggeration of the section.

6. Calculate the gradient between the tumulus at 964824 and Rollington Farm (969827).

7. What evidence is there that man has lived in this area for a long time?

8. What reasons can you give for the location of Corfe Castle village? Describe its layout.

9. The area may be divided into three east-to-west zones, each with its own distinct form of relief. Draw a sketch map at *half* the scale of the map and divide it into the three different relief areas. Is there a corresponding difference in the vegetation of these areas? Write a paragraph of description of each of the three areas.

10. Study the vegetation and drainage in square 9784. What type of woodland is it? Can you suggest what the wood is used for? Can you explain its unusual form of drainage?

One-inch Maps   (1 : 63 360)

Successive series of one-inch maps have been produced by the Ordnance Survey for over 150 years, but this scale is now being replaced by 1 : 50 000. Traditional users of the one-inch map were holidaymakers—walkers, cyclists, youth hostellers—and also motorists who wanted to find alternative routes to avoid traffic congestion or to explore country lanes.

Most of the conventional signs are the same on both 1 : 50 000 and one-inch maps. The main differences are that, on one-inch maps, (i) motorways are shown in red, (ii) orchards are shown as lines of black trees, (iii) woodland is green with tree symbols.

We show one extract from a 1 : 63 360 map:

Map 8:   Sheet 83 (Penrith)

Map 8   (1 : 63 360 (one inch to one mile), Sheet 83 (Penrith))

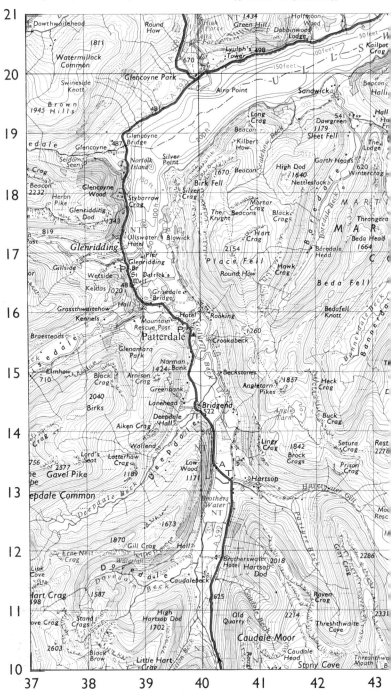

©Crown copyright 1976

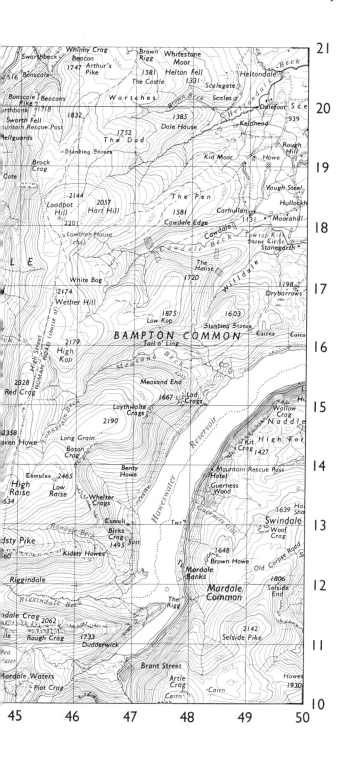

Map 8   (1 : 63 360 (one inch to one mile), Sheet 83 (Penrith))

Questions

1. Give the grid reference of the Youth Hostel in Patterdale. Give the height and grid reference of the highest point in the area.
2. Measure (a) the bearing, (b) the straight line distance, (c) the road distance along the A 593 from spot height 625 at 402113 to the Ullswater Hotel at 388171. (Distances should be measured to the nearest tenth of a mile.)
3. List the conventional signs in square 4013.
4. Draw a section between the spot heights 1424 at 393150 and 1260 at 408157, using a vertical scale of one tenth of an inch to one hundred feet. Calculate the vertical exaggeration of the section.
5. Calculate the gradient between spot height 1842 at 417137 and the end of the lane at 413131.
6. What is the feature which runs north to south across the western side of square 4214 between Heck Crag and Buck Crag? Why is this symbol used on the map instead of contours? Is it possible to calculate its approximate height?
7. Describe, briefly, the relief and drainage of the area between the A 592 road and the Haweswater Reservoir. What agent has been responsible for the formation of this type of landscape? (Study the shape of the section drawn for Question 4 and the feature of which Blea Water at 450108 is the centre.)
8. Why are there so few settlements and roads in this area? Describe and explain the location of settlements and roads.
9. What types of natural vegetation can you see in this area? Is there any farmland? If there is any, describe and explain its location.
10. What differences can you notice between the streams Hayeswater Gill (flowing through square 4213) and Bannerdale Beck (flowing through square 4215)?
11. The words crag, beck, pike and fell occur several times in this area. Say what you think each of these words signifies.
12. How can you tell that the two bodies of water (Haweswater and Ullswater) are lakes and not part of the open sea?

Glossary

abrasion: the process by which a rock surface is worn away by one of the agents of erosion, using the material which the agent is transporting (the *load*) as a tool. Thus the sea uses beach sand and pebbles to undercut the cliff, the wind uses sand. This process may also be called *corrasion*.

acid rocks: igneous rocks with a high proportion—usually over 65 per cent—of silica, e.g. granite, rhyolite.

alluvium: the finer material carried and laid down by a river on its flood plain, a delta or in lakes. It is often called *silt*. In a broader sense the word alluvium is sometimes used to denote all the unconsolidated material laid down by a river (adjective: alluvial).

anemometer: a meteorological instrument used to measure wind speed. The two main types are the cup anemometer and the tube anemometer.

annual range of temperature: it is used mainly to express the temperature difference between the two months of the year which have the highest and lowest *mean monthly average temperatures.*

anticyclone: an area of high atmospheric pressure, sometimes called a high.

antipodes: the two points at opposite ends of any diameter of the earth.

aquifer: a rock layer which allows water to pass through it, e.g. chalk, sandstone, and which holds water when underlain by an *impermeable* layer.

arid: very dry. It is defined in two main ways: (i) less than 254 mm of rain per year, (ii) where evaporation exceeds precipitation.

aspect: the direction in which a slope faces. It is usually related to the amount of sunshine received by the slope.

attrition: the wearing down of fragments in the load into smaller particles, as a result of their constant friction with each other during transport by stream, wind or the sea.

axis: the line between North and South Poles about which the earth rotates. It is tilted at an angle of $23\frac{1}{2}°$ from the vertical.

backing: a change of wind direction in an anti-clockwise direction, e.g. from south through south-east to east. See also *veering.*

back slope: the more gentle slope of a *cuesta*. It is sometimes called the *dip slope.*

barchan: a sand dune in the shape of a crescent. It lies transversely to the wind and its horns point in the same direction as the wind.

barometer: a meteorological instrument used for measuring the pressure of the atmosphere.

base level: the lowest level to which a stream or river erodes its bed. It is the same as sea-level, under normal conditions of erosion.

basic rocks: igneous rocks with a low proportion—usually less than 55 per cent—of silica, e.g. gabbro, basalt.

Beaufort Scale: a scale of thirteen wind speeds (0–12), related to the wind's effect on surface features such as waves, trees, dust, smoke and houses.

catchment area: the total area drained by a river and its tributaries and bounded by the watershed of the river system.

Celsius: the scale of temperature on which 0° represents the melting point of ice and 100° the boiling point of water. It is more commonly called *Centigrade*.

Centigrade: see *Celsius*.

compression: the horizontal pressures on rocks which usually result in rock folding and, sometimes, faulting. It is also used of air which is subjected to pressure so that the body of air is made to occupy a smaller volume, e.g. water compresses air in a crack in the rock as a wave breaks or as the tide rises. See *hydraulic action*.

condensation: the process by which vapour changes into liquid form. It is important in meteorology as air which cools below its *dew point* results in the many forms of *precipitation*.

confluence: the place where two streams or rivers meet.

corrasion: see *abrasion*.

craton: a large, stable part of the earth's surface composed of very old, hard rocks and hardly affected by earth movements. It is often called a *shield* or *shield area*.

cuesta: a hill with one gentle slope (*back slope*) and one steep slope (*scarp slope*) usually formed by the outcrop of a gently inclined layer of sedimentary rock. It is sometimes called an *escarpment*.

deflation: the removal by wind of fine, loose material (e.g. sand, dust) from the earth's surface.

denudation: the wearing away of the earth's surface by all natural means. It is often divided into *weathering, mass wasting* and *erosion*.

depression: an area of low atmospheric pressure, sometimes called a *low*.

dew point: the temperature at which the water vapour in cooling air *condenses*.

dip: the maximum angle at which a rock layer is inclined from the horizontal.

dip slope: see *back slope*.

diurnal range: the difference between the highest and lowest temperatures in any one day.

divide: see *watershed*.

doldrums: the belt of calm air along the equator, forming part of the equatorial low-pressure belt.

drainage: the flow of water along the earth's surface by means of natural or artificial channels.

drowned valley: see *ria*.

drowning: the effect of rising sea-level on a land mass.

earth movement: a movement in the earth's crust caused by internal forces.

emergence: a rise in the level of the land in relation to sea-level.

equator: an imaginary line around the earth midway between the poles and at right angles to the earth's axis. It is also the 0° parallel of latitude.

equinox: the two days each year, about 21st March and 21st September, when the sun is overhead at the equator. On these dates the periods of daylight and darkness are of equal length all over the world.

erosion: the process by which the earth's surface is worn away by those agents (ice, sea, wind and rivers) which also transport and deposit the eroded fragments. See also *weathering*.

eruption: the volcanic process by which material is poured or thrown out from a volcano on to the earth's surface or into the atmosphere in a solid, liquid or gaseous state.

escarpment: see *cuesta*.

evaporation: the process by which liquid is changed into vapour.

exfoliation: the peeling off of layers of an exposed rock surface, due to alternate heating and cooling. It is especially characteristic of areas such as deserts, which have a large *diurnal range* of temperature. It is sometimes called *onion weathering*.

Fahrenheit: the temperature scale on which 32° represents the melting point of ice and 212° the boiling point of water.

fault: a crack or fracture in the earth's crust caused by *compression* or stretching.

fjord: a deep, steep-sided inlet of the sea formed when a rising sea-level drowns a glaciated valley.

fluvio-glacial: the effects of melt water flowing from the ice of a glacier or ice-sheet.

freeze–thaw process: see *thaw–freeze process*.

glacial: the cold period of an Ice Age during which the ice-covered part of the earth's surface has increased. (See *interglacial*.)

glaciation: the processes and features associated with the action of ice.

great circle: a circle drawn on the earth's surface whose centre is the centre of the earth. The shortest distance between any two points on the earth will be part of the circle.

guyot: a mountain of volcanic origin rising from the sea floor, with a flat top well below sea-level. See also *seamount*.

hectare: a metric unit of area equivalent to 2·47 acres (100 hectares = 1 km²).

hemisphere: half a sphere. The earth is divided into the northern and southern hemispheres by the equator.

hog's back: a *cuesta* whose *back slope* is as steep as its *scarp slope*. It is formed by a steeply dipping layer of sedimentary rock.

horizon: a layer in a *soil profile*.

humidity: see *relative humidity*.
hydraulic action: the erosive power of water resulting from its power and movement. It also includes the *compression* of air in cracks by waves.
hygrometer: a meteorological instrument used for measuring relative humidity.
hygrophyte: a type of vegetation which requires a plentiful water supply (adjective: hygrophytic).

impermeable rock: rock which does not allow water to pass through it.
interglacial: the time between two glacial periods, the result of an increase in temperature.
inversion of temperature: a temporary state of the atmosphere in which temperature increases with altitude for a short distance.
iso-: a prefix meaning equal. It is used to denote lines of equal value drawn on a map, for example: isobar, a line joining all points of equal barometric pressure; isotherm, equal temperature; isohyet, equal rainfall.

jet stream: a westerly air current at high altitude (about 12 000 m). The speed varies seasonally from 60 knots in summer to between 100 and 200 knots in winter.
joint: a natural crack in a rock. In an igneous rock, it results from shrinkage as magma cools and goes solid, and it can lie in any direction. In a sedimentary rock, it usually lies at right angles to the bedding and results from shrinkage as the rock dries out.

karst: an area of limestone topography in Yugoslavia, now used to describe *any* area of characteristic limestone scenery.

lacustrine: to do with a lake, e.g. lacustrine delta.
lapse rate: the rate at which temperature falls with altitude. It varies with the humidity of the air and with latitude but, on average, it is 1 °C for every 100 m of ascent.
lee, leeward: the side away from the wind or the sheltered side, usually in relation to a range of hills or mountains. See also *windward*.
load: the material carried by an agent of transportation such as the sea, rivers, ice and wind.

magma: rock in a molten and gaseous state at high temperature and pressure.
mass wasting: the downhill movement of surface material as a result of gravity, brought about by lubrication after heavy rain or melting snow.
mean monthly average temperature: a single temperature calculated at a weather station for each month of the year by (i) calculating the *daily* average temperature after each day, (ii) calculating the *monthly* average temperature for that month from these, at the end of each month, (iii) after a long period of recording (usually thirty years) taking all the monthly averages for each month in turn and from them calculating a mean (average) for that particular month.

meridian: a line of longitude.

millibar: a unit of atmospheric pressure (mb).

onion weathering: see *exfoliation*.

orogeny: a mountain building period.

outcrop: the surface exposure of a rock.

parallel: a line of latitude.

pedology: the scientific study of soils.

periglacial: processes and features around the edge of an ice-sheet.

permeable rock: rock which allows water to pass through either because it is *porous* or because it is *pervious*.

pervious rock: allows water to pass through because it has joints or cracks.

pH value: the degree of acidity of a soil as indicated on a numerical scale.

porous rock: contains spaces (pores) through which water may pass.

precipitation: the water which reaches the earth's surface from the atmosphere in solid or liquid form.

range of temperature: the difference between the highest and lowest temperatures, usually over a specific period of time such as a day (see *diurnal range*) or a year (see *annual range*).

rejuvenation: the overall effects on a land mass of a drop in *base level*, caused either by a drop in sea-level or by *emergence*. It is especially important in so far as it influences rivers.

relative humidity: the proportion of water vapour in the air expressed as a percentage of the total amount that the air could hold when *saturated*. The figure varies with temperature and air pressure.

ria: a deeply branching inlet of the sea formed when rising sea-level invades the valleys of a river system; a *drowned valley*. See *fjord*.

salinity: the proportion of dissolved salts in sea water, usually expressed in parts per thousand ($^o/_{oo}$) by weight.

scarp slope: the steeper slope of a *cuesta*.

seamount: a mountain, usually of volcanic origin, rising from the sea-floor. It has a prominent crest below sea-level. See also *guyot*.

sediment: material deposited by water.

seif dune: a ridge-like sand dune which follows the direction of the wind, often for hundreds of kilometres.

shield area: see *craton*.

silt: see *alluvium*.

snow line: the lower limit of permanent snow cover. It varies seasonally (there are winter and summer snow lines) and with latitude (4 900 m on the equator, sea-level at the poles).

soil erosion: the removal of soil by wind and water, which results from man's misguided agricultural activities.

soil profile: a vertical section through the soil from the surface to the underlying rock. It is divided into several *horizons*.

solstice: the two days each year, about 21st June and 21st December, when the sun is overhead at one of the tropics. On these dates the period of daylight is longest in the hemisphere where it is summer and shortest in the hemisphere where it is winter.

solution: the process by which a solid is dissolved in a liquid.

stratum: a layer of sedimentary rock of distinctive character (plural: strata).

strike: the direction, usually expressed as a compass bearing, of the outcrop of a rock. It lies in the horizontal plane at right angles to the dip.

submergence: a rise in sea-level in relation to the land. See *drowning*.

saturated: used geographically in two senses to describe (i) the state when the atmosphere can hold no more water vapour, that is, *relative humidity* is 100 per cent, (ii) the state when an *aquifer* is holding its maximum content of water.

temperature inversion: see *inversion of temperature.*

thaw–freeze process: an active form of weathering in temperature conditions which frequently fluctuate above and below freezing point. Water in cracks alternately freezes and thaws and, because expansion takes place as water turns to ice, angular rock fragments are broken off.

tidal range: the difference between water level at high tide and low tide.

topography: the description of the surface features of an area.

tropic: the two parallels of latitude $23\frac{1}{2}°$ N (Cancer) and $23\frac{1}{2}°$ S (Capricorn) which are the limits of movement of the vertical overhead noonday sun.

unconformity: an interruption in the sequence of deposition of sedimentary rocks, shown by younger, overlying rocks which have a different *dip* from the older underlying rocks. The difference in age between the two sets of rock indicates a period of denudation of the older set.

veering: a change of wind direction in a clockwise direction, e.g. from south-east through south to south-west. See also *backing.*

watershed: the line, usually marked by the crest of a ridge, which separates two *catchment areas*.

water-table: the upper surface of the *saturated* part of an *aquifer*.

weathering: the *in situ* break up of surface rocks by those means which cannot themselves move the resulting fragments, for example, the weather, chemical and organic activity. See also *erosion*.

windward: the side towards the wind or the exposed side, usually in relation to a range of hills or mountains. See also *leeward.*

xerophyte: a type of vegetation adapted by some means to withstand dry conditions (adjective: xerophytic).

Suggested Further Reading

Briault, E. W. H. and Hubbard, J. H.: *An Introduction to Advanced Geography*. Longman (Harlow, 1968).

Calder, N.: *The Restless Earth*. BBC Publications (London, 1972).

Cooke, R. U. and Johnson, J. H.: *Trends in Geography*. Pergamon (Oxford, 1969).

Davies, G. M.: *The Dorset Coast: A Geological Guide*. Black (London, 1956).

Dury, G. J. (ed.): *Essays in Geomorphology*. Heinemann (London, 1967).

Dury, G. H.: *The Face of the Earth*. Penguin (Harmondsworth, 1970).

Gass, I. G., Smith, P. J. and Wilson, R. C. L. (eds.): *Understanding the Earth*. Artemis Press (Horsham, 1972).

Gresswell, R. K.: *Geology for Geographers*. Hulton Educational Publications (Amersham, 1966).

Hancock, J. C. and Whitely, P. F.: *The Geographer's Vademecum*. Philip (London, 1971).

Hanwell, J. D. and Newson, M. D.: *Techniques in Physical Geography*. Macmillan (London, 1973).

Holmes, A.: *Principles of Physical Geology*. Nelson (London, 1965).

Howe, G. M. and Thomas, P.: *Welsh Landforms*. Macmillan (London, 1963).

Leip, H.: *The Gulf Stream Story*. Jarrolds (Norwich, 1957).

Miller, T. G.: *Geology and Scenery in Britain*. Batsford (London, 1953).

Monkhouse, F. J.: *Landscape from Air*. Cambridge University Press (London, 1959).

Monkhouse, F. J.: *Dictionary of Geography*. Arnold (London, 1970).

Moore, W. G.: *A Dictionary of Geography*. Black (London, 1967).

Pounds, N. J. G.: *The Earth and You*. John Murray (London, 1963).

Sawyer, K. E.: Landscape Studies: *An Introduction to Geomorphology*. Arnold (London, 1970).

Sparks, B. W.: *Geomorphology*. Longman (Harlow, 1970).

Stamp, L. D.: *Applied Geography*. Penguin (Harmondsworth, 1969).

Strahler, A. M.: *Physical Geography*. John Wiley (Chichester, 1969).

Swinnerton, H. H.: *The Earth Beneath Us*. Penguin (Harmondsworth, 1958).

Trueman, A. E. (revised by J. B. Whittow and J. R. Hardy): *Geology and Scenery in England and Wales*. Penguin (Harmondsworth, 1971).

The Geographical Digest, published annually by Philip (London).

Philip's Modern School Atlas. Philip (London).

New Naturalist Series. Collins (London).

Answers to Questions

(where appropriate)

Unit One

5. (a) Time of a point to the west is *behind*. Longitude difference is $180°$ $\therefore$ time difference is $\frac{180}{15} = 12$ hours. 12 hours behind 1800 hours Tuesday is *0600 hours Tuesday*.

(b) Time of a point to the east is *ahead*. Longitude difference is $240°$ $\therefore$ time difference is $\frac{240}{15} = 16$ hours. 16 hours ahead of noon Friday is *0400 hours Saturday*.

(c) Time of a point to the west is *behind*. Sydney, Australia is $151°$ E, New York is $76°$ W $\therefore$ longitude difference is $227°$. Time difference is $\frac{227}{15} = 15\frac{2}{15}$ hours = 15 hours 8 minutes.
15 hours 8 minutes behind 1800 hours Sunday is *0252 hours Sunday*.

(d) Time difference is 14 hours $\therefore$ longitude difference is $14 \times 15° = 210°$. 2000 hours is *ahead* of 0600 hours $\therefore$ direction is *to the east*. $210°$ to the east of $150°$ west is *60° E longitude*.

(e) Time of a point to the west is *behind*. Calcutta is $88°$ E, New Orleans is $90°$ W. Longitude difference is $178°$ $\therefore$ time difference is $\frac{178}{15} = 11\frac{13}{15}$ hours = 11 hours 52 minutes. 11 hours 52 minutes behind 0400 Tuesday is *1608 hours Monday*.

Unit Nine

11. (a) 6 oktas cloud; wind: south-west, 33–37 knots; temperature: $7°$C; present weather: rain and drizzle.

(b) 3 oktas cloud; wind: north-east, 18–22 knots; temperature: $11°$C; present weather: rain showers.

(c) No cloud; wind: south-east, 3–7 knots; temperature: $17°$C.

(d) 8 oktas cloud; wind: west-south-west, 63–67 knots; temperature: $4°$C; present weather: hail showers.

(e) 1 okta cloud; calm; temperature: $16°$C.

(f) Sky obscured; wind: north-west, 1–2 knots; temperature: $-6°$C; present weather: fog.

12.

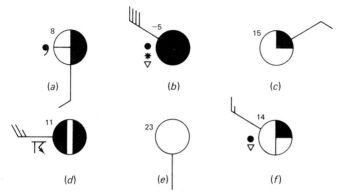

(a) (b) (c)

(d) (e) (f)

13. Weather Map *A*
  (a) Depression or low-pressure system.
  (b)

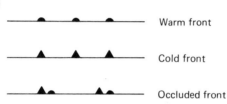

——————●——————●—————— Warm front

——————▲——————▲——————▲—— Cold front

——————▲●——————▲●—————— Occluded front

  (c) (i) Ocean Weather Ship *M*: 7 oktas cloud; wind: east, 38–42 knots; temperature: 4 °C.
  (ii) Gibraltar *N*: 6 oktas cloud; wind: south-west, 13 17 knots; temperature: 14 °C.
  (iii) Sardinia *P*: 5 oktas cloud; calm; temperature: 3 °C; present weather: mist.
  (iv) Northern Norway *Q*: 8 oktas cloud; wind: south-west, 1–2 knots; temperature: −16 °C; present weather: snow.

(d) Southern England	Iceland
8 oktas cloud	7–8 oktas cloud
Wind: mainly south, 18–32 knots	Wind: north-east, speed variable 8–12 knots in east, up to 37 knots in west
Temperature: 9–11 °C	Temperature: −1 to −2 °C
Rain widespread	Snow in the west

(e) Conditions are typical of the warm front and warm sector of a depression; heavy cloud and frontal rain as warm air rises over cold air along the	Wind is north-east because the centre of the depression is to the south and the anti-clockwise circulation of air brings in *very* cold air (NB February).

warm front. Wind is southerly
as part of the anti-clockwise
circulation of air around a
depression centred off north-
west Scotland. Wind is strong
as a result of a steep
barometric (pressure) gradient
(that is, isobars are close
together).

Temperature is below freezing
and snow is falling in the west.
Winds are strong as a result of
a steep barometric gradient.

14. Weather Map *B*
   (*a*) (i) Between 948 and 944 mb, (ii) between 1 024 and 1 028 mb.
   (*b*) *X* = depression or low-pressure centre; *Y* = anticyclone or high-pressure centre; *Z* = ridge of high pressure.
   (*c*) *A* = warm front; *B* = cold front; *C* = occluded front.
   (*d*) (i) Ocean Weather Ship *K*: 8 oktas cloud; wind: south-west, 38–42 knots; temperature: 15 °C; present weather: rain.
   (ii) The Shetlands *L*: 1 okta cloud; wind: south-west, 8–12 knots; temperature: 3 °C.
   (iii) North-west Spain *M*: sky obscured; wind: south, 3–7 knots; temperature: 9 °C; present weather: fog.

   (*e*)

Southern Ireland	Central and southern France
8 oktas cloud everywhere Wind: south-west to south-east, 22–47 knots Temperature: 7–12 °C Rain everywhere	Cloud variable, 0–8 oktas Wind: variable, south-east to north-west, 2–27 knots Temperature: 1–9 °C Dry

   (*f*) A warm front lies across Ireland and frontal rain is falling from heavy cloud. Wind direction is determined by a centre of the 'low' off north-west Ireland around which air moves anti-clockwise: winds are strong because barometer gradient is steep. Temperatures are surprisingly high for 0600 in January and there is a marked difference between warm sector (12 °C) and cold sector (7–9 °C) temperatures.

   A ridge of high pressure projects into central and southern France from an anticyclone in southern Spain. Wind direction varies greatly as air moves *outwards* from the ridge in a clockwise direction. Wind speed is light inland but stronger on the coast because the pressure gradient varies. Temperatures are lower, despite location further south, probably because of continentality.

15. Weather Map *C*
    (*a*) (i) Between 980 and 984 mb, (ii) between 1 028 and 1 032 mb.
    (*b*) *A* = cold front; *B* = warm front; *C* = warm sector of a depression; *D* = anticyclone; *E* = trough of low pressure.
    (*c*) (i) Stavanger *S*: 8 oktas cloud; wind: south-west, 18–22 knots; temperature: 9 °C; present weather: rain. Conditions here are typical of a station close to a warm front, giving thick cloud and rain. Wind is strong because the pressure gradient is steep and south-west as part of the anti-clockwise circulation of air in a depression.
    (ii) The Faroes *F*: 8 oktas cloud; wind: north-west, 13–17 knots; temperature: 1 °C; present weather: rain and snow. This station is in the cold sector of the depression, north-west wind (i.e. very cold), with rain and snow. Winds are less strong than at *S* because the pressure gradient is less steep.
    (iii) Paris *P*: sky clear; calm (no wind); temperature: −2 °C; present weather: fog. This is an 0600 hours chart and the low temperature is almost certainly the result of radiation (NB fog). There is no wind (see the widely spaced isobars), and the stillness of the air assists the development of fog. It should be noted that, despite the latitude difference, Paris is 3 °C cooler than the Faroes.
    (*d*)

Central Europe	West Scotland
Variable cloud, mainly 0–4 oktas: one station 8 oktas; one, sky obscured.	8 oktas everywhere
Wind: generally calm, but varying between south-west and north. Speed less than 7 knots	Wind: between north-west and south-west; stronger, 18–32 knots
Temperatures low, mostly −2 to 4 °C, but one station 10 °C	Temperature: 11–12 °C
Mist and fog widespread	Rain everywhere
Central Europe is dominated by an anticyclone and, at 0600 hours, radiation during the night resulting from the clear skies has lowered temperatures, mostly to below freezing. Such conditions are conducive to radiation fog which obscures the sky at one station. The one station with higher temperatures (10 °C) has cloud cover. Calms or very light winds are widespread because of the gentle pressure gradient.	Western Scotland has conditions typical of the cold front of a depression. Frontal rain is falling everywhere from thick cloud. Temperatures are warmer than in central Europe, as warm, maritime winds blow from the west as part of the anti-clockwise air circulation around a depression. Winds are stronger because the pressure gradient is steeper.

(*e*) (i) Air reaching south and south-eastern England comes from the cold continent to the south, and though slightly warmed crossing the Channel, is only 8–9 °C. In southern Ireland the temperatures of 13 °C result from the warmer air brought in from south-west, probably from the Gulf Stream.

(ii) Winds of 28–32 knots in west Denmark result from the steep pressure gradient in the North Sea, whereas the lower wind speed (calm to 12 knots) in western France results from the gentler pressure gradient associated with the anticyclone in southern France.

16. Weather Map *D*

(*a*) (i) Below 936 mb, (ii) over 1 024 mb.

(*b*) *A* = cold   front;   *B* = occluded   front;   *C* = warm   front; *D* = depression.

(*c*) Ocean Weather Ship *K*: 8 oktas cloud; wind: south-west, 38–42 knots; temperature: 11 °C; present weather: rain.

Station *X*: 8 oktas cloud; wind: south-west, 33–37 knots; temperature: 11 °C; present weather: thunderstorms.

Station *Y*: 8 oktas cloud; wind: south-east, 3–7 knots; temperature: −1 °C; present weather: snow.

Station *Z*: Sky obscured; wind: north-west, 13–17 knots; temperature: 6 °C; present weather: fog.

Station *W*: Missing or doubtful data.

(*d*) Ocean Weather Ship *K* has a wind speed of 38–42 knots because of the steep pressure gradient (that is, many isobars close together), whereas Station *L* has calm conditions resulting from its location in an area with a very gentle pressure gradient (that is, isobars spaced well apart).

(*e*)

Southern Britain	Germany
Cloud variable, 4–8 oktas	Heavy cloud, 7–8 oktas
Wind: south-west, 13–37 knots	Wind: south and south-east 3–17 knots
Temperature: 8–11 °C	Temperature: −2 to 5 °C (one exceptional station, 15 °C)
Thunder and rain showers	Rain showers and mist
Southern Britain lies to the south of a deep depression giving south-west winds, which blow strongly as a result of the steep pressure gradient. Maritime air gives surprisingly high temperatures for a midnight in January and this is probably	Germany lies between a deep depression off north-western Scotland and an anticyclone in eastern Europe, giving a south and south-east air stream. Winds are light as barometric gradient is gentle. Temperatures are lower in this continental location. Rain,

responsible for the thunderstorms.

mist and fog are all associated with the approaching warm front and at one station, drizzle obscures the sky.

Unit Eleven

12. (*a*) **Temperature**

Graph *A* is a southern hemisphere station because the lowest temperatures are in the middle of the year. Temperatures range from 14–24 °C and all months are well above freezing point so that station is *warm temperate* (that is, the hottest months are not hot enough for a tropical climate). Graph *B* is in the northern hemisphere and temperatures range between −15 and 16 °C. Winters are cold with five months below freezing.

(*b*) **Rainfall**

Graph *A* has a distinct *winter* maximum with five very dry summer months. Graph *B* has a distinct *summer* maximum but the annual total is not so great. The winter months are very dry, probably with much snow.

Graph A. A warm temperate climate with a winter maximum of rainfall can only be a Mediterranean climate in the southern hemisphere. Thus the location is either in South Africa, central Chile, south-western Australia or the Adelaide region of Australia.

Graph B. A large range of temperature with five months below freezing point and a distinct summer maximum of rainfall can only be a cool temperate interior climate. The location is either in central North America (the prairies) or central and eastern Europe (the steppes).

Ordnance Survey Map Answers

Map 1 (1 : 50 000, Sheet 198 (Brighton and the Downs))

1. 206063; 218053; 242051.
2. (*a*) 004 degrees grid, (*b*) 6·7 km, (*c*) 8·7 km.
3. National Trust, always open; National Trust, opening restricted; contours; triangulation pillar, 121 m; hachures, part of a field system; parish boundary: bridleway; footpath; road used as public right of way; unfenced track; electricity transmission line; bracken, heath and rough grass.
4. Starting at about 15 m above sea-level, the surface rises gradually for 1·5 km to a height of 46 m. Then, a steep rise to 198 m in 0·5 km which is followed by a very gentle descent for several km, crossing a system of valleys to the coast at sea-level (NB there are no cliffs). The landform is an *escarpment* or *cuesta*, with its steep scarp slope facing north and its more gentle dip or back slope dropping gradually southwards to the sea.
5.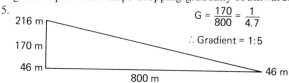

$$G = \frac{170}{800} = \frac{1}{4.7}$$

∴ Gradient = 1:5

6. **Square 2110:** a steep-sided, west-facing valley rising from 61 m to over 183 m; the lower valley sides are concave, the upper slopes convex.
   Square 1911: a flat, low-lying riverside area at about 15 m.
7. This area is part of the level flood plain of the river Adur. The mainstream has embankments on both sides to stop flooding and the riverside land is covered by a complex system of drainage ditches which make cultivation of the heavy clay soil possible.
8. The upper 9 km of the river meanders southwards, first across the flat, low-lying clay valley, then through a water gap cut in the chalk escarpment, where the river flows on a layer of its own alluvium. The tidal river has embankments on both sides, for almost the whole of this distance. South of the A 27(T) road bridge, the river widens into an estuary in which expanses of mud are exposed at low tide. The river mouth is protected both from storm waves and from natural sedimentation by a breakwater on each side.
9. These are dry valleys, typical of the chalk escarpment which is part of the South Downs. They may be seen both as 'combes' in the steep scarp slope and as an intricate system of dry valleys in the dip slope.
10. Longshore drift takes place along this coast in an easterly direction, and the short black lines are groynes built to prevent movement of beach material eastwards. Shoreham-by-Sea has been built on what appears to be a flat, low-lying spit formed by this drift, which has diverted the mouth of the Adur eastwards.
11. There is an abundance of *antiquities*, all on the high chalk lands: Motte and Bailey (237110), cultivation terraces (208098), field systems (2409, 2308), fort (229084), and three tumuli (burial mounds). The absence of antiquities on the low-lying clay land suggests that it was originally marshy, heavy soil, perhaps with dense woodland. It only became habitable when it had been cleared and drained.
12. A line of small villages and hamlets grew up in the northern strip between Fulking and Bramber, probably many centuries ago, along the spring line at the foot of the chalk escarpment. The clay valley to the north was almost certainly marshy and prone to flooding when the villages were first established, so the track joining the villages avoided the marshy lowland. The steep scarp slope of the chalk cuesta lies to the south of the villages and the track between the villages avoided this too. Thus movement between the villages was easiest along the line between the marshy lowland and the steep scarp slope.

   The coastal strip of more recent settlement is broken only by the river Adur. Shoreham-by-Sea is a port and industrial town, shown by its 'works' at 227049 and 246079, and by its locks, piers, lighthouse and lifeboat station. The remaining coastal settlement is probably residential (people commuting daily to London) and devoted to tourism (Brighton is 6 km to the east, Worthing 3 km to the west).

   The empty space between the two strips consists of rolling, waterless and often windswept chalk downland, which appears to be wholly devoted to farming except for small areas of rough grass in squares 2307 and 2308.

13. (a) This road pattern is made up of the access and exit roads between the A 27(T), which is probably a dual carriageway, and the A 283 which runs north to south at a lower level.

(b) These are converging electricity transmission lines which suggest that there is a power station just off the south-east corner of the map. It is probably coal- or oil-powered, with its fuel reaching it by sea.

14. (a) Shoreham Airport is located on very flat ground. It is also near enough to an area of considerable population to ensure regular use and good roads give easy access. It is far enough out of the built-up area for safety purposes.

(b) The 'works' has good road and rail connections, and it has electricity supplied by transmission line. It appears that the railway line running north beside the Adur has been kept open this far especially to serve the works; the railway line to the north is no longer in use. This area is chalk, so it is probably a cement works as it is backed by large quarries.

Map 2 (1 : 50 000, Sheet 194 (Dorchester and Weymouth))

1. 844869; 823807; 816802.
2. (a) 164° grid, (b) 5·2 km, (c) 6·4 km.
3. 7 km.
4. Minor road (partly unfenced); multiple track railway; railway bridge; meandering river; drainage ditches; unfenced track crossing the river by two bridges; footbridge across the river; four patches of wood; electricity transmission line; heather, bracken and rough grass, marshland; large buildings (part of Nuclear Research Station).
5. *Southward continuation is overleaf*

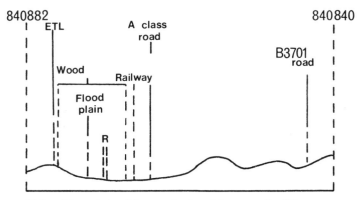

ETL: Electricity Transmission Line   R: River

840840   840795

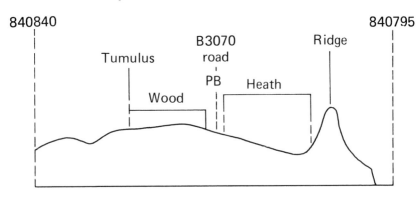

6.

$$G = \frac{106}{900} = \frac{1}{8.4}$$

∴ Gradient = 1:8

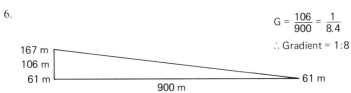

7. (a) (i) A steep-sided, east-to-west ridge rising from 76 m to over 168 m; the ridge has a narrow, flat summit.

(ii) A rounded, gently sloping spur between 76 m high in the north and approximately 130 m in the south on its flat summit. A small dry valley runs northward from 107 m to below 76 m. The western flank of the spur is steeper than its northern and eastern flanks. The extreme north-east of the square is part of a larger, north-pointing dry valley.

(iii) The absence of contours suggests that this area is very flat and low-lying, between 15 m and 30 m.

(b) 91 m.

8. Wood; marsh; bracken, heath and rough grass. Much of the area does not have any of these forms of vegetation, and we may deduce from this that it is farmland.

9. The river flows from west to east (see the 15 m contour in square 8387). It meanders extensively in this section of its course; parts of the river appear to be braided but this may be part of man's attempt to drain the flood plain more efficiently. Most of the flood plain has been drained and is probably used for cattle rearing. It may be liable to flood after heavy rain.

10. The gently rolling nature of the surface, the almost total absence of surface water (except in the extreme east) and the numerous dry valleys suggest that this is a chalk area (Section 3.2(b)).

11. The whole area has antiquities: Wool Bridge; Bindon Abbey (855868); Stony Weir (854871); Lulworth Castle (854822); Water Barrows (8681); Burngate Farm (835816); dyke (838802); chapel (831798); eight groups of tumuli.

12. In addition to residential and agricultural purposes, man uses this area for a Nuclear Research Station (Winfrith Heath); Lulworth Camp (8380) and 'Danger Areas' together suggest army use as firing ranges; tourism.

13. (a) **Wool.** This large village has grown up at a point where the flood plain narrows slightly (study contour for 15 m) so that crossing the river here at Wool Bridge is easier. Today, seven roads converge to cross the new bridge. The proximity of several antiquities suggests that this settlement is an old foundation and its growth may have been associated with Bindon Abbey, 1 km to the east. There is a good water supply, with fertile land nearby. In recent years it has probably expanded because the workers at the nearby Research Station have settled there.

(b) **West Lulworth.** This village has grown up on the northern, sheltered side of an east-to-west ridge, very close to a gap which gives access to Lulworth Cove. As this Cove is the only area of sheltered water along the entire coast, West Lulworth probably had its origin as a fishing village and, perhaps, the cove became important as an anchorage for small coastal craft.

Map 3 (1 : 50 000, Sheet 121 (Lincoln))

1. 799615; 786562; 802591; 812563.

2. (a) 15·1 km, (b) 046 degrees grid.

3. **Square 7856,** A class road; bridge over river; river; lake, stream; spot height (13 m); parish boundary; footpath (right of way); buildings.
   Square 7964: trunk road; embankment; secondary road; road bridge over railway; minor roads; unmetalled tracks (some unfenced); buildings; contour; multiple track railway; level crossing; footpath (right of way); parish boundary.

4. (a) Part of an airport. (b) Ferry for 'foot passengers' only. (c) There is little evidence of wood, marsh, heath, bracken and rough grass.

5. The highest point is between 30 m and 46 m, probably in square 8357. There are thirteen level crossings on the two stretches of railway. This large number suggests that the land surface here is very flat, a conclusion verified by the small number of well-spaced-out contours, the river's meandering course, the airport, two disused windmills, and the absence of cuttings and embankments along the railway lines, which are both very straight.

6. The river flows northwards, and becomes tidal north of point 809611, where there are lock gates and a weir. The river's course is very sinuous and it meanders for 15·1 km across a flat, low-lying flood plain, crossing ten grid squares. Bridges may obstruct navigation on the river so their approaches must be built on embankments to raise them sufficiently high (see A 1(T) road crossing).

7. This road pattern is because of the access and exit roads between the A 1(T) and other roads at that point, especially the A 6065.

8. There are nine villages here (South Muskham, North Muskham,

Cromwell, Carlton-on-Trent, Besthorpe, the Collinghams, Langford, Winthorpe, Holme). Only North Muskham and Holme can be called riverside villages and little of either is built on the river bank. These settlements may be of recent origin, since the Trent flood plain has been drained. The remaining seven villages were probably sited away from the river and above its flood level. These villages are good examples of *ribbon settlements* or *street villages*; those to the west of the Trent have been by-passed by the A 1(T) road.

Map 4 (1 : 25 000, Sheet SD 77 (Ingleborough))

1. 741 745; 734 764.
2. (*a*) 4·9 km, 32·8 km.
   (*b*) (i) 007 degrees grid, (ii) 240 degrees grid, (iii) 307 degrees grid.
3. *B* class road, fenced; unclassified road, partly unfenced; several fenced and unfenced tracks; contours; buildings; cliffs; springs; river; streams; deciduous trees; field boundaries; boulder-strewn surface.

4.
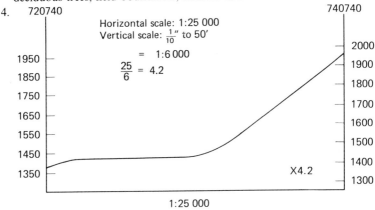

5.
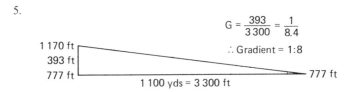

6. **Hard Gill** rises at 1 600 ft. The upper 100 ft is a small rapid headstream but the **V**-shaped contours become more pronounced downstream. Below 1 200 ft it runs swiftly through a deep, steep-sided valley. The stream disappears just below 1 100 ft but the valley beyond this point is still steep-sided.
   Chapel Beck is part of a larger stream which flows slowly from approx-

imately 800 ft to below 750 ft. The valley floor is flat but the sides of the valley become steeper away from the river and there are three scars (steep cliffs) parallel to the river.

7. From the flat summit of Ingleborough Hill the surface drops steeply from 2 300 ft to 1 500 ft. Below this, the slope becomes increasingly gentle to about 1 300 ft, where the first of three parallel *scars* causes the surface to drop steeply to 975 ft; below this the ground slopes gently down to the old quarry.

8. After dropping steeply for several hundred feet the streams disappear between 1 200 and 1 300 ft. This is characteristic of jointed limestone country where streams disappear and flow underground. Supporting evidence that this is a limestone area comprises over twenty 'pot-holes' (swallow holes) into which streams have disappeared in the past, numerous caves, expanses of bare limestone pavement (730753), probably with clints and grykes, and the scars which are probably the outcrops of nearly horizontal limestone strata.

9. Most of the area is bleak, infertile, windswept upland with extensive bare rock surfaces, steep slopes and poor pasture. The only roads and settlements are in the comparatively sheltered valley of Chapel Beck along which movement is easiest, though there is an unfenced track running steeply up the valley of Hard Gill to about 1 200 ft, where it becomes a footpath which continues steeply to the summit of Ingleborough Hill.

Map 5 (1 : 25 000, Sheet SH 61 (Barmouth))

1. 628141; 626157; 616128.
2. (a) 315 degrees grid, (b) 2·35 km, (c) 2·5 km.
3. HWMOT; LWMOT; streams; mud; sand; tidal water; footpaths; embankments; unfenced track and track fenced on one side only; single line railway; railway station; contours; marsh; deciduous woodland with a fence; field boundaries; footbridge; buildings.
4.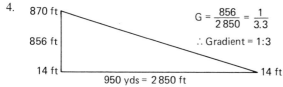
5. A knoll or isolated hill.
6. (a) To the north of the road is an area which is almost completely devoid of contours. It is a very flat, low-lying area, except for several 'islands' of higher ground, of which Fegla Fawr is the biggest (630146). The flatness here is confirmed by numerous drainage ditches, embankments along the HWMOT and patches of marsh.

   South of the road there are many contours close together, indicating steep, hilly terrain which rises to a height of over 1 100 ft in the extreme south-east.

(*b*) The flat, low-lying area was probably formed as a result of river-borne sediment being deposited in the estuary. As this alluvial area grew larger it encircled the isolated areas of high ground. It is likely that the post-glacial readjustment of sea-level (Section 5.4) resulted in a slight emergence (uplift) of the land. Since then, the alluvium has been drained and embanked to form agricultural land, which is most probably used for cattle farming.

7. (*a*) At low tide the estuary consists of several large stretches of sand with smaller patches of mud near high-water mark. In places the sandbanks extend for more than a kilometre from the shore. The river flows to the sea between the sandbanks.

(*b*) At high tide the sandbanks are covered by the sea to give a large expanse of shallow, sheltered water from the north shore to the south, as shown by HWMOT lines on each side.

8. This is a north-pointing sand spit, partially recurved. Prevailing winds are south-westerly on this west-facing coast of Cardigan Bay, giving rise to a northerly movement of beach material along the coast (this is *longshore drift*). When this northward-moving material reaches the southern entrance of the estuary, deposition begins at an angle to the coast: the spit grows slowly northwards away from the coast and in the sheltered water behind it, deposition of river-borne material goes on. As the spit slowly gets longer, so this area of deposited material grows larger (Section 5.3).

The uneven shape of the spit on its inland side may be the result of its end having been *recurved* by winds from the north-west. Much of the southern end of the spit merges gently into the low land behind it, but the northern end still retains the characteristic shape of a sand spit. The twice-daily tidal flow keeps open a narrow entrance to the estuary and prevents the spit from closing it completely.

9. Drainage ditches, field boundaries and some tracks suggest that man uses this area for agriculture.

10. The main roads on both sides of the estuary run along the edge of the steep, hilly country. The road follows the coast exactly in the north, whereas in the south it separates the hills from the flat, reclaimed land. Roads built in this position are most easily constructed as they avoid both the high ground with its steep slopes and the low-lying ground with its drainage ditches, marshes and embankments.

11. Barmouth has grown up in a very exposed position, facing south-west. It is on the north side of the estuary because there is navigable water at this point and the extent of tidal coverage is smallest (that is, HWMOT and LWMOT are close together). The only flat land on which a town could grow and have access to the sea is that between the northern hills and the coast. Originally Barmouth probably grew along the road; even today, the town has not extended far into the hills but rather across the flat land to the west where the railway station, Marine Hotel and other buildings have been built. It is a small port, probably handling coastal traffic and, perhaps, fishing. There is no evidence of industry and the inhabitants

probably commute daily to nearby towns to work. The railway line runs across the estuary on a long bridge which was probably easier and cheaper to construct than building a railway line along the northern shore of the estuary.

Map 6 (1 : 25 000, Sheet ST 17 (Cardiff))

1. 180766; 183758; 178764.
2. (*a*) 046 degrees grid, (*b*) 2·3 km, (*c*) 2·7 km.
3. **Square 1773** consists largely of flat, low-lying land (saltings) crossed by the meanders of the tidal river (the Ely). Railways with extensive sidings run along each side of the river; those in the north are associated with buildings. Only in the extreme south-west does the land surface rise to a height of just over 100 ft.
   Square 1977 is a built-up area of houses and schools, with a close network of streets.
4. (*a*) Apart from the fringe of dry land along the west side, this area consists largely of an expanse of mud (Penarth Flats) at low tide, crossed by a narrow channel of water.
   (*b*) At high tide the sea reaches the coast as is shown by HWMOT.
5. There is a lock at the entrance to every dock, because water must be retained in the docks while the tide rises and falls outside. Such a dock is called a *tidal basin* and the lock enables ships to pass in and out, even though the levels of water inside and outside the dock may be different.
6. The black lines represent sidings, that is, branches of the main railway line. The buildings close to the dockside are installations such as warehouses and storage sheds. These suggest that the main activity in the docks is commercial, including the importing and exporting of many kinds of goods.
   The smaller inlets are *dry docks* or *graving docks* for repairing ships. The difference in size between these and the commercial docks is obvious: only one ship at a time occupies each dry dock but many ships can be berthed end to end along the dockside in the tidal basin, to be loaded and unloaded.
7. These large blocks of buildings are in a central position and their proximity to the main railway stations (183758, 188766), the docks, the City Hall and the Sports Stadium (180762) suggests that this area is the shopping and business centre of Cardiff—the Central Business District (CBD). There are twelve churches but only two schools. There are more schools on the northern and southern edges of the shopping centre nearer to the residential areas.
   In square 1977, the buildings consist of a network of streets of back-to-back terrace houses, mostly without gardens. There is a large number of churches and schools to serve this residential area. The pattern of buildings is different in the south central part of the square: their shape is irregular and they are bigger, suggesting a shopping centre.

8. This is an area of parkland, an open space on both sides of the river Taff for relaxation, leisure and recreation. It probably consists of patches of woodland and grass with flower beds (e.g. Sophia Gardens). The layout is more geometrical to the east and there are several (black) public buildings including the City Hall and the Castle. This area appears to be the administrative centre of Cardiff with, perhaps, the library, museum and court rooms.

9. Other features which typify a large town are the network of railway lines and sidings with several stations and 'halts' serving the residential areas, the goods depot (192762) and railway connections with the docks, the large number of schools and churches, several hospitals, the prison and extensive residential areas.

10. The large, rectangular buildings, the network of railway sidings, its 'out-of-town' location, and the circular 'shapes' associated with it suggest that this is some form of industrial installation, perhaps with oil storage tanks, or a gas works with its gas holders.

Map 7 (1 : 25 000 (Second Series) Sheet SY 87/97 SZ 07 (Corfe Castle))

1. 961820; 964824; 959824.

2. (a) 323 degrees grid, (b) 2·7 km, (c) 2·9 km.

3. An almost conical hill (knoll) with very steep slopes, especially on the north side.

4. Main road; secondary road; several tracks, both fenced and unfenced; road bridge over railway; single track railway; railway siding; footpaths; spot heights for 92 ft; contours; buildings; deciduous wood; scrub; bracken heath and rough grass; lakes; church with tower and field boundaries.

5.

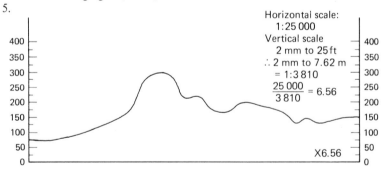

6.

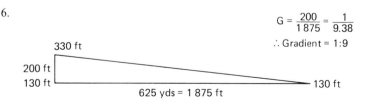

7. Five tumuli (two in hilltop locations); field system (970812); Corfe Castle, The Rings and Morton's House (all in Corfe Castle village).

8. This is an excellent example of a 'gap' settlement. There are, in fact, two gaps separated by the knoll on which Corfe Castle stands. The easiest access to the Castle is from the south because the land to the south is higher than that to the north (notice the shorter hachures to the south). The village probably grew on this side to make it easier for the villagers to take speedy refuge in the Castle. The Corfe river flows through the lower, easterly gap, which is used by four roads and a single track railway. This is the easiest route between the two sides of the ridge, because it does not involve climbing the steep sides of the ridge, but it may involve a longer journey.

   The map suggests that the original village of Corfe grew up immediately south of the Castle, where the church, Town Hall and Morton's House can be seen, and spread along the minor road in square 9581 leading to Corfe Common. The pattern of the field (or garden) boundaries for the houses along this road is different from that of the surrounding area. It consists of large gardens behind the houses, which contrast with the much larger fields away from the village. The part of the village along the main road has probably grown up more recently and this is a good example of a ribbon settlement or street village (Section 13.10). The houses at Town's End (963812) are probably very recent; this appears to be an estate of semi-detached houses.

9.

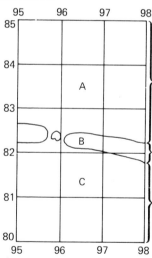

A Low-lying heathland, mostly below 900 ft. The slightly undulating surface is covered with coniferous forest, scrub, bracken and heath. There is only farmland in the extreme south.

B A steep-sided, flat-topped ridge with a distinct gap in which stands a knoll. There is some scrub and rough grass, but most of the ridge has large fields on its top and south side, and much of the north side is forested. The absence of surface drainage and the dry valley at 970823 suggest that the ridge might be a hog's back formed by a steeply-dipping chalk layer.

C Low, rolling country below 250 ft, extensively farmed but with patches of wood, scrub and rough grass.

10. This large area (almost 1 km²) is probably a plantation belonging to the Forestry Commission because the trees are all coniferous and there are numbers of unfenced access tracks or rides. The drainage pattern in the centre of the plantation indicates that the flat valley bottom has been artificially drained by means of a close network of ditches. These also help to drain the higher, forested parts of Wytch Heath. A smaller but similar pattern is seen on the west side of the plantation, draining that side of the low, south-pointing spur on which forest has been planted.

Map 8 (1 : 63 360 (one inch to one mile), Sheet 83 (Penrith))

1. 399157; 2 718 ft at 441110.
2. (a) 348 degrees grid, (b) 3·8 miles, (c) 4·3 miles.
3. Deciduous wood, partly unfenced; A class road; several tracks, both fenced and unfenced; buildings; contours; AA telephone box; GPO telephone box; heath, bracken and rough grass; footpath; streams; road bridges over streams; National Trust, always open; spot height at 512 ft.

4.

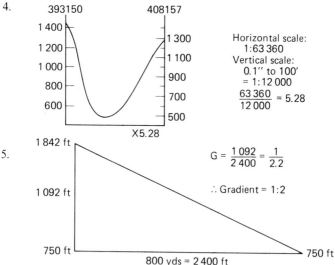

5.

6. This is a steep inland cliff, known here as a *crag*. The symbol is used when slopes are so steep that contours cannot be drawn separately. It is possible to calculate the approximate height of such a cliff by comparing the contour heights at the top and bottom at the same point on the cliff. Thus, at 419149 the top is about 1 650 ft and the bottom (by the *H* in Heck) is 1 300 ft, making the cliff about 350 ft high.

7. This is an area of high hills (more than 20 points over 2 000 ft) with steep slopes and inland cliffs, sometimes over 1 000 ft high. Valley floors are frequently flat and sometimes occupied by lakes. There are several smaller bodies of water at higher levels than the large lakes, surrounded on three sides by steep slopes.

Drainage is locally radial and streams flow west, north and east from the highest ground at High Street (4411). The upper part of several valleys is very steep and streams flow swiftly but the valley profile becomes more gentle towards the lower end.

This is an excellent example of an area which has undergone mountain glaciation, typical features of which are the U-shaped valleys, corries (450108) and arêtes (High Street).

8. Much of this area is inhospitable, particularly in winter when most of the high ground is likely to be snow-covered, winds are strong, and snow and rainfall heavy. The hills can be treacherous even in summer, for sudden mists may blanket their slopes. Only in the valleys is there any shelter, and only the more easily accessible valleys have roads and settlements. Roads follow the valleys very closely (e.g. the A 592) and any branch roads soon peter out along the tributary valleys. The road to the east of the area follows the lake shore exactly and it, too, ends just before it reaches the steep valley head. Settlements are generally very small.

9. Apart from some patches of woodland on the lower valley sides, most of the area is covered by heath, bracken and rough grass. Small areas of farmland do exist, but only on the flat valley floors because only here is there sufficient shelter and good soil (probably drained alluvium).

10. **Hayeswater Gill** is very steep and fast-flowing; it drops 650 ft in less than a mile.

Bannerdale Beck rises at about 1 400 ft and drops swiftly to 1 000 ft. Below this its gradient becomes progressively more gentle, and its lower 300 ft of descent is spread over nearly two miles of stream length.

The cross-section of the valley of Hayeswater Gill is decidedly V-shaped whereas that of Bannerdale Beck is clearly U-shaped. You may notice that the shape of the contours in each valley gives a rough indication of the shape of its cross-section.

11. Crag = cliff; beck = stream; pike = peak or summit; fell = a high area of steeply sloping, bracken-covered surface.

12. First, there is no evidence of tidal rise and fall. Second, there are no cliffs beside the water. Third, the contour along the lake shore is well above sea-level, indicating that the water level is also at the height. For example, the surface of Haweswater is at approximately 850 ft while that of Ullswater is just below 500 ft.

Index

(M) indicates reference to a map.